PROCEEDINGS

New Technologies for Astronomy

Jean-Pierre Swings
Chair/Editor

25–26 April 1989
Paris, France

ECO2

The Congress of
EPS—European Physical Society
Europtica—The European Federation for Applied Optics
SPIE—The International Society for Optical Engineering

Cooperating Organizations
ANRT—Association Nationale de la Recherche Technique
Associazione Elettrotecnica ed Elettronica Italiana
CNES—Centre National d'Etudes Spatiales
ICG—International Commission on Glass
GIFO—Groupement Industriel Français pour l'Optique
GNEQP—National Group on Quantum Electronics and Plasma Physics
Office of Solar Heat Technologies, U.S. Department of Energy
SEE—Société Française des Electriciens, des Electroniciens
   et des Radioélectriciens
SPSE—The Society for Imaging Science and Technology

Published by
SPIE—The International Society for Optical Engineering
P.O. Box 10, Bellingham, Washington 98227-0010 USA
Telephone 206/676-3290 (Pacific Time) • Telex 46-7053

Volume 1130

SPIE (The Society of Photo-Optical Instrumentation Engineers) is a nonprofit society dedicated to advancing engineering and scientific applications of optical, electro-optical, and optoelectronic instrumentation, systems, and technology.

The papers appearing in this book comprise the proceedings of the meeting mentioned on the cover and title page. They reflect the authors' opinions and are published as presented and without change, in the interests of timely dissemination. Their inclusion in this publication does not necessarily constitute endorsement by the editors or by SPIE.

Please use the following format to cite material from this book:
    Author(s), "Title of Paper," *New Technologies for Astronomy,* Jean-Pierre Swings, Editor, Proc. SPIE 1130, page numbers (1989).

Library of Congress Catalog Card No. 89-62612
ISBN 0-8194-0166-8

ECO2
NEW TECHNOLOGIES FOR ASTRONOMY

Volume 1130

CONTENTS

ECO2
NEW TECHNOLOGIES FOR ASTRONOMY

Volume 1130

ECO2
NEW TECHNOLOGIES FOR ASTRONOMY

Volume 1130

ECO2
NEW TECHNOLOGIES FOR ASTRONOMY

Volume 1130

CONFERENCE COMMITTEE

Chair
Jean-Pierre Swings, Institut d'Astrophysique/Université de Liège (Belgium)

Cochairs
Jean-Claude Fontanella, ONERA Châtillou (France)
Fritz Merkle, European Southern Observatory (FRG)

Session Chairs
Session 1—Adaptive Optics
Richard Wade, Royal Observatory Edinburgh (UK)

Session 2—New Techniques for Ground-Based Astronomy
Fritz Merkle, European Southern Observatory (FRG)

Session 3—New Technologies for Space Astronomy
Fritz Merkle, European Southern Observatory (FRG)

Session 4—Imaging and Spectroscopy in Astrophysics
Patrick Wayman, Dunsink Observatory (Ireland)

Session 5—The Infrared Space Observatory
Jean-Pierre Swings, Institut d'Astrophysique/Université de Liège (Belgium)

TECHNICAL ORGANIZERS ECO2

Technical Program Committee

Chairman: S. Lowenthal, IOTA (France)
Vice-Chairman: C. Puech, Thomson CSF (France)

EPS—European Physical Society
J. J. Braat, Philips Eindhoven (Netherlands)
O. D. D. Soares, University of Porto (Portugal)
J.-P. Huignard, Thomson CSF (France)
O. J. Lokberg, University of Trondheim (Norway)
E. Jakeman, Royal Signals and Radar Establishment (UK)

Europtica—The European Federation for Applied Optics
H. Arsenault, Université Laval (Canada)
J. Seeley, University of Reading (UK)
R. Torge, Carl Zeiss (FRG)
L. H. J. F. Beckmann, Oldelft (Netherlands)

SPIE—The International Society for Optical Engineering
D. B. Ostrowsky, Université de Nice (France)
E. W. Kreutz, RWTH Aachen (FRG)
A. Monfils, Université de Liège (Belgium)
R. B. Johnson, University of Alabama, Huntsville (USA)
R. Jacobsson, Spectrogon AB (Sweden)

Coopted members
S. Huard, ENSP, Marseille (France)
L. B. Jeunhomme, Photonetics (France)
M. Bourdinaud, CEA Saclay (France)
J.-P. Laude, Jobin-Yvon (France)

Joint Policy Committee

EPS—European Physical Society
H. Tiziani, Institut für Technische Optik, Universität Stuttgart (FRG) JPC Vice Chairman
H. A. Ferwerda, University of Groningen (Netherlands)
G. Thomas, Executive Secretary EPS (Switzerland)

Europtica—The European Federation for Applied Optics
P. Bozec, ESSILOR (France)
H. Walter, Optische Werke G. Rodenstock (FRG)
P. Zaleski, ESIC (France)

SPIE—The International Society for Optical Engineering
L. R. Baker, Sira Ltd. (UK) JPC Chairman
B. J. Thompson, University of Rochester (USA)
W. L. Wolfe, Optical Sciences Center, University of Arizona (USA)

Technical Organizing Committee

I. Abram (France)	R. Frey (France)	S. Lowenthal (France)	A. M. Sessler (USA)
N. Abramson (Sweden)	V. Fridkin (USSR)	H. A. Macleod (USA)	R. Sigel (FRG)
W. Arden (FRG)	A. Gabriel (France)	J. Madey (USA)	G. T. Sincerbox (USA)
W. Arnold (USA)	M. L. Gaillard (France)	H. Maitre (France)	W. Sohler (FRG)
H. Arsenault (Canada)	L. Garifo (Italy)	J. P. Marioge (France)	C. G. Someda (Italy)
D. Attwood (USA)	L. Garnero (France)	P. Mazzoldi (Italy)	O. D. D. Soares (Portugal)
J. Ballard (UK)	C. N. de Graaf (Netherlands)	F. Merkle (FRG)	L. Solymar (UK)
T. Barbee (USA)	P. Greve (FRG)	J. Midwinter (UK)	M. Soskin (USSR)
H. Bartelt (FRG)	R. Grosskopf (FRG)	T. Mochizuki (Japan)	I. J. Spalding (UK)
R. Benattar (France)	K. Grosskopf (FRG)	A. Monfils (Belgium)	C. Steenbergen (USA)
M. Billardon (France)	J. B. Grun (France)	G. M. Morris (USA)	A. Steventon (UK)
B. Boelger (Netherlands)	P. Günther (Switzerland)	G. Mueller (FRG)	W. Stewart (UK)
M. Bourdinaud (France)	F. L. Herr (USA)	C. Nissim (France)	O. Svelto (Italy)
J. Braat (Netherlands)	M. Howells (USA)	G. Ohm (FRG)	J. P. Swings (Belgium)
H. Braeuninger (FRG)	S. Huard (France)	Y. Okamura (Japan)	K. Tada (Japan)
P. Bricard (France)	J. P. Huignard (France)	A. Orsag (France)	R. Torge (FRG)
O. Bryngdahl (FRG)	K. Jain (USA)	D. B. Ostrowsky (France)	T. Takagi (Japan)
F. Canal (Spain)	L. Jeunhomme (France)	G. Otrio (France)	L. Thylen (Sweden)
A. Carenco (France)	H. J. Kahlert (FRG)	R. di Paola (France)	A. Todd-Pokropek (UK)
D. P. Casasent (USA)	A. Katzir (USA)	M. Papuchon (France)	W. Tolksdorf (FRG)
J. P. Castera (France)	C. Klingshirn (FRG)	Y. Petroff (France)	T. Tschudi (FRG)
H. J. Caulfield (USA)	K. Koizumi (Japan)	S. M. Pizer (USA)	J. Tsujiuchi (Japan)
P. Chavel (France)	E. Kraetzig (FRG)	D. Pohl (Switzerland)	M. A. Viergever (Netherlands)
A. Consortini (Italy)	E. W. Kreutz (FRG)	A. Quenzer (France)	P. R. Vinogradov (USSR)
R. Daendliker (Switzerland)	S. Kubota (Japan)	F. K. Reinhart (Switzerland)	C. Warde (USA)
P. Dhez (France)	M. Lacombat (France)	A. Renleri (Italy)	B. S. Wherett (UK)
H. Doetsch (FRG)	P. Lagasse (Belgium)	G. C. Righini (Italy)	C. Wilkinson (UK)
G. Duchossois (France)	J. P. Laude (France)	G. Roosen (France)	T. Wilson (UK)
J. Duvernoy (France)	S. H. Lee (USA)	B. E. A. Saleh (USA)	S. Wittekoek (Netherlands)
J. C. Fontanella (France)	H. U. Lemke (FRG)	G. Schmall (FRG)	M. Wittig (Netherlands)
A. Franks (UK)	W. Lobsiger (FRG)	E. Sein (France)	R. Wolfe (USA)
			R. Zander (Belgium)

INTRODUCTION

The use of high performance detectors in most wavebands has enabled (and, fortunately, still does) astronomers to make the best possible observations with their telescopes, and has led to results having very good spectral, spatial, and temporal resolution(s). Further advances are foreseen with the future availability of very large ground-based telescopes, e.g., ESO's Very Large Telescope (VLT) (for which active and adaptive optics will be implemented), array detectors (especially in the infrared) and, of course, sophisticated space telescopes such as Infrared Space Observatory (ISO) and Hubble Space Telescope (HST), ultraviolet and optical.

Conference 1130 has thus been divided into five sessions, specifically devoted respectively to adaptive optics, new techniques for ground-based astronomy, new technologies for space astronomy, imaging and spectroscopy in astrophysics, and the Infrared Space Observatory.

In each of these sessions, surveys of the present techniques, projects, and efforts were presented. They were then followed by more detailed and specialized contributions. The presentations covered a very wide wavelength range, from the UV to the IR, as well as a remarkable variety of techniques, such as wavefront sensors for high frequency adaptive optics, telescopes of various sizes (from a few centimeters to tens of meters), polarimetry, aperture synthesis, and beam combination for ground-based or space-borne interferometry, speckle, CCD arrays, bidimensional IR arrays, IR cameras, photopolarimeters for ISO, etc. In addition, beautiful astrophysical results were shown during several sessions of Conference 1130; equally beautiful results are expected in a reasonable future, based on the techniques described in this proceedings.

Jean-Pierre Swings
Institut d'Astrophysique/Université de Liège (Belgium)

PLENARY SESSION

EUROPEAN SPACE AGENCY (E S A)

STRATEGY FOR EARTH OBSERVATION INTO THE 21ST CENTURY

P. Goldsmith and G. Duchossois

The Earth's environment and specifically the means to monitor and preserve it are being increasingly recognised as matters of major concern. Mankind is now appreciating that his activities may be disturbing the delicate balance which determines his environment on all scales from the local to the global. Linked to these environmental concerns is the realisation that the Earth has limited resources on which increasing demands are being placed. Thus better and more organised information about the behaviour of the environment and factors influencing the Earth's natural resources is essential if valid political decisions are to be made. This can only be achieved effectively on the basis of a better understanding of the Earth when viewed as a single system in which the physical, chemical and biological interactions between the atmosphere, the oceans, the land and ice regions, and the Solid Earth are all taken into account.

Observations of the Earth from space form the only effective means of providing the necessary temporal and spatial data on the full global scale needed to achieve this goal.

1. **The Problems leading to the Rationale of the Earth Observation Strategy**

   Some of the most prominent examples of the major environmental/resource challenges facing mankind today are:

   (a) **CLIMATE CHANGE**

   Possible changes in climate due to the increasing concentration of the so-called "greenhouse gases", such as CO_2, in the atmosphere caused by such activities as the burning of fossil fuels and deforestation.

   (b) **OZONE DEPLETION**

   The danger associated with increased ultra-violet flux at the Earth's surface due to the catalytic destruction of stratospheric ozone (viz, the ozone hole). The injection of man-made chloro-flurocarbons into the atmosphere is the major cause of this phenomenon.

   (c) **ACID RAIN**

   Increased acid deposition (acid rain) resulting in damage to lakes, trees, soils, etc. The increased deposition is linked with the injection into the atmosphere of sulphureous compounds contained in fossil fuels and their subsequent chemical modification and ultimate washout and deposition as acidic material.

(d) <u>PHOTOCHEMICAL OXIDANT FORMATION</u>

Increased oxidant content of the lower atmosphere producing damage
to vegetation. These oxidants result from photo-chemical reactions
involving hydrocarbons, nitrogen oxides, etc. injected into the
atmosphere from pollution sources of which automobiles are a prime
example.

(e) <u>DESERTIFICATION, DEFORESTATION</u>

Man's direct activities such as overgrazing and purposeful deforestation not only upset the local ecological balance, but there is
also the danger that these activities constitute one of the
influential factors in determining possible climatic changes,
through resulting changes of the reflectivity of the Earth's
surface to solar radiation and changes in the hydrological cycle.
They could also influence the carbon dioxide balance.

(f) <u>EARTHQUAKES AND VOLCANOS</u>

Earthquakes and volcanic activity are of course <u>not</u> the result of
man's activities. But their catastrophic potential is such that
the possibility of increased understanding of the Earth's crust and
interior could lead to some early warning system, cannot be
neglected. Increased volcanic activity has the potential of
effecting climate as is well illustrated in the aftermath of the
Krakatau eruption.

The current awareness of these problems is primarily due to a combination of better, but still inadequate, theoretical numerical models and
the output of the currently limited methods of monitoring these changes
set against the background of the natural variability.

Scientists now emphasize that Earth Observation from space provides the
only viable and cost-effective means of acquiring the necessary input
data into their models whilst also monitoring the conditions of the
Earth on the local, regional and global scales.

Whilst current numerical and theoretical models of climate, complicated
as they are, allow predictions of the effect of further increases in the
Greenhouse gases (CO_2, CH_4, etc.) at the present time these models by no
means contain an adequate representation of the full system.   These
predictions must be treated with some caution.   For instance, one of
the most comprehensive models gives, for a doubling of CO_2, a predicted
increase in the mean temperature of the Earth's surface of 5.2°K with an
increase of over twice that in regions North of 70° N in the Arctic
winter.   The model results are very sensitive to cloud radiation feedback and the surface fluxes which is illustrated by the fact that when
the same model is modified to better represent liquid water and ice
crystals in the atmosphere, the predicted mean temperature increase is
reduced to 3° K.

It is a combination of improved theoretical work linked with a better
observational base, of which observations from space must make up the
major component, that will lead to reliable assessments of the environmental damages that mankind is now facing.   From this foundation an ESA
long-term strategy has been formulated with the fundamental aim of meeting the need for better basic observations.

2.   The Strategy

The concerns which must be addressed can be grouped into four broad categories:

(a)   Environmental problems arising from climatic change, especially where man's activities are starting to affect the delicate thermo-dynamic and ecological balance must be tackled, together with the all-pervasive pollution problems.

(b)   Both the non-renewable and renewable resources must be monitored and managed to the best advantage.

(c)   Satellite meteorology is now at an operational level following a decade of successful satellites, which has resulted in the establishment of EUMETSAT. The need to continue and improve on the system is fully accepted especially as the data from these satellites make a major input into the assessment of the environmental problems.

(d)   Finally, there are aspects of the Solid Earth which are best studied using space techniques. It is also acknowledged that the definition of the Earth's geoid would make a considerable contribution to the oceanographic data base so essential to understanding the atmospheric/ocean interactions which are a major driver controlling the Earth's climate.

From the foregoing a more detailed ESA strategy has been developed to address these problems and to foster the evolution of satellite remote sensing from the experimental through to the operational phase. ESA will seek to achieve these objectives by supporting the main Earth-science disciplines and by demonstrating how remote sensing can be utilised to realise the full potential socio-economic benefits of Earth observation. There is therefore a twin-pronged concept to lead the way for eventual commercial exploitation whilst at the same time providing the basic global observational data required to support the fundamental research needed to address the major environmental problems which in themselves have major considerable socio-economic implications.

The goal of operational remote sensing will only be achieved when continuity of data over long periods, measured by decades, can be assured so that user communities may flourish after being nurtured to act in concert and encouraged to exploit the data. To this quintessential requirement must be added timely delivery of data and strong coordination with the relevant user communities.

Four major space-programme elements have been identified for implementing this strategy and achieving the European goals:

1.   An environmental-Monitoring Programme;

2.   An Earth Resources Management Programme;

3.   An Operational Meteorology Programme;

4.   A Solid Earth Programme.

Each of these programmes requires the measurement and monitoring of a number of basic parameters some of which are common to two or more of the programmes.Thus the four programmes must be seen as an integrated whole.

3. Implementation of the Strategy

The implementation of these programmes starts with the European Remote Sensing Satellite, ERS-1, to be launched in 1990. This provides the means to demonstrate the value of data derived mainly from microwave sensors to the scientific and application communities in the areas of oceanography, ice, vegetation and pollution monitoring. ERS-1 data will make a fundamental contribution to the World Climate Programme and its World Ocean Circulation Experiment WOCE. These communities all emphasize the need for data of the ERS-1 type to be continued to fill the gap between the end of ERS-1 and the beginning of the polar platform era in 1997. Thus the first requirement is for an ERS follow-on satellite to be launched in 1994 at the latest, so consolidating Europe's leading role in this aspect of Earth observation.

The means of meeting the needs of the environmental, Earth resources and some aspects of that of operational meteorology in the longer term is seen to be the exploitation of the polar platform being developed within the Columbus Programme of the Agency. In order to best meet the strategy it is argued that a launch frequency be established that will cater for the need for continuity of data into the next century and also which will allow the possibility for different polar orbits to meet the differing observational requirements. An ideal scenario would be one allowing a double continuous series of launches as illustrated in Figure 1, making use of the same basic platform bus.

The operational meteorological requirements will be met by embarking an operational meteorological package provided by EUMETSAT on at least one series of polar platforms. In addition there will be a need to continue and improve the current operational Meteosat programme from geostationary orbit. The performance of this Second Generation Meteosat will be decided as the result of inputs from EUMETSAT. The Agency will contribute to its costs to cover the new technology that will be required. It is expected that the first launch will be in the late 1990s.

For the first Solid-Earth mission in the mid-1990s, ESA has defined a single dedicated spacecraft - ARISTOTELES - with a primary gravity field mapping mission, followed by a geodetic task for precise positioning.

The Earthnet programme provides, and will continue to provide, the payload data handling function for the Earth Observation programme. In this way it acts as an essential link between the space segments, including non-ESA components, and the European user communities. An additional task is that it will be the means of promoting Earth Observation activities so as to help nurture future independent operational or commercial entities.

The Earth Observation Preparatory Programme must continue in order to prepare for the future polar orbiting missions.

Thus the programmes that need to be adopted to fulfil the aims of the strategy, lead in turn to the proposal for a number of interlinked satellite systems that together constitute the practical means for implementing the programmes, namely:

1.   A successor to ERS-1 (in the medium term)

2.   Second-generation Meteosat

3.   A dedicated Solid Earth mission - ARISTOTELES

4.   The Polar Platform missions (in the longer term).

A fundamental aspect is that observations primarily directed towards one problem area usually impact significantly on others.   For example, the improved definition of the geoid provided by the Solid Earth Programme, when taken in conjunction with radar altimeter measurements from other satellites, would make a significant contribution towards a fuller description of the synergism between the general global sea level rise and oceanic circulation needed for the Climate Change Programme. Similarly, the requirements of operational meteorology will also make vital inputs to the Climate Change and Land Management Programmes.   The proposals that constitute the strategy for Earth observation contained in this report are mutually interdependent, and should be considered and hopefully adopted in their entirety.   This interdependency is illustrated in Figure 2.   The programmatics of the strategy after ERS-1 and ERS-2 are given in Figure 3.

4.   Concluding Remarks

A major part of the strategy is to encourage the development of operational and commercial user communities in the expectation that in the long term these communities will shoulder an increasingly larger proportion of the financial burden.   In this respect it is recognised that governmental and inter-governmental organisations will be major customers.   One of the roles of Earthnet will be to spearhead the promotion of Earth-observation products for these users.

A basic strategy driver is the need for continuity: firstly to meet the scientific, application and operational needs, and secondly to give potential commercial/operational users the confidence to invest in the development of the necessary ground processing and infrastructure in the expectation of long-term growth.   Only by anticipating this will it be possible to realise the full socio-economic benefits of the programme.

An over-riding aspect of the strategy is that it must be seen as part of a much larger international endeavour to address the major problems now facing mankind.   This is fully recognised by the Agency and its proposals have been drafted in close consultation not only with user communities in Europe but also with our international partners.

The benefits associated with the proposed programme are industrial as well as political and scientific.   To address the problems highlighted here and realise the programme advanced new technologies will have to be exploited.   By participating in the programme European industry will be in a position to retain its pre-eminence so helping to safeguard the economic well-being of Europe.

The problems facing mankind are daunting and it would be unrealistic not to acknowledge their political dimension. The strategy outlined above recognises this and seeks to place Europe in a position to make major contributions to these issues. At the same time, on a more parochial level, it will ensure that European politicians receive the best possible independent advice when debating alternative courses of actions.

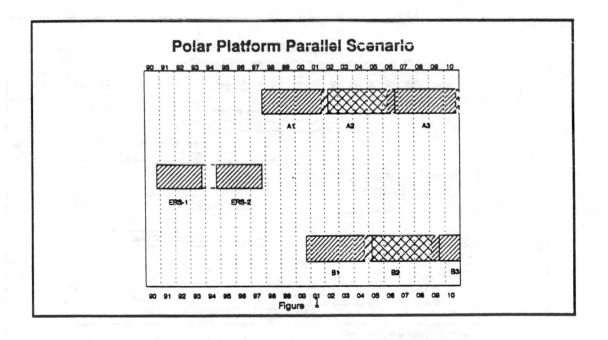

Figure 1

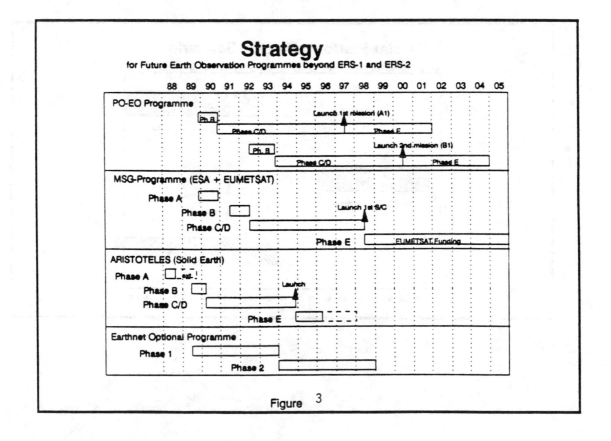

Figure 2   CONTRIBUTION OF SPACE PROJECTS TO PROGRAMME OBJECTIVES

PROGRAMME ELEMENTS / SPACE PROJECTS	ERS-1 ERS-2	ARISTO TELES	EPOP A SERIES	EPOP B SERIES	METEOSAT 1ST GEN. (+ LASSO)	METEOSAT 2ND GEN.
ENVIRONMENTAL MONITORING	✳	✳	✳	✳	✳	✳
EARTH RESOURCES MANAGEMENT	◇	◇	◇	✳	◇	◇
OPERATIONAL METEOROLOGY	✳		✳	◇	✳	✳
SOLID EARTH	◇	✳	◇	◇	◇	

✳ - MAJOR CONTRIBUTION

◇ - USEFUL CONTRIBUTION

Strategy

for Future Earth Observation Programmes beyond ERS-1 and ERS-2

Figure 3

SESSION 1

Adaptive Optics

Chair
Richard Wade
Royal Observatory Edinburgh (UK)

A Survey of Present Efforts in Astronomical Adaptive Optics

Jacques M. Beckers and Fritz Merkle

European Southern Observatory
D-8046 Garching bei München, FRG

ABSTRACT

Astronomical adaptive optics improves the angular resolution of both solar and stellar telescopes. In addition to giving astronomers the ability to resolve the objects under study better, adaptive optics will : (i) enhance the contrast of pointlike sources against the sky and telescope (thermal) background, (ii) increase the spectroscopic resolution of most spectrographs, and (iii) improve the sensitivity of optical interferometers.
We review the status of a number of efforts underway at various observatories around the world to implement adaptive optics on both large solar and stellar telescopes.

1. INTRODUCTION

The increased collecting area of very large telescopes results in an increase in sensitivity over smaller telescopes thus shortening exposure times. Their increased (diffraction limited) angular resolution results, however, in a unique new capability of the telescopes which cannot be obtained in other ways with the smaller telescopes. This angular resolution can be achieved by eliminating seeing effects either by image recovery techniques using post-detection analysis of speckle observations or by image reconstruction before detection using adaptive optics. The latter method is much to be preferred when possible. Its astronomical benefits lie, in addition to direct high resolution imaging of astronomical objects from planets to distant galaxies, in improved spectral resolution because of the narrower slits that can be used, in improved detection of point sources against the sky background, and in the vastly improved conditions for interferometric imaging with telescope arrays.

A number of papers have already been written reviewing the principles and properties of astronomical adaptive optics[2,,4,13,14,16,17,18,19]. We refer to those papers for a detailed description. This paper summarizes the principles and expected performance of adaptive optics and describes the programs for their astronomical implementation currently underway. It is an update of a paper given earlier on the same topic[5].

2. PRINCIPLE OF ADAPTIVE OPTICS

The principle of adaptive optics is shown in Figure 1. It uses a wavefront sensor (mostly Hartmann-Shack sensors used at visible wavelengths) to sense the wavefront tilts on stars or on small ($<$ few arc sec.) extended objects within the usable field of view of the telescope. This field of view is limited to the so-called isoplanatic patch (= the area on the sky within which the atmospheric wavefront disturbances are approximately the same). The wavefront correction is made with a small, agile optical component (generally a deformable mirror) placed at an image of the pupil or at a conjugate of an average atmospheric seeing layer to achieve the speed required.

Both the wavefront sensor and the adaptive mirror need to have sufficient spatial and temporal resolution to resolve the significant wavefront spatial and temporal variations. The former are of the magnitude of the Fried's parameter r_0. This parameter increases with wavelength from $r_0=10$ cm in the visible for 1 arc sec seeing to $r_0=60$ cm in the K band (2.2 microns) and $r_0=380$ cm at 10 microns. The durations of the temporal variations also increase proportional to the Fried's parameter so that the number of photons available for the wavefront sensing increases as the cube of this parameter. One can use therefore fainter and fainter stars for wavefront sensing when going to longer and longer wavelengths. In addition to the larger number of stars which become available, the diameter of the isoplanatic patch also increases leading to the rapid increase in sky coverage for astronomical adaptive optics shown in Figure 2.

In addition to the wavefront sensor and the adaptive mirror an adaptive optics system usually includes a digitally controlled servo system, which couples the wavefront error signals to the mirror actuators using sophisticated control algorithms and appropriate temporal and spatial filtering, and an optical system which couples the adaptive optics to the telescope and the astronomical instrument.

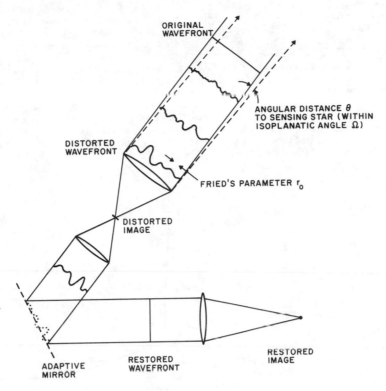

Fig. 1   Principle of Adaptive Optics.

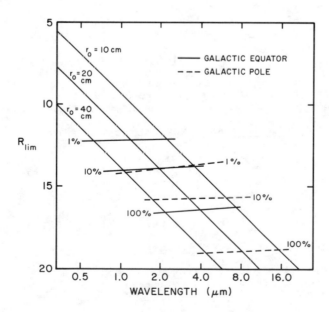

Fig. 2   Sky coverage by Adaptive Optics for Different Values of the Fried Parameter r_0.

3. EXPECTED PERFORMANCE OF ADAPTIVE OPTICS

A perfect adaptive optics system will fully restore the wavefront to give an image for a point source equal to the Airy disk. A number of imperfections will cause this to be not the case. Among these are: (a) limited spatial and temporal resolution of the wavefront sensor and adaptive mirror, (b) time lag between the wavefront measurement and the wavefront correction, (c) deviations from perfect isoplanatism, (d) failure to correct for amplitude variations (scintillation), (e) chromatic effects related to the wavefront sensing at visible wavelengths while observing in the IR, (f) noise in the wavefront sensing, and (g) imperfections in the wavefront control algorithms.

Roddier et al[21], Gaffard et al[11], and Smithson et al[24] have determined the point spread function resulting from most of these imperfections. It is schematically shown in Figure 3. It closely approximates a combination of the original seeing disk with the Airy disk of a fully corrected telescope. The fraction of the energy (Σ) in the Airy spike is a

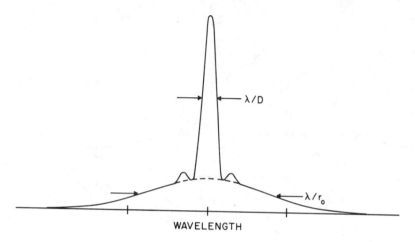

WAVELENGTH

Fig. 3   Point Spread Function for Imperfect Adaptive Optics.

good measure of the performance of the adaptive optics system. It is approximately equal to the so-called Strehl Ratio S. For a perfect system $\Sigma = 1.0$, for a system with a spatial resolution near the Fried parameter $\Sigma \approx .8$ when a wavefront sensing object is used at the center of the isoplanatic patch, and $\Sigma \approx .4$ when the object is at the edge of this patch.

Since the seeing changes with time one expects the value of Σ to also change. Absolute photometry using the Airy spike will therefore be difficult. Relative photometry over a small area at the center of the isoplanatic patch should be possible. The main use of adaptive optics will therefore be in studies of morphology, high resolution spectroscopy, relative photometry, and interferometry (using the coherent radiation in the Airy spike).

4. CURRENT PROGRAMS IN ASTRONOMICAL ADAPTIVE OPTICS

Table I summarizes the programs which are now in progress which aim at implementing adaptive optics on astronomical telescopes. In other types of optical systems (military related) adaptive optics appear to have been successfully used for some time giving one confidence that this technology will become soon a component of astronomical telescopes.

The first three of these programs are being interfaced with their telescopes now. We fully expect adaptive optics to become a common feature of large telescopes in the 1990's.

5. HEADLINES OF ONGOING ASTRONOMICAL OPTICS EFFORTS

The astronomical adaptive optics systems listed in section 4 use a variety of components and have different scientific goals. This section summarizes each system.

5.1 ESO/Meudon/Onera/CGE

This adaptive optics system named "COME ON" is intended to be used at the ESO La Silla 3.6 meter telescope in a so-called polychromatic adaptive optics mode in which the wavefront is sensed at visible wavelength but corrected for observations at near infrared wavelengths. It serves as a prototype for the 8 meter Very Large Telescope (VLT) units. The Hartmann-Shack wavefront sensor is built by ESO, its fast electronic processor by ONERA, the 19 element PZT actuated continuous faceplate mirror by CGE and the Observatoire de Meudon will do the integration of the system including the optics and the IR array detector. It will be mated with the telescope in 1989.

TABLE I Current Programs in Adaptive Optics

Location	Principal Investigator	Number of Elements	Proposed Use (telescope diam.)	Ref.
ESO/Meudon/ ONERA/CGE	Kern/Merkle/ Fontanella/Gaffard	19	IR Stellar at La Silla (3.6m)	17
NOAO-KPNO	Goad/Beckers	37/55	IR Stellar (3.8m) and IR Solar (1.5m) at Kitt Peak	6,12
Lockheed-PARL	Smithson	19/37	Visible Solar at Sac Peak	23
NOAO-SPO	Dunn	13	Visible Solar at Sac Peak (.76m)	7,8
Center for Astrophysics	Nisenson	36	Visible Speckle Interferometry	20
Univ. Chicago	Kibblewhite	81	Near IR Stellar at Apache Point (3.5m). Uses Laser Star	15
Univ. Hawaii	Roddier	TBD	Visible Stellar	21,22
J. Hopkins Univ.	Durrance	19	Stellar Coronography at Las Campanas (1.0m)	9
Chengdu PR China	Jiang Wenhan	19	Visible Solar (LEST, 2.4m)	29

5.2 NOAO-KPNO

Also a polychromatic system is to be used at the Kitt Peak 3.8 meter telescope as well as for solar observations at the 1.5 meter McMath telescope. The 55 PZT actuator continuous surface faceplate mirror was built by ITEK, the Hartmann-Shack wavefront sensor by Adaptive Optics Associates (AOA). Figure 4 shows the first results obtained with this system on a laboratory light source with fixed optical aberrations. The servo loop is fast enough to correct atmospheric variations and it is expected that stellar image correction will occur in 1989.

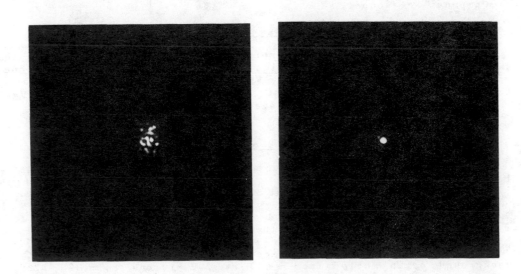

Fig. 4   Correction of Optical Aberrations by the NOAO-KPNO system using a laboratory light source. Left: uncorrected, Right: corrected.

5.3 Lockheed-PARL

To be used for solar observations at the Sacramento Peak 76 cm vacuum telescope. Uses a Hartmann-Shack wavefront sensor observing small sunspots (pores) and a 19 element (51 actuator) segmented adaptive mirror which is planned to be upgraded to a 37 segment mirror soon. Because of the mirror segmentation a direct control of the <u>tilt</u> is possible by the wavefront <u>tilt</u> sensor. The mirror surface continuity is controlled by a laser source interferometric system. Acton and Smithson[1] report that the system is functioning giving diffraction limited resolution even in 2 arc sec seeing (presumably working in the partial adaptive optics mode discussed in section 6).

5.4 NOAO-SPO

A developmental program aimed at creating an optimum adaptive optics system for solar observations ultimately to be used with the Large Earthbased Solar Telescope (LEST). At this moment a continuous faceplate 12 actuator mirror is compared with a 13 segment mirror[8],[26]. Different wavefront sensing techniques are being explored including ones using Liquid Crystal Display[27] and Hartmann-Shack devices possibly using solar feature correlation tracker techniques[28].

5.5 Center for Astrophysics

A Hartmann-Shack AOA sensor/continuous faceplate PMN actuated mirror which aims at partial adaptive optics correction at visible wavelengths. It will be used with image recovery techniques developed for speckle interferometry.

5.6 University of Hawaii

The Roddiers propose to use both wavefront curvature sensing and correction to achieve diffraction limited imaging. Because both sensing and actuating involves wavefront curvature it may be possible, for bright sources, to simplify the control of the system.

5.7 University of Chicago

An adaptive optics program being started aims at diffraction limited imaging of the 3.5 meter ARC telescope at Apache Point in New Mexico. It aims at making use of artificial stars to increase sky coverage (see section 7). It will probably use a 9 x 9 element segmented mirror and a Hartmann-Shack sensor.

5.8 Johns Hopkins University

This program has as specific goal coronographic observations of stars aimed at planet detection. The adaptive optics function is to decrease scattered light around the parent star and to enhance the contrast of eventually existing planets against the remaining scattered light background. It will use a 19 element membrane adaptive mirror coupled to the 40 inch Las Campanas telescope.

5.9 Institute of Optics and Electronics, Chengdu

With the goal of developing adaptive optics for LEST the IOE is exploring modal multidithering techniques for adaptive optics systems. It has been very successful at correcting laboratory images (similar to Figure 4) and it has reported successful correction of atmospheric effects on light sources in horizontal paths at 340 meter distance. In the future incorporation of a system at the Yunnan Observatory in Kunming is foreseen.

6. USE OF PARTIAL ADAPTIVE OPTICS

An adaptive optics system designed to work at the 2.2 micron K-Band at an 8 meter diameter telescope with .75 arc sec seeing at visible wavelengths (Fried parameter = 13.5 cm at .5 micron and 80 cm at 2.2 microns) will contain about 100 adaptive elements. When using an on-axis object for wavefront sensing it results in $\Sigma \approx 80\%$ at 2.2 microns. At shorter wavelengths Σ will decrease to about 50% at 1.2 microns, 20% at .9 microns and 9% at .7 microns because of the decrease in Fried's parameter. However the width of the Airy spike (Fig. 3) decreases and the width of the seeing disk slightly increases with decreasing wavelength resulting only in a small decrease of its contrast against the background seeing halo (from $\approx$ 400 at 2.2 microns to $\approx$ 390, 220 and 160 at 1.2 microns, .9 micron and .7 micron respectively). For a number of astronomical programs such a partial adaptive optics system would therefore be quite powerful. The advantage of such a partial system lies of course in the small, realizable number of actuators and in the increased sky coverage. A full adaptive optics system for example at .7 micron would require 1600 or more actuators. In addition brighter stars would be needed for the wavefront sensing so that its sky coverage would be much less.

A partial adaptive optics system would be especially beneficial for interferometric imaging with telescope arrays. At the ESO VLT 8 meter telescopes, for example, it results at .7 microns in the light gathering power corresponding to that of a 2.4 meter telescope (equal to the Hubble Space Telescope) but with the coherent radiation inside an Airy disk corresponding to that of an 8 meter telescope with a width of about .02 arc sec (vs $\approx$ .1 arc sec for the HST).

7. EXTENDING THE SKY COVERAGE

Foy and Labeyrie[10] proposed the use of artificial stars for wavefront sensing. These stars would be created by illuminating the neutral sodium layer at $\approx$ 100 km elevation with a laser tuned to one of the sodium D lines. The incoherent back scattered radiation would create an extended small (1 to 2 arc sec) object in the center of the field of view which could be used for wavefront sensing at any position in the sky. Thompson and Gardner[25] experimented with this technique and showed that a star with V = 14 was feasible. Kibblewhite[15] estimates that current laser technology would be capable of creating at best a V = 10 star. From Figure 2 it can be seen that this would increase the sky coverage substantially (eg from < .1% at .75 microns to 100%). The trick in getting bright artificial stars is to make the laser duty cycle (pulse width x number of pulses/sec) as large as possible since increasing the energy only does not increase the artificial star brightness significantly due to a saturation of the upper atomic level population by stimulated emission in the sodium layer.

8. EXTENDING THE ISOPLANATIC PATCH

Beckers[3] suggested a way to increase the size of the isoplanatic patch by using a technique called "Multiconjugate Adaptive Optics". It achieves this by imaging different layers of the atmosphere onto different adaptive mirrors. The array of adaptive mirrors therefore corrects the atmospheric wavefront distortions in detail, at each height, resulting in the increase of the area on the sky that is corrected. In order to do this it is necessary to measure the wavefront distortion as a function of height in the atmosphere. That is accomplished by a technique called "Atmospheric Tomography" which measures the wavefront distortion using an array of artificial stars. No numerical simulation or experimentation of this technique have as yet been done. Preliminary analysis indicates an improvement of the isoplanatic patch diameter of about two times the number of layers used, the amount of improvement being very dependent on the atmospheric optics structure and on the heights being imaged.

9. CONCLUSION

Adaptive optics coupled to large 8 meter class telescopes will lead to major changes in ground based optical astronomy. The incorporation of the present first steps in adaptive optics on astronomical telescopes will already bring major advances in our capabilities to do astronomy. From there on one might foresee an ongoing program of improvements using more actuators, artificial stars, multiconjugate systems, and other refinements still unthought of. Ground-based telescopes will as a result compete favorably with space-based systems but at a fraction of the cost (however only at wavelengths transmitted by the atmosphere). In the next few years the completion of the first adaptive optics systems will be at least as exiting to astronomical research as will be the completion of large telescopes being planned or in construction. The combination of both will move astronomy forward with a major enhancement of capabilities.

10. REFERENCES

1. D.S. Acton and R.C. Smithson, Bulletin Am. Astr. Soc. 20, 1010 (1988).

2. J.M. Beckers, Fifth Erice Workshop on Towards Understanding Galaxies at Large Redshifts (R.G. Kron and A. Renzini eds.), Kluwer Academic Publ., 319 (1988).

3. J.M. Beckers, ESO Symposium on Large Telescopes and Their Instrumentation (M.H. Ulrich ed.), 696 (1988).

4. J.M. Beckers and L. Goad, Ninth Santa Cruz Summer Workshop on Instrumentation for Ground-Based Optical Astronomy (L.B. Robinson ed.), Springer Verlag, 315 (1988).

5. J.M. Beckers and F. Merkle, JNLT and Related Engineering Developments, (T. Kogure and A. Tokunaga eds.), Astronomy and Space Science, in press (1989).

6. J.M. Beckers, F.J. Roddier, P.R. Eisenhardt, L.E. Goad, and K.L. Shu, Proceedings SPIE 628, 290 (1986).

7. R.B. Dunn, LEST Technical Report No. 28, <u>Adaptive Optics in Solar Observations</u> (F. Merkle, O. Engvold and R. Falomo eds.), 243 (1987).

8. R.B. Dunn, G. Streander and O. von der Lühe, Preprint of SPO Symposium (1988).

9. S. Durrance, <u>Active Optics,</u> Proceedings SPIE 1114-12 (1989).

10. R. Foy and A. Labeyrie, <u>Astron. and Astrophys.</u> 152, L29 (1985).

11. J.P. Gaffard and Corinne Boyer, <u>Applied Optics</u>, 26, 3772 (1987).

12. L. Goad and J.M. Beckers, <u>Active Optics</u>, Proceedings SPIE 1114-09 (1989).

13. J.H. Hardy, <u>Proceedings SPIE</u>, 332, 252 (1982).

14. J.H. Hardy, <u>Active Optics</u>, Proceedings SPIE 1114-01 (1989).

15. E. Kibblewhite, private communication (1989).

16. F. Merkle, Ninth Santa Cruz Summer Workshop on <u>Instrumentation for Ground-Based Optical Astronomy</u> (L.B. Robinson ed.), Springer Verlag, 366 (1988).

17. F. Merkle, ESO Symposium on <u>Large Telescopes and Their Instrumentation</u> (M.H. Ulrich ed.), 639 (1988).

18. F. Merkle, <u>J. Opt. Soc. Am.</u>, A5, 904 (1988).

19. F. Merkle and J.M. Beckers, <u>Active Optics</u>, Proceedings SPIE 1114-05 (1989).

20. P. Nisenson, private communication (1989).

21. F. Roddier and C. Roddier, <u>Proceedings SPIE</u> 628, 298 (1986).

22. N. Roddier and F. Roddier, <u>Active Optics</u>, Proceedings SPIE 1114-11 (1989).

23. R.C. Smithson, M.L. Peri and R.S. Benson, LEST Technical Report No. 28, <u>Adaptive Optics in Solar Observations</u> (F. Merkle, O. Engvold and R. Falomo eds.), 179 (1987).

24. R.C. Smithson and M.L. Peri, LEST Technical Report No. 28, <u>Adaptive Optics in Solar Observations</u> (F. Merkle, O. Engvold and R. Falomo eds.), 193 (1987).

25. L.A. Thompson and C.S. Gardner, <u>Nature</u>, 328, 229 (1987).

26. O. von der Lühe, Optical Engineering 27, 1078 (1988).

27. O. von der Lühe, LEST Technical Report No. 28, <u>Adaptive Optics in Solar Observations</u> (F. Merkle, O. Engvold and R. Falomo eds.), 155 (1987).

28. O. von der Lühe, Astronomy and Astrophysics, in press (1989).

29. Jiang Wenhan, Lui Yueai, Shi Fang, Tang Guomao, LEST Technical Report No. 28, <u>Adaptive Optics in Solar Observations</u> (F. Merkle, O. Engvold and R. Falomo eds.), 133 (1987).

COME-ON: AN ADAPTIVE OPTICS PROTOTYPE DEDICATED TO INFRARED ASTRONOMY.

Pierre KERN[1,2], Pierre LENA[1], Pierre GIGAN[1],
Jean-Claude FONTANELLA[3], Gérard ROUSSET[3],
Fritz MERKLE[4], Jean-Paul GAFFARD[2].
1.Université Paris 7 et Observatoire de Paris, Laboratoire associé au CNRS n°264,
Place J.Janssen, 92195 Meudon, France,
2.Laboratoires de Marcoussis (CGE), Route de Nozay, 91460 Marcoussis, France.
3.Office National d'Etudes et de Recherches Aérospatiales,
av. de la Division Leclerc, 92322 Chatillon sous Bagneux, France,
4.European Southern Observatory, Karl Schwarzschild-Str.2
Garching bei München, Federal Republic of Germany,

ABSTRACT

The paper presents the status of the COME-ON (CGE Observatoire de Meudon ESO ONERA) experiment. This instrument, developed and tested by several European laboratories, is an adaptive optical system with a 19 actuators deformable mirror and a Hartmann Shack type wavefront sensor. The wavefront sensing is performed at visible wavelengths; a special computer drives the deformable mirror which should achieve diffraction limited infrared imagery with large optical telescope. The different components and their individual characteristics are described. The results of the tests of some components are given: 19 actuators deformable mirror, tip-tilt mirror. The expected performances are summarized and possible applications of the instrument to astronomical sources are presented. The isoplanaticity aspect, the required temporal bandwidth and reference source brightness is discussed. The conclusions of the experiment will be used for the design of adaptive optics for the ESO Very Large Telescope.

1. INTRODUCTION

Drastically limited by the atmospheric turbulence effects, the large telescopes require special techniques to recover their intrinsic spatial resolution. For years already, several solutions have been implemented and substantial improvements are now obtained by post processing. Real time processing in an alternate way, would give major benefits which will be discussed in section two. In the perspective of the future very large telescopes, it is obvious that the so-called adaptive optics might become a common instrument in the next years. New telescopes design will take in account this possibility in several observing modes.

In the framework of the ESO VLT, a consortium of several European laboratories has proposed an adaptive optics prototype[1]. They join their competences in the different fields of real time atmospheric turbulence corrections. Under management of ONERA, the instrument is aimed for nearly diffraction limited imaging at the focus of a 4 m class telescope for near infrared wavelengths (2-5 µm). In section two, the atmospheric characteristics which have scaled this instrument is given . In section three the characteristics of some elements are described. Section four discusses the limitations and several aspects of the use of the instrument for infrared astronomy, and outlines some of the main limitations.

2. WHAT IS THE INSTRUMENT DESIGNED FOR ?

The main characteristics of the propagation through the atmospheric turbulence and the means to compensate for induced perturbations have been described in detail in the literature. Some of the main papers are mentioned below, and their results are used in this section to justify the design of the instrument. The so-called Fried parameter r_o,[2] [3] [4] gives the main constraint; r_o is a measurement of the spatial coherence of the wavefront in the entrance pupil plane of the telescope at a wavelength λ. It varies as $\lambda^{5/6}$. A telescope with a diameter larger than r_o has a long exposure angular resolution limited to:

$$\alpha = \frac{1.22\ \lambda}{r_o}$$

An adaptive optics system evaluates the shape of the corrugated wavefront and provides in real time the controls to a deformable mirror for a partial or a full correction of the wavefront, leading to images of enhanced resolution. The three main components are a wavefront sensor, a phase corrector and a control system able to drive the corrector with the measurements provided by the sensor. From the values of r_o the following parameters can be calculated, where N is the number of actuators needed to perform a correction at the diffraction limit with a 4 meter class telescope, θ_o is the isoplanatic patch or the angular field of view within which the perturbation are correlated, $\bar{h}$ is the equivalent height of the turbulent layer (6 km), τ_o is the coherence time, and $\bar{v}$ is the mean wind speed in the turbulent layers (10 m/s).

It has to be noticed that for astronomical sources, the instrument under construction is expected to use an off-axis reference source, which must be within the isoplanatic patch. One of the main limitation discussed below is the possibility to get a reference source bright enough and close enough to the astrophysical object in order to provide a significant reference information.

λ (µm)	0,5		1,65	2,2		3,85		5		10
r_o (m)	0,1	0,2	0,4	0,6	1,2	1,2	2,4	1,6	3,8	3,6
$N \approx (D/r_o)^2$	1600	400	100	44	12	10	3	6	2	1
$\tau_o \approx r_o/v$ (ms)	10	20	40	60	120	120	240	160	380	360
$\theta_o \approx r_o/h$ arcsecond	3	6	14	20	40	41	82	55	110	120

Table 1: Main parameters (calculated for D=4m, $\bar{v}$=10m/s, $\bar{h}$=6km).

The main features of the system have been fixed by these parameters :

- a 19 actuators deformable mirror,

- a Shack- Hartmann wavefront sensor with 5x5 or 10x10 subapertures,

- a sampling rate up to 150 Hz which leads to an effective bandwidth of about 30 Hz,

- the reference source is the visible counterpart of the infrared object to be corrected, or an off-axis visible reference source within the isoplanatic angular patch.

The instrument is designed to achieve diffraction limited images at the focus of the 3,6 m telescope of ESO at La Silla in the L band of the atmosphere (3.85 µm) under average seeing condition and in the K band (2.2 µm) under good seeing conditions.

3. DESCRIPTION OF THE DIFFERENT COMPONENTS AND THEIR CHARACTERISTICS

3.1. General layout

The philosophy for this instrument design is to have a laboratory test bench at the focus of a telescope. All the main components will be exchangeable in order to test in the future new developments in the area of deformable mirrors, wavefront sensing, wavefront computers and infrared cameras. The optical layout and the general synoptic are given in figure 1[5]. Figure 2 is a view on the experiment as currently tested at the Observatoire de Paris-Meudon.

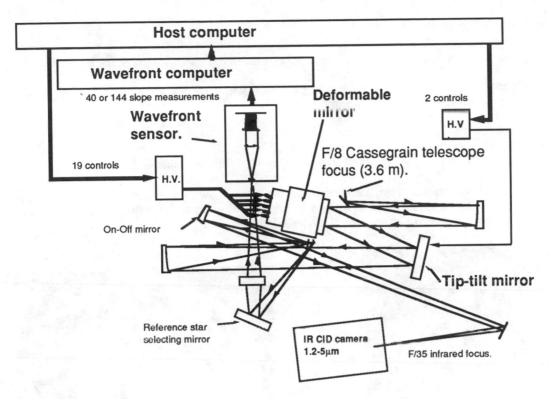

Figure 1: Schematic layout of the adaptive system.

Figure 2: Opto-mechanical mount of the COME-ON experiment.

Figure 3: COME-ON 19 actuators deformable mirror.

3.2. Adaptive mirror and tip-tilt mirror

The COME-ON 19 piezoelectric actuators deformable mirror built by CGE, has the following characteristics[6]:

useful diameter:	70 mm
amplitude of the corrections:	±15 μm (optical path) with ±1500 Volts
distance between the actuators:	17.5 mm
mechanical bandwidth (see figure 6):	5 kHz
thickness of the silicon front plate:	1 mm
mirror flatness:	λ/4 (λ=.638 μm)
temperature range:	from 20 to -10°C (with the above flatness)

The figures 3, 4 and 5 give a view of the mirror and some interferograms showing the flatness just after polishing and typical deformations produced by the actuators. The temperature cycling tests have been successfully conducted in a climatic room. Figure 6 gives the frequency response of an actuator. It shows a first resonance at 3.6 kHz.

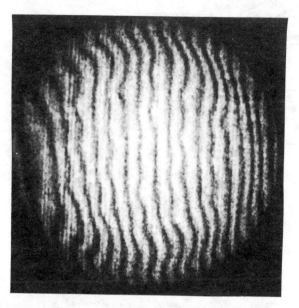

Figure 4: Interferogram of the deformable mirror after polishing without stress.

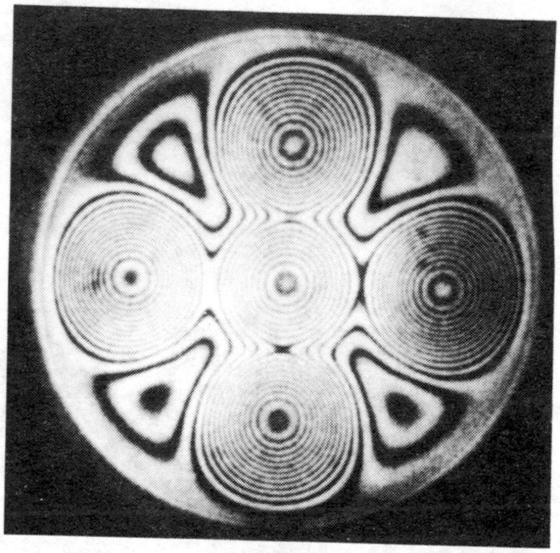

Figure 5: Interferogram of the deformable mirror with 5 of the actuators driven by 600 Volts.

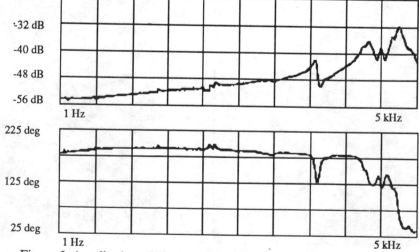

Figure 6: Amplitude and phase frequency responses of an actuator.

The tip-tilt mirror (figure 9), designed and built at Observatoire de Paris, will correct for the overall tilt fluctuation. It has a gimbal mount with two axis in the plane of the mirror. Four piezoelectric translators (two per axis) work in push-pull mode and are associated with four displacement transducers. These sensors and these piezoelectric translators work in closed loop and give a good linearity, an adjustable damping and a negligible drift. The measured characteristics are listed below :

diameter of the mirror :	80 mm ,
range on each orthogonal axis:	400 arc seconds,
sensibility:	0.3 arc second,
bandwidth :	140 Hz (at -3 dB point in closed loop) (Figure 7),
setting time:	2.5 ms (for an amplitude of 5 arc seconds) (Figure 8).

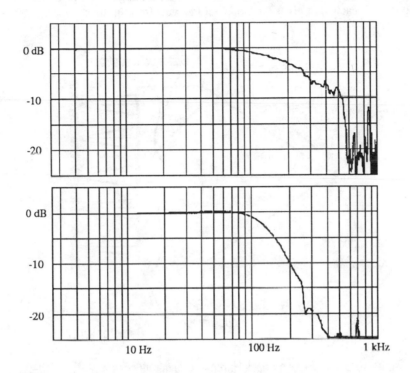

Figure 7: Transfer functions of the tip-tilt mirror in outside axis(above) and inside axis (below).

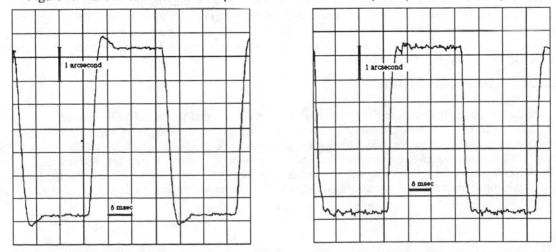

Figure 8: Step response of the tip-tilt mirror on inside axis (right) and on outside axis (left).

Thermal tests have been conducted at the Observatoire de Paris, in order to measure its dynamical characteristics in the temperature range of use (from -15°C to 20°C). In order to avoid extra optical elements in the optical setup, this mirror is placed close to the deformable mirror, but out of the pupil plane. Modification of the wavefront out of the image pupil plane results in infrared background modulation in the output infrared signal. This influence can be shown to be negligible for small apertures as in this experiment. It has been shown also that thermal background modulations induced by deformable mirror and tip-tilt mirror is negligible when used with an infrared detector array[7].

3.3. Wavefront sensor.

The Shack-Hartmann wavefront sensor was chosen in the project because of its simplicity, compactness and achromaticity. In such a wavefront sensor a lenslet array placed in a pupil plane defines subapertures (figure 10) of suitable dimensions according to the seeing conditions. The individual on-axis images of the plane wave are shifted when the wavefront is disturbed. The shift of each spot gives the slope[8] of the wavefront in the subaperture. The seeing conditions give the number of subapertures.

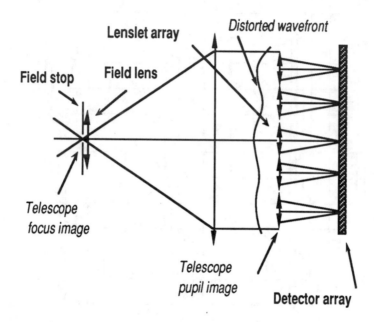

Figure 10: Principle of a Shack Hartmann wavefront sensor.

The Shack Hartmann sensor used here has been built at ESO. The spot patterns are imaged on a 100 x 100 Reticon array through a two stages Proxitronix intensifier coupled to the detector array with a fiber plate. In the present case, either 5x5 or 10x10 subapertures are used to match the sampling of the wavefront at infrared wavelengths. The pixel size is 60 μm and the lenslets diameter is 1mm. The instrument contains its own calibration source. It provides to the wavefront computer a video signal with a frame rate up to 500 per second.

3.4. Wavefront computer and host computer

In order to calculate the controls for the deformable mirror, the video signal produced by the wavefront sensor has to be processed. The purpose of the wavefront computer designed and developed at ONERA is to return to the host computer the local slope measurements of the wavefront. It is a hard wired programmable processor which first digitizes the output signals of the wavefront sensor. A second stage corrects for the inhomogeneities of the pixel responses. A third stage gives the X-Y centroid positions within each subaperture. The last stage returns on the VME bus of the host computer the local slope of the wavefront. The wavefront computer was successfully tested with an acquisition rate up to 1.5 MHz (i.e. 150 frames per second).[5]

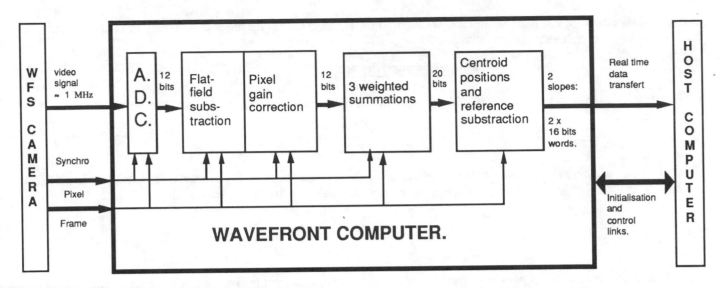

Figure 11: Block diagram of the ONERA wavefront computer.

Figure 9: COME-ON Tip-tilt mirror.

Figure 11bis: Wavefront computer

In the host computer[9], the command matrix is multiplied by the measurements provided by the wavefront computer. The control signals are sent to the deformable mirror, and to the tip-tilt mirror via a high voltage amplifier. The modal strategy was preferred, allowing a temporal filtering adapted to the different mode orders.

3.5. Imaging detector.

The system was designed to fit with the infrared 32x32 array camera of the Observatoire de Paris[10]. This camera was built in the background of the ISO (Infrared Space Telescope) with CID (Charge Injected Device) InSb detectors of SAT (Société Anonyme de Télécommunications). This camera design was adapted to fit with the COME-ON instrument. Different magnifications allow the sampling of diffraction pattern in the K and L bands (2.2 µm and 3.85 µm). In the future, the new ESO infrared camera will also be applicable[11].

4. EXPECTED PERFORMANCE.

The different limitations of the COME-ON system will be briefly reviewed in this paragraph. Their consequences will be characterized by their contribution to the phase variance σ^2_φ at the output of the system.

4.1. Detection error.

This is due to photon noise effects on the calculation of the centroids position in the wavefront sensor. Assuming that the wavefront sensor detector is really photon noise limited, it can be shown that the related error is[8] :

$$\sigma^2_d \approx 2.\frac{\pi^2}{n'_A} \qquad (rad^2) \quad (1)$$

where n'_A is the number of photons detected within a subaperture. This error is expressed at λ_A, mean wavelength of the wavefront sensor spectral bandwidth. For a correction at an infrared wavelength λ, the effective error is:

$$\sigma^2_d \approx 2.\frac{\pi^2}{n'_A}\left(\frac{\lambda_A}{\lambda}\right)^2 \qquad (rad^2) \quad (2)$$

In the COME-ON situation this error is plotted in Figure 12 (curve I) assuming 10 x 10 subapertures, an integration time of 1/125 s, a reference source of visual magnitude 12, a 500-800 nm spectral bandwidth, an overall transmission-quantum efficiency of 0.05.

4.2. Prediction error.

This error is due to the time lag of the system and requires a complete modeling of the system to be accurately determined. A rule of thumb relation has been proposed[12]:

$$\sigma^2_p \approx \left(\frac{\bar{v}}{r_o}.\frac{0.4}{f_c}\right)^{5/3} \qquad (rad^2) \quad (3)$$

where f_c is the 3 dB cut-off frequency of the system. In the present situation, with a sampling rate of 125 Hz, f_c can be roughly estimated to 25 Hz, which leads to the curve II of the figure 12.

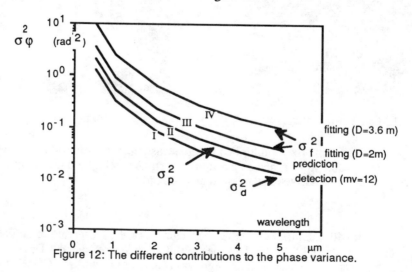

Figure 12: The different contributions to the phase variance.

4.3. Fitting error.

Due to its finite number of actuators, the mirror cannot compensate perfectly well for the degraded wavefront. It is assumed that with 10x10 subapertures the phase measurement error is negligible compared to 19 actuators mirror fitting error. Such an error can be described by[13]:

$$\sigma^2_f \approx K \left(\frac{1}{\sqrt{N}} \cdot \frac{D}{r_0} \right)^{5/3} \quad \left(rad^2 \right) \quad (4)$$

where K is a coefficient which depends on the mirror geometry and influence function of the actuators.

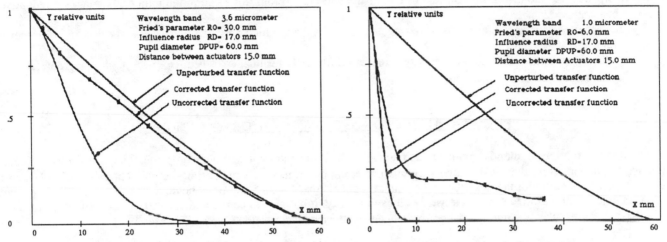

Figure 13: Calculated OTF of the COME-ON deformable mirror for two different wavelengths. (reference 14).

In the COME-ON geometry this coefficient can be derived from the reference[14], where the effective optical transfer function of the mirror has been calculated (see figure 13). The best fit of these results is given by K=0.3. Therefore the relation (4) is very similar to the expression given by Noll, for the Zernike polynomials[15] The corresponding curve as a function of r_0 is plotted in figure 12 (curve III and IV) for two diameters of telescope (D = 2 m, D = 3.6 m). It can be clearly seen that this error is the main cause of the limited performance of the system. In the next step (COME-ON+) it is foreseen to use a new technology mirror with a larger number of actuators, in order to overcome this limitation.

4.4. Anisoplanatism effects.

These effects have been calculated in reference [16]. The anisoplanatism effects can be seen as a degradation of the fitting of the mirror to the wavefront, and then characterized by F, a multiplicative factor to σ^2_f. This factor is function of the vertical turbulence profile, of N and of the field angle θ. It is plotted on figure 14 for different values of λ and D.

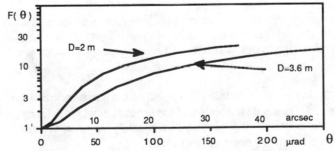

Figure 14: Increase of phase variance with field angle
(modal control with the 20 first Zernike polynomials).

4.5. Overall optical transfer function (O.T.F.) of the system.

The total variance of the phase is the sum of the independent contributions listed above:

$$\sigma^2_{\varphi} = \sigma^2_d + \sigma^2_p + F. \sigma^2_f \quad (rad^2) \quad (5)$$

For spatial frequencies larger than r_o, the resulting long exposure O.T.F. can be approximated by[13]:

$$\langle S \rangle = \tilde{S}_{d.l.} \exp - \sigma^2_{\varphi} \quad (6)$$

where $\tilde{S}_{d.l.}$ denotes the diffraction limited O.T.F. of the telescope. From this relation the major advantages of adaptive optics can be understood:

- in the Fourier space, high spatial frequencies are enhanced, which should improve the speckle interferometry methods,
- in the image space, the encircled energy is increased (the only residual error being exp-σ^2_{φ}), allowing detection of weak sources on noisy backgrounds.

5. CONSEQUENCES ON ASTRONOMICAL OBSERVATIONS.

The main limitation of adaptive optics in astronomy will be induced by the isoplanatic patch. The probability to find a reference bright enough in that field can be very small, keeping out of reach a large part of the sky. The table below[17] gives the coverage of the sky with the described technique. It appears that for 3.85 μm and above, a 4 meter class telescope can operate in a diffraction limited mode at most positions in the sky. It has also to be pointed out that the isoplanatic patch after correction, decreases when the number of corrected modes, in the modal correction scheme increases [16].

λ (μm)	1.2	2.2	3.85	10
r_o (m)	.30	.60	1.15	3.6
θ arcsecond	9	20	40	125
m_v lim	9	12	14	18
$C_p(\%)$	0	.1	10	100
$C_e(\%)$	0	.3	30	100

Table 2: Requirements for reference sources (from reference 17), m_v lim is the magnitude limit for the visible reference source, C_p is the sky coverage at the galactic pole, and C_e at the equator.

From these enhancements, which are feasible if a bright enough reference source is available within the isoplanatic patch, several improvements of astronomical observations are to be pointed out. The three main advantages expected from adaptive optics are:

- in imagery and spectrometry: the signal-to-noise ratio increases in the same order as the encircled energy, inducing a significant reduction in the exposure time. This is of great advantage for small field imaging or spectroscopy. The residual fitting error with adaptive optics results in a halo around the source which may not permit coronography and accurate photometry.

- in speckle imagery: it has been demonstrated that even with a partial correction[14], significant improvements may be expected. The exposure time could be longer[18] and the spectral bandwidth larger, which should improve signal to noise ratio. Moreover, the enhancement of high spatial frequency wing in the OTF should reduce the amount of post processing in speckle interferometry or image deconvolution.[19]

- in infrared imagery: the contribution of the sky background to the infrared signal will be reduced, improving the signal to noise ratio[20, 5]. With the same array detectors than for conventional imagery the focal length is increased to properly sample the resolved image. The induced smaller throughput allows a reduction of the parasitic thermal counterpart to the signal.

6. CONCLUSION

Basically designed to demonstrate the advantages and limitations of present technology adaptive optics in the field of astronomy, COME-ON will provide a unique tool to define the next generation instruments in the background of the new giant telescopes. Several points will be investigated by such an instrument: effects of isoplanatic patch size, coherence time and evolution of these parameters with the number of used modes.

Apart from these, different astrophysical programs are considered to be conducted at the diffraction limit: evolution of the SN1987A, subarcsecond imaging of the Galactic centre, studies of proto planetary structures. The instrument will be tested first at the end of 1989 in France at the 1.52m OHP telescope, before operation begins at the ESO 3.6m telescope at La Silla, Chili.

The instrument provides a bench to test new components either for wavefront sensing or for correction. The improvements to overcome the actual limitations are in the number of actuators, in the wavefront sensor and in the bandwidth of the control system. New components should be tested on an upgraded version of the actual bench named COME-ON+.

NOTE

This paper was also presented during the Technical Symposia on Aerospace Sensing in Orlando(March 1989), and will be published in the SPIE proceeding 1114.

REFERENCES

[1] P. Kern et al., Adaptive optical system for infrared observation, Proc. SPIE 860, (1987).

[2] F.Roddier, The effect of Atmospheric Turbulence in Optical Astronomy, Progress in Optics, Ed. E. Wolf, North Holland (1981).

[3] D.L.Fried, Optical resolution through a randomly inhomogenous medium for very long and very short exposure, J.O.S.A., 56, 1372 (1966).

[4] J.H. Hardy, Active optics in Astronomy, ESO-Proc., Garching, (1981).

[5] P.Kern et al., Prototype of an Adaptive optical system for infrared astronomy, ESO-Proc on Very Large Telescope and their Instrumentation, Garching, March 21-24, 1988.

[6] J.P.Gaffard, First tests on the 19-actuators deformable mirror for the COME-ON project, ESO-Proc on Very Large Telescope and their Instrumentation, Garching, March 21-24, 1988.

[7] F.Roddier, P.Eisenhardt, Proc. SPIE 628, 314 (1986).

[8] J.C.Fontanella, Analyse de surface d'onde, déconvolution et optique adaptative, J. Optics, vol 16, n°6, (1985).

[9] J.C. de Miscault, E.Hannonge M.Séchaud, G.Rousset, Adaptive optics system command definition and use of interaction matrix, ESO-Proc on Very Large Telescope and their Instrumentation, Garching, March 21-24, 1988.

[10] F.Lacombe, D.Tiphène, D.Rouan, P.Léna, M.Combes, Imagery with infrared arrays, I.Ground-based system and astronomical performances. Astron. Astrophys (1989) in press.

[11] G.Finger, A.F.M.Moorwood, Proc SPIE 865 (1987).

[12] D.P.Greenwood, Bandwidth specification for adaptive optics systems. J.O.S.A., vol 67, n°3, March 1977.

[13] J.W.Hardy, Active Optics in astronomy, ESO-Proc. on Scientific importance of high angular resolution at optical and infrared wavelengths. Garching, March 1981.

[14] J.P.Gaffard, C.Boyer, Adaptive optics for optimisation of image resolution, A.O (1987).

[15] R.J.Noll, Zernike Polynomials and Atmospheric Turbulence, J.O.S.A. vol.66 207 (1976)

[16] F.Chassat, submitted to J. Optics, Calcul du domaine d'isoplanétisme d'un système d'optique adaptative fonctionnant à travers la turbulence atmosphérique.1989.

[17] D.Mourard, N.Mercouroff, Optique adaptative, Rapport de stage de l'école Polytechnique (1986).

[18] F.Roddier, Interferometric imaging in optical astronomy, Physics Reports 1988.

[19] J.Primot, G.Rousset, J.C.Fontanella, Image deconvolution from wavefront sensing: Atmospheric turbulence simulation cell results, ESO-Proc on Very Large Telescope and their Instrumentation, Garching, March 21-24, 1988.

[20] P. Léna, Array imaging at high angular resolution, Proc of the Workshop on Ground based Astronomical Observations with IR Array Detectors, University of Hawaï at Hilo, (1987).

Deconvolution of turbulence-degraded images from wavefront sensing

J. Primot, G. Rousset, T. Marais and J.C. Fontanella,

Office National d'Etudes et de Recherches Aérospatiales,
BP 72, 92322 Châtillon Cedex, France

ABSTRACT

In this high-resolution technique, both wavefront phase and speckle image are recorded simultaneously. The image processing leads to a high signal-to-noise ratio than in speckle interferometry.

1. INTRODUCTION

The angular resolution of large ground-based telescopes is limited essentially by atmospheric turbulence. The optical resolution limit is of the order of one arc-second however large the aperture diameter may be. The turbulent atmosphere induces random spatial and temporal fluctuations in the wavefront coming from the object which drastically degrade the image.

Different post processing techniques have been proposed to overcome this natural limitation. They can be divided into two classes. The first one includes methods based on the processing of monochromatic short-exposure speckled images: i.e. speckle interferometry for example. The second one includes methods based on pupil plane interferometry.

The originality of the presented technique lies in the processing of data coming from both focal and pupil planes. In addition to an imaging camera, a wavefront sensor is conjugated with the entrance pupil to determine the wavefront simultaneously with the image. This makes possible to calculate the instantaneous optical transfer function, including the atmosphere. Hence, spatial frequencies which have not completely disappeared from the image can be corrected. Moreover, the lost spatial frequencies are different for each recorded image because of the random temporal evolution of the turbulence. Thus, the whole object frequency spectrum can be restored from a sufficiently large set of short-exposure images and associated wavefronts. The technique and some preliminary results have already been published[1].

2. PRINCIPLE

Let us consider an incoherent object O imaged by an optical system after transmission through turbulent atmosphere. The recorded intensity of the monochromatic short-exposure image at the instant i is I_i. The optical transfer, including the atmosphere, is characterized by the point spread function S_i which is assumed to be independent of its location in the image plane. This assumption is valid only in a limited field of view, called isoplanatic patch, which is of the order of a few arc-seconds for visible wavelengths. I_i is related to O by a convolution product; this can be expressed in the Fourier space:

$$\tilde{I}_i = \tilde{O} \cdot \tilde{S}_i \tag{1}$$

where the symbol $\sim$ denotes the Fourier transform of a function, and $\tilde{S}_i$ is the instantaneous optical transfer function. $\tilde{O}$ is calculated by an approach similar to the one used in Speckle Holography rather than a direct division in the Fourier space. We can thus define an estimator $\tilde{O}_e^M$:

$$\tilde{O}_e^M = \frac{\left\langle \tilde{I}_i \cdot \tilde{S}_i^* \right\rangle}{\left\langle \tilde{S}_i \cdot \tilde{S}_i^* \right\rangle} \tag{2}$$

where $\langle \ \rangle$ denotes the average over M records and $*$, the conjugate complex quantity.

It should be noticed that, as M approaches infinity, the denominator is equal to the square of the "speckle modulation function" related to the turbulence. In fact, $\tilde{O}_e^M$ corresponds to the best least-squares estimation of the object Fourier transform according to the considered set of measured data.

3. INSTANTANEOUS OPTICAL TRANSFER FUNCTION ESTIMATION

The image degradation along the propagation axis is induced by the optical path fluctuations due to the atmospheric turbulence. In a first approximation, which is usually called near-field approximation[3], wavefront amplitude fluctuations are neglected. Therefore the optical transfer function $\tilde{S}_i$ can be determined by the autocorrelation of $e^{i\Phi}$ by measuring the distorted wavefront phase Φ in the optical system pupil.

In order to estimate the distorted wavefront, we use a Hartmann-Shack wavefront sensor for the following reasons. First, it works with polychromatric radiation. As the atmosphere introduces essentially geometrical and not chromatric aberrations, it is possible to sense the wavefront in a large spectral bandwidth, e.g. the wavelengths not used for the imaging. Secondly, it works with extended sources within the isoplanatic patch.

This type of sensor allows the measurement of the local slopes of the phase in two perpendicular directions[1]. The phase is then reconstructed by a modal technique. The coefficients of the expansion of the turbulent phase Φ upon the Zernike polynomials are deduced from the gradients by a least-squares fitting.

4. NOISE LIMITATIONS OF THE METHOD

For low light level, the variance σ_Φ^2 on the reconstructed wavefront is the sum of two terms. The first one σ_{pn}^2, is related to the propagation of the photon noise induced error on the local slope measurements; the second one σ_m^2 is related to the necessarily limited size of the considered set of Zernike polynomials. The detailed calculation of these two terms can be found in[2]:

$$\sigma_\Phi^2 = \sigma_{pn}^2 + \sigma_m^2 \quad (rad^2) \tag{3}$$

$$\sigma_{pn}^2 \approx \frac{20 \ N_{sp}}{v \cdot N \cdot p} \quad (rad^2) \tag{4}$$

$$\sigma_m^2 \approx 0.25 \cdot (N/N_{sp})^{5/6} \quad (rad^2) \tag{5}$$

where N_{sp} is the number of subapertures of the Hartmann-Shack wavefront sensor, N, the number of speckles in the image, p, the number of photons by speckle, and v, the ratio between the spectral bandwidth devoted to the wavefront sensing and the spectral bandwidth devoted to the recording of the speckled images.

The optimal number of subapertures is deduced from the minimization of σ_Φ^2, so:

$$N_{sp} \approx v^{1/2} \cdot p^{1/2} \cdot N/10 \tag{6}$$

and

$$\sigma_\Phi^2 = 4 \cdot v^{-1/2} \cdot p^{-1/2} \quad (rad^2) \tag{7}$$

Let us now consider $\tilde{O}_e^M$, the estimator defined in eq. (2). If the denominator is assumed to be a good approximation of the speckle modulation function (in fact, there is a problem of bias which will not explained here), the error on the reconstructed object has two uncorrelated origins. The first one is related to the photon noise in the recorded speckled images, the second one, to the computed OTF according to the wavefront sensing error. This property allows the estimation of the signal-to-noise ratio of the method for low light level[1,2]:

$$SNR \approx \sqrt{M} \cdot p^{1/2} \cdot W^{1/2}(f) \cdot T_0^{1/2}(f)$$

where W(f) is the normalized energy density of the object, and $T_0(f)$, the ideal OTF.

This value can be compared with the SNR of the speckle interferometry:

$$SNR_{S1} \approx \sqrt{M} \cdot p \cdot W(f) \cdot T_o(f)$$

Thus, this new method for high-resolution imaging gives a higher signal-to-noise ratio for low light level. It is also a better way to restore the object, as the complexity of the object increases ($W(f) < 1$) and as the considered spatial frequency increases ($T_o(f)$ goes to zero).

5. EXPERIMENTAL RESULTS

An experiment has been carried out in ONERA in order to prove the capabilities of the method. The turbulence is artificially generated by mixing cold and hot air in a cell (cf figure 1). The ratio D/r_o is estimated at 13. The observed object is a slide of Mickey mouse (copyright the Walt Disney Company). Figures 2a and 2b show the unperturbed image and the associated point spread function; figures 2c and 2d, a typical short-exposure image and associated point spread function calculated from the wavefront sensing; figure 2e, the deconvolution obtained from a set of 200 records. The phase Φ is reconstructed over 56 Zernike polynomials.

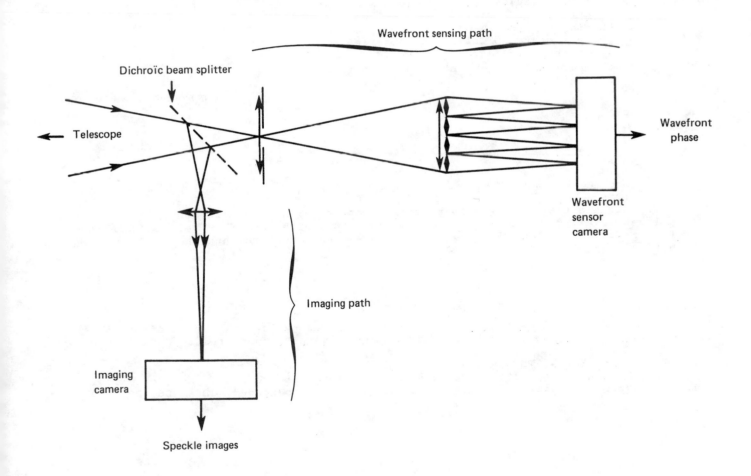

Figure 1 – Experimental set up for simultaneous imaging and wavefront sensing.

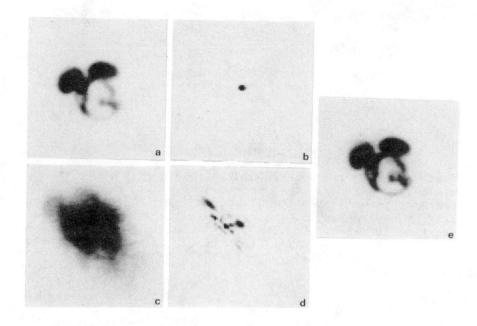

Figure 2 - Laboratory results of speckle image processing from the measurement of the wavefront:

    a) the unperturbed image,
    b) the associated point spread function,
    c) one turbulence degraded image ($D/r_0 = 13$),
    d) the corresponding point spread function,
    e) the best estimate of the object from 200 records.

6. CONCLUSION

This technique seems to be a very promising method for high resolution imaging especially for low light level. Compared to Knox and Thompson algorithm or other related techniques, it is not sensitive to speckle noise, and does not require hypothesis on turbulence stationarity.

REFERENCES

1. J. Primot, G. Rousset and J.C. Fontanella, "Deconvolution from wavefront sensing: a new technique for compensating turbulence-degraded images", submitted to JOSA A in December 1988.
2. J. Primot, Ph. D. Thesis, to be published.
3. J.W. Goodman, "Statistical optics", a Wiley Interscience Publ., New York, 1984.
4. R.J. Noll, "Zernike polynomials and atmospheric turbulence", JOSA, 66, 207, 1976.

THEORETICAL AND EXPERIMENTAL EVALUATION OF ISOPLANATIC PATCH SIZE FOR ADAPTIVE OPTICS(*)

by F. Chassat

MATRA ESPACE, 31, Rue des Cosmonautes,
Z.I. du Palays, 31077 Toulouse Cedex, France

G. Rousset and J. Primot
Office National d'Etudes et de Recherches Aérospatiales (ONERA)
BP 72, 92322 Châtillon Cédex, France

ABSTRACT

Correlation functions of the Zernike-polynomial expansion coefficients of turbulence induced aberrated wavefronts are presented and experimentally confirmed using laboratory-generated Kolmogorov turbulence. These functions are convenient for characterizing the anisoplanatic error for adaptive optics. The isoplanatic patch-size of such systems is evaluable according to their specific working parameters. We find, for example, with a 4 m telescope working at 3.5 μm and sensing the wavefront phase fluctuation on 20 Zernike polynomials, an isoplanatic patch about 22 arcseconds wide.

1. INTRODUCTION

Anisoplanatism is a source of performance degradation in high-resolution imaging techniques which are devised to overcome the effects of atmospheric turbulence[1]. It turns out that in many systems, phase corrections are determined from the turbulence perturbations on a propagation path and have to be applied to a slightly different path. This mismatch effect can be investigated by means of a phase expansion of the aberrated wavefronts in an adequate set of polynomials. In part 2, the phase is expanded in the set of Zernike polynomials and the correlations of the expansion coefficients between two directions of propagation are derived. In part 3, a laboratory experiment has been carried out to validate this theoretical analysis. Finally, in part 4, the evaluation of the influence of anisoplanatism is characterized for an adaptive optics system and is given in terms of the root-mean-square fluctuation error of the compensated phase.

2. CORRELATION OF THE COEFFICIENTS FOR A ZERNIKE-POLYNOMIAL EXPANSION OF THE WAVEFRONT PHASES FROM TWO POINT SOURCES OBSERVED THROUGH A TURBULENT MEDIUM

2.1. General considerations

According to G.C. Valley and S.M. Wandzura[2], and as will be shown in part 4, it is useful to expand aberrated wavefronts in an orthogonal set of polynomials and to characterize the correlation between two different wavefronts by the correlations of their polynomial expansion coefficients. In particular, these correlations are very convenient for investigating the isoplanatism error of many adaptive optics systems. Assuming the receiver is a uniformly illuminated circular aperture, the appropriate expansion functions are the Zernike polynomials. The latter are often preferred to the Karhunen-Loeve polynomials for modal control of adaptive optics systems[3] because of their analytical expressions, and because they correspond to the classical aberrations familiar to optics engineers[4]. The properties of these polynomials are well described by R.J. Noll[5] whose notation is adopted in the following paragraphs.

2.2. Zernike-polynomial expansion coefficient correlation

Let's consider two distant point-sources S_1 and S_2 which transmit monochromatic waves of wavelength λ through a turbulent medium (see Figure 1). The angles between the optical axis of the telescope circular aperture of diameter $D = 2 R$ and the propagation directions of the two incoming plane-waves are α_1 and α_2. We note $\alpha = |\alpha_1 - \alpha_2|$ the angular distance between the two sources.

We expand the phase Φ_1 and Φ_2 of the two received wavefronts in the set of the Zernike polynomials Z_j :

$$\Phi_1 (R\varrho,\Theta) = \sum_{j} a_j^{(i)} Z_j (\varrho,\Theta) \qquad (i=1,2) \tag{1}$$

(*) This paper has been presented at SPIE'89 Technical Symposia on Aerospace Sensing-ORLANDO - 27-31/03/1989.

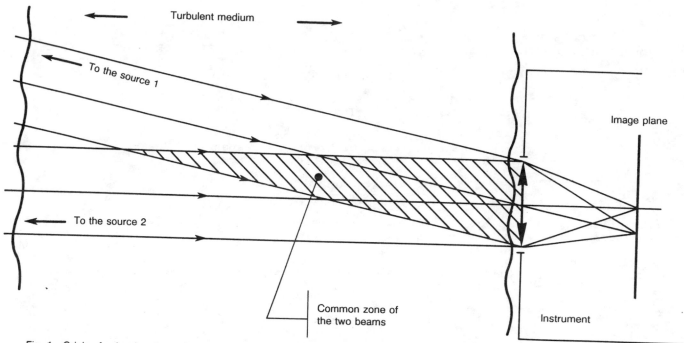

Fig. 1 - Origin of anisoplanatism : the waves coming from distinct sources encountered different disturbances on their paths to the telescope.

with ϱ and Θ, the normalized radial coordinate and the azimuthal coordinate over the telescope pupil; $a_j^{(1)}$ and $a_j^{(2)}$ are the two sets of expansion coefficients.

The dependence on the field angle of the expansion coefficient correlations is then derived by calculating the functions :

$$C_{jj}(\alpha) = \langle a_j^{(1)} a_j^{(2)} \rangle \tag{2}$$

where the brackets $\langle \rangle$ denote an ensemble average according to the statistical properties of the turbulence.

Assuming fully developed Kolmogorov turbulence, we find the final formulation[6,2] :

$$C_{jj}(\alpha) = (D/r_0)^{5/3} \frac{\int_0^L dh \; C_N^2(h) \; \sigma_j(\alpha h/R)}{\int_0^L dh \; C_N^2(h)} \tag{3}$$

where :

- L is the thickness of the turbulent medium;

- $C_N(h)$ is the structure constant of the refractive index fluctuations versus the distance h between a turbulent layer and the telescope pupil;

- r_0 is the Fried parameter, characterizing the transverse coherence length of the turbulence and defined by :

$$r_0 = [0.423 \; 4\Pi^2/\lambda^2 \int_0^L dh \; C_N^2(h)]^{-3/5} ; \tag{4}$$

- σ_j is an expression (see reference 6) depending on the order j of the Zernike polynomial and on the power spectrum of the refractive index fluctuations, which has been modelled according to Kolmogorov's law by a $k^{-11/3}$ slope profile.

As we can see, these functions have to be calculated for each particular $C_N(h)$ profile.

The results in the case of a uniform C_N along the propagation path are plotted on the curves of Figure 2. As an example, we show the correlation functions for polynomials having a radial degree n=2 (Figure 2a), and n=3 (Figure 2b). We notice the difference between the profiles of the two 3rd order astigmatisms (polynomials 5 and 6), or between the two 3rd order comas (polynomials 7 and 8). This is due to the relative orientation of the polynomials in the telescope pupil with respect to the virtual axis defined by the two point-sources.

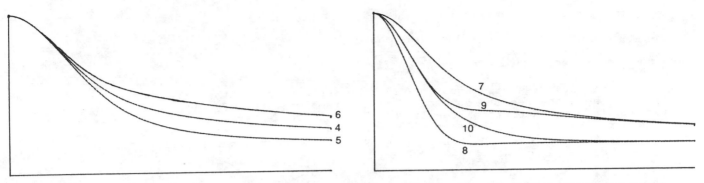

Fig. 2 - *Normalized correlation functions of Zernike-polynomial expansion coefficients for polynomials having a radial degree n = 2 (a) and n = 3 (b) (evaluation for a uniform C_N profile).*

We observe also that the loss of correlation increases with the radial degree of the polynomial as theoretically shown in references 2, 6. We thus obtain a classification of these correlation functions versus the radial degree of the polynomials.

3. EXPERIMENTAL EVIDENCE

An experiment was carried out in order to validate the above theoretical results. The experimental set-up and the results are briefly presented here.

3.1. Experimental set-up

Two pin-holes in an opaque plate are illuminated with a tungsten lamp and are situated in the focal plane of a collimating objective (see Figure 3). Both resulting collimated beams copropagate in an atmospheric turbulence simulation cell where turbulence is produced by mixing hot and cold air. At the exit of the cell, a lens corresponding to the telescope pupil images the two pin-holes on the Hartmann-Shack wavefront sensors, i.e., each wavefront sensor senses the wavefront coming from one pin-hole. Two synchronized C.C.D. cameras with light intensifiers (micro-channel plates) allow us to make simultaneous short-exposure records of the wavefront. The analogical signals delivered by the cameras are digitally converted and stored in a computer.

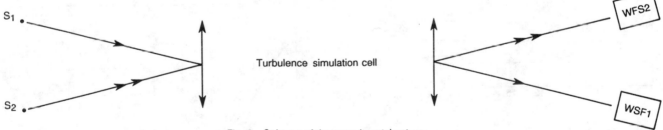

Fig. 3 - *Schema of the experimental set-up.*

The r_0 experimental value in the turbulence simulation cell was estimated to be about 5 mm for visible wavelengths around 0.6 µm. As the cell exit pupil is 30 mm wide, the D/r_0 value is about 6. The Hartmann-Shack wavefront sensors are identically designed with 12 by 12 lenslets. We can thus calculate 100 Zernike coefficients at most, because of the accuracy of the computer algorithm used to evaluate the Zernike-polynomial expansion coefficients[7]. Moreover, from a statistical point of view, we need at least 400 records, at a sampling rate below 5 Hz, in order to obtain a good ensemble average of the Zernike coefficients from the experimental data.

3.1. Experimental results

The correlation functions for the analysed Zernike polynomials are evaluated as follows

$$\left| \frac{C_{JJ}(\alpha)}{C_{JJ}(0)} \right|_{exp} = \frac{\overline{a_J^{(1)} \cdot a_J^{(2)}} - \overline{a_J^{(1)}} \cdot \overline{a_J^{(2)}}}{[\overline{(a_J^{(1)})^2} - (\overline{a_J^{(1)}})^2]^{1/2} \, [\overline{(a_J^{(2)})^2} - (\overline{a_J^{(2)}})^2]^{1/2}} \qquad (5)$$

where $\overline{x}$ denotes the mean value over the 400 recorded data of x.

We recall that in the case of the theory presented above,

$$\langle a_J{}^{(i)} \rangle = 0, \quad \langle (a_J{}^{(i)})^2 \rangle = C_{JJ}(0) \quad (i=1,2) \tag{6}$$

so equation (5) coincides with equation (1).

The experimental results [equation (5)] are represented by the full square dots in Figure 4. We have shown the results for the radial degrees n=2 and n=3, with the solid-line curves showing again the theoretical results of Figure 2. The experimental data reproduce within a .1 wide error-bar (in the scale of the normalized unit of Figure 4) around the theoretical curves. Agreement is good and confirms the predicted theoretical profiles.

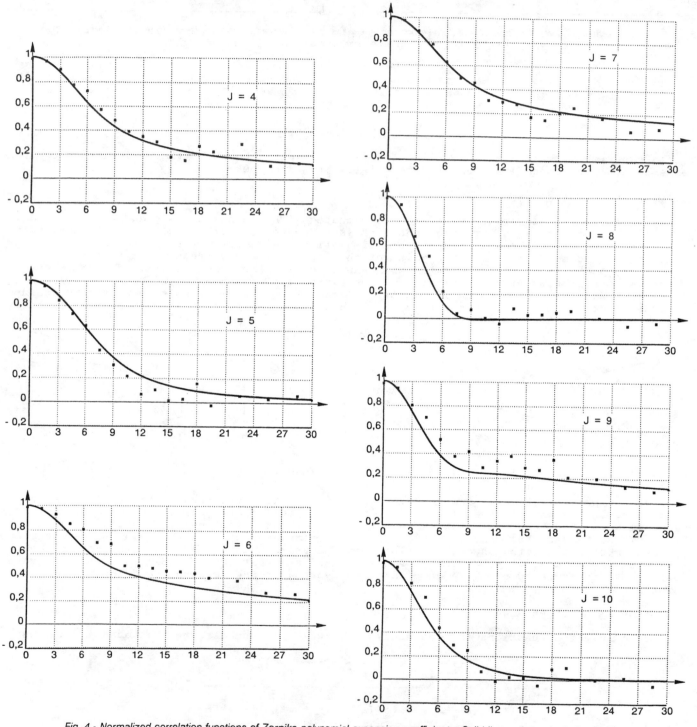

Fig. 4 - Normalized correlation functions of Zernike-polynomial expansion coefficients. Solid lines : theoretical evaluation (for a uniform C_N profile). Full squares : experimental measurements.

4. THEORETICAL EVALUATION OF THE ANISOPLANATIC ERROR FOR AN ADAPTIVE OPTICS SYSTEM

The correlation functions presented above allow us to characterize the error due to the anisoplanatism effect of many very high-resolution imaging techniques. Nevertheless, the calculation for the anisoplanatic error evaluation must remain very close to the particular process of the considered turbulence compensation system.

The purpose of the following paragraphs is to evaluate the anisoplanatic error for an adaptive optics system. It is an example of the use of the Zernike coefficients correlation functions.

4.1. Principle

The experimental set-up of an adaptive optics system is schematically shown in Figure 5. It corresponds to the case of a high-resolution imaging system compensating in real-time the turbulence-induced phase fluctuations. The anisoplanatic problem occurs, for instance, when the observed object (P) cannot be used as the source for the wavefront sensing. Then a distinct source (R) is needed in order to evaluate the phase perturbations and to derive the corrections to apply on the optical beam coming from (P). In the following discussion, we assume that the phase corrections (which are performed for example by means of a deformable mirror[9]) can be completely expressed with the Zernike polynomials having a radial degree less than or equal to N.

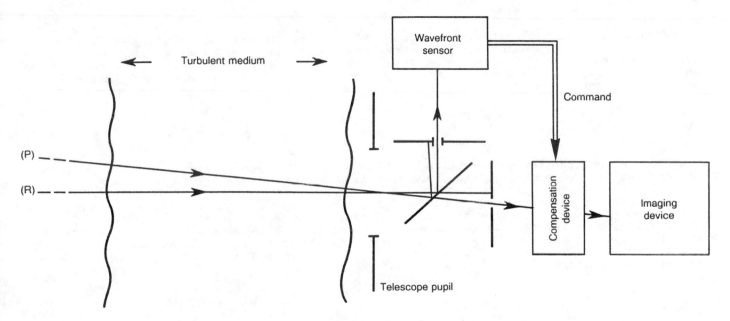

Fig. 5 - A sketch of an adaptive optics system.

4.2. Calculation of the compensation error

We are concerned with the evaluation of the error after corrections in terms of the root-mean-square fluctuation of the compensated phase. We assume for simplicity's sake that (P) and (R) are point-like sources.

Let $\tilde{\Phi}_P$ and $\tilde{\Phi}_R$ be the two incident wavefronts in the telescope pupil. We assume that the wavefront sensor measures the Zernike coefficients up to the J^{est} polynomial, and that the compensation system reproduces these Zernike polynomials exactly. Therefore, the wavefront sensing leads to the estimation of $\tilde{\Phi}_R$ by Φ_R :

$$\Phi_R = \sum_{j=2}^{J} a_j^{(R)} Z_j \qquad (7)$$

The piston mode Z_1 is neither considered nor needed (it is recalled that $\langle (a_1)^2 \rangle$ is theoretically infinite).

Then, after compensation of $\tilde{\Phi}_P$ by Φ_R we obtain the phase Φ_C which can be written :

$$\Phi_C = \tilde{\Phi}_P - \Phi_R = (\tilde{\Phi}_P - \Phi_P) + (\Phi_P - \Phi_R) \qquad (8)$$

This formulation exhibits the two origins of the residual error :

$$* \quad \widetilde{\Phi}_P - \Phi_P = \sum_{j=J+1}^{\infty} a_j^{(P)} Z_j \tag{9}$$

is the error due to the limited degree of freedom of the compensation system[5],

$$* \quad \Phi_P - \Phi_R = \sum_{j=2}^{J} (a_j^{(P)} - a_j^{(R)}) Z_j \tag{10}$$

is the anisoplanatism induced error on the analysed Zernike polynomials.

We then calculate the ensemble average value of the root-mean-square fluctuation of Φ_C :

$$\Delta_c = [\iint_{pupil} d^2r \langle (\Phi_c(r))^2 \rangle]^{1/2} \tag{11}$$

and we find in terms of the correlation functions[6] :

$$\Delta_c^2 = \sum_{j=J+1}^{\infty} C_{jj}(0) + 2.\sum_{j=2}^{J} (C_{jj}(0) - C_{jj}(\alpha)) \tag{12}$$

The case of a classical atmospheric C_N profile was considered here (Hugnagel, 1974[8]). To reduce numerical computations of the correlation functions, we add in equation (12) the correlations for each radial degree n. This leads to the calculation of the mean correlation functions corresponding to each radial degree n, noted C_{nn}. Without any approximation[6], the equation (12) thus becomes :

$$\Delta_c^2 = \sum_{n=N+1}^{\infty} (n+1) C_{nn}(0) + 2.\sum_{n=1}^{N} (n+1)(C_{nn}(0) - C_{nn}(\alpha)) \tag{13}$$

Let us notice that for a correction including all the polynomials of a radial degree less than or equal to N, we have to take into account $N(N+3)/2$ polynomials.

The $\Delta_c(\alpha)$ profiles are plotted for different values of N in the Figure 6. The $\Delta_c(0)$ values show the on-axis error due to the finite number of polynomials used for the compensation, as presented above in equation (9). It corresponds to the first term in the right-hand side of equation (13). This is therefore the lowest possible residual error which is only reached for a nearly zero field of view imaging device. Notice that this error decreases while increasing N.

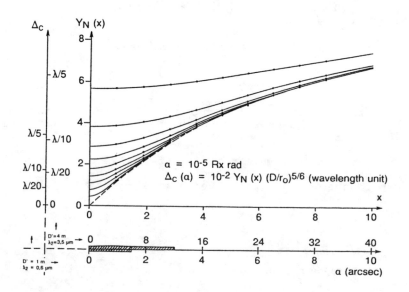

Fig. 6 - Solid line : root-mean-square fluctuation of the residual error (in wavelength unit) of the compensated phase. Dashed line : estimated profile of the inferior envelope of the solid line curves. Second set of axes : cases with $D = 4$ m, $\lambda = 3,5$ µm, $r_0 = 1$ m and with $D = 1$ m, $\lambda = 0,6$ µm, $r_0 = 12$ cm.

Moreover, the curves show the evolution of the error versus the field-angle for different values of N. We note that the advantage in considering more polynomials gets smaller and smaller while increasing angles. This is due to the fact that the anisoplanatic error (equation (10)), which participates in equation (13) by the second term of its right-hand side, increases while increasing N for any value of α. In fact, if $N' > N$, an angle $\alpha_{N,N'}$ can be defined such that :

$$\Delta_c(\alpha, N') < \Delta_c(\alpha, N) \quad \text{for } \alpha < \alpha_{N,N'}$$

and

$$\Delta_c(\alpha, N') > \Delta_c(\alpha, N) \quad \text{for } \alpha_{N,N'} < \alpha$$

We can then deduce the optimum number of polynomials needed in a range of angular separation between the two point sources (see Figure 7). The angular range in Figure 7 corresponds to higher angles than in Figure 6, but we would observe the same phenomenon for small angles by considering higher radial degrees.

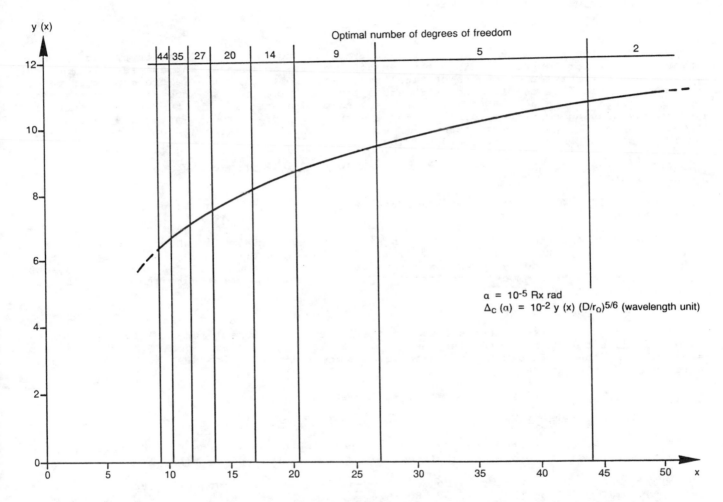

Fig. 7 - Lowest root-mean-square fluctuation of the residual error, versus the angle, and corresponding to an optimum number of corrections (represents the same curve as the dashed-line one in Figure 6).

Finally, if we define the isoplanatic patch size as the larger angle corresponding to $\Delta_c < \lambda/10$, we can then deduce from Figure 6 the different isoplanatic patch sizes for different degrees N and for an adequate device (N = $N_{optimum}$) by using the estimated behaviour shown by the dashed line. To give realistic examples, we added a second set of axes to figure 6, showing explicitly the cases of a 4 m telescope working at an infrared wavelength (3.5 μm), and of a 1 m telescope at visible wavelength (0.6 μm), both in the same atmospheric conditions[8]. The isoplanatic patch-sizes (assuming the reference source is at the center of the field of view) vary between 12 and 24 arsec for the 4 m telescope, and between 1.5 and 3 arcsec for the 1 m, depending on the number of polynomials used in the compensation system (hachured range on the horizontal axis in Figure 6). We notice that the isoplanatic patch size increases quickly at the beginning, while considering more and more polynomials. But, it rapidly reaches an optimum from which there is no gain in considering more polynomials. For the 4 m telescope, we have the isoplanatic patch sizes versus the number of polynomials:

```
12    arcsec  <———>  9 polynomials  (N=3)
19.6    "     <———> 14     "        (N=4)
22      "     <———> 20     "        (N=5)
22.8    "     <———> 27     "        (N=6)
23.4    "     <———> 35     "        (N=7)
23.8    "     <———> 44     "        (N=8)
24      "     <———> 54     "        (N=9)
```

It shows that the optimum is reached for about 27 polynomials and that the gain is negligible for higher values of N, compared to the great number of polynomials needed.

These results expressed in terms of the root-mean-square fluctuation of the compensated phase have now to be compared with previous ones, which were expressed by many authors in terms of the optical transfer function[10,11].

5. CONCLUSION

The correlation functions of the Zernike-polynomial expansion coefficients proved to be a convenient tool for characterizing the anisoplanatism influence on an adaptive optics system. The confirmation of the theoretical analysis, provided by the laboratory experiment, allows us to calculate isoplanatic patch sizes for adaptive optics according to particular design features (such as the r_0 value, the telescope diameter and the number of polynomials used in the sensing-correcting system). For the criterion of a root-mean-square fluctuation of the compensated phase less than $\lambda/10$, the isoplanatic patch (assuming the reference source is at the center of the field of view) is:

- 22 arcsec wide, for the 4 m telescope with $r_0 = 1$ m and 20 Zernike polynomials for the corrections.

- 3 arcsec wide, for the 1 m telescope with $r_0 = 12$ cm and 54 polynomials for the corrections.

We have shown that the isoplanatic patch size has an optimum value which is reached for a finite number of polynomials. Consequently, if off-axis reference sources are used with an adaptive optics system designed with numerous degrees of freedom, it could be advantageous to use it in a working-mode with less degrees of freedom according to the source angular separation.

6. ACKNOWLEDGMENTS

The authors would like to thank J.C. Fontanella and J. Laurent for helpful discussions and encouragement. Thanks are also due to G. Fertin, F. Mendez and M. Billard for their technical assistance. This work was partially supported by Direction des Recherches, Etudes et Techniques (DRET), France.

7. REFERENCES

1. D.L. Fried, "Anisoplanatism in adaptive optics", J. Opt. Soc. Am., 72, p. 52, 1982.

2. G.C. Valley, S.M. Wandzura, "Spatial correlation of phase-expansion coefficients for propagation through atmospheric turbulence", J. Opt. Soc. Am., 69, p. 712, 1979.

3. J.Y. Wang, J.K. Markey, "Modal compensation of atmospheric turbulence phase distortion", J. Opt. Soc. Am., 68, p. 78, 1978.

4. M. Born, E. Wolf, Principles of Optics. Pergamon Press, New-York, p. 464, 1975.

5. R.J. Noll, "Zernike polynomials and atmospheric turbulence", J. Opt. Soc. Am., 66, p. 207, 1976.

6. F. Chassat, "Theoretical evaluation of the isoplanatic patch size of an adaptive optics system working through the atmospheric turbulence", J. of Opt., 24, 1989.

7. J. Primot, G. Rousset, J.C. Fontanella, "Deconvolution from wavefront sensing: a new technique for compensating turbulence-degraded images", J. Opt. Soc. Am., (submitted).

8. R.E. Hufnagel, "Variations of atmospheric turbulence". in Digest of Technical Papers, Topical Meeting on Optical Propagation through Turbulence, Boulder, 1974.

9. J.W. Hardy, J.E. Lefebvre, C.L. Koliopoulos, "Real-time atmospheric compensation", J. Opt. Soc. Am., 67, p. 360, 1977.

10. D.L. Fried, "Varieties of isoplanatism", SPIE, 75, p. 20, 1976.

11. F. Roddier, C. Roddier, "Modelling atmospheric effects in adaptive optics systems for astronomical telescopes", SPIE, 628, p. 298, 1986.

Segmented mirrors for atmospheric compensation

Bill Hulburd

Thermo Electron Technologies Corporation
9555 Distribution Avenue
San Diego, California 92121-2305

ABSTRACT

An optical wavefront propagating through the atmosphere will be perturbed by local variations in the refractive index of the atmospheric gases. When accumulated over long optical path distances they will impart a spatial and temporally random distortion to the wavefront. These distortions have a characteristic spatially coherence length r_o, and an atmospheric decorrelation time τ_o. In directed energy applications, atmospheric distortions can reduce the peak target energy densities of large diameter laser beams by orders of magnitude. The problem is not solved through the use of larger apertures; once the aperture size increases beyond one or two τ_o the far-field spot remains constant in size. Hence, for large aperture systems, the overall performance is set by the spatial coherence of the atmosphere and not by the systems' exit pupil.

An adaptive optics (AO) system can compensate for the degrading effects of the atmosphere and significantly restore diffraction limited performance. A segmented or deformable mirror with appropriate control signals can "pre-distort" the outgoing beam to cancel the atmospheric aberration. To be effective, the system must measure and correct wavefront variations over spatial resolution elements on the order of one r_o and generate the compensation in a time less than τ_o.

TTC is currently producing its third generation of segmented mirrors for atmospheric compensation. Advanced systems for short wavelength operation with five hundred segments have been tested and proven as part of integrated adaptive optical systems, see Figure 1. These systems have excellent optical figure, wavefront fitting, and dynamic performance as well as low cost. The segmented mirrors' inherent modularity has eliminated the classic optical fabrication problems associated with large optics. Using TTC's third generation technology it is now practical to produce segmented wavefront correctors with more than 10,000 segments for compensation of short wavelength systems with apertures of 4 m and beyond.

1. WAVEFRONT FITTING

Each segment of the segmented mirror can be independently adjusted in tip, tilt and piston to approximate a smooth and continuous wavefront. Given an aperture filled with an array of vanishingly small segments it would be possible to exactly match the desired wavefront shape. Nonetheless, for economically feasible numbers of segments, it is still possible to provide an excellent match between the segmented mirror and an ideal wavefront corrector. The fitting error for an aberration with a Kolmogorov spectrum is given by

$$\Delta\phi^2 = 0.18 \left(\frac{d}{r_o}\right)^{5/3}$$

where $\Delta\phi^2$ is the wavefront rms phase error in radians, d is the segment diameter and r_o is the atmospheric coherence length. For a value of $(d/r_o) = 1$ the resultant Strehl contribution is 0.84. Figure 2 shows a photograph of the actual far-field spot of a segmented mirror correction of an aberration with a Kolmogorov spectrum. The photo is inductive of a Strehl of 0.60 which is due to the combination of wavefront sensor and segmented mirror errors. However, in the absence of external aberrations the segmented mirror is capable of Strehl performance in excess of 0.90.

2. THE EFFECT OF SEGMENT-TO-SEGMENT GAPS

In general the discontinuities caused by segment gaps are of minor impact on overall segmented mirror performance. There are two principal optical effects caused by the gaps, these are

- a loss of energy through the gaps, in proportion to the ratio of gap area to segment area;

- diffraction of energy from the central lobe of the diffraction pattern, also in proportion to the ratio of gap area to segment area.

There is no applicable broadening of the central lobe of the diffraction pattern due to moderately small gaps. Figure 3 and 4 show the far-field spot and encircled energy in far-field spot as a function of radius. The curves represent a segmented mirror without gaps, and with 2% overall gap area. The curves appear to differ only in scale indicating that the overall effect of the gaps is a reduction in the energy in the central lobe. The loss is equivalent to twice the ratio of gap area to segment area. The bulk of the energy diffracted by the gaps goes into a series of spots on orthogonal lines extending out from the central lobe. The spots are very dim compared with the central lobe, and they have spatial frequencies in multiples of the segment sized features on the mirror. These spots extend a long way out from the central lobe and are typically visible for distances three orders of magnitude greater than the width of the central lobe.

3. OPERATION WITH N-λ LONGITUDINAL TRUNCATION

One important feature of segmented mirrors is their ability to operate with n-λ longitudinal truncation. In applications where narrowband radiation is to be used the segment stroke can be reduced to as little as plus or minus one half wave (± l/2) and still operate effectively. This may create a wavefront with discrete phase steps at segments boundaries. However, if these steps are made to be exactly an integer number of waves the reflected wavefront will phase properly, and the mirror will have diffraction limited optical performance. The fitting error associated with the use of broad band radiation with a segmented mirror with n-λ steps is given by

$$\Delta\phi^2 = (2\pi n_{rms})^2 \left(\frac{\Delta\lambda}{\lambda}\right)^2$$

where n_{rms} is the number of wave steps used to keep the segments in a ± l/2 range. It is possible to operate in an n-λ mode with moderate fitting errors for laser linewidths on the order of several nanometers. Segmented mirrors operating in an n-λ mode can utilize actuators with reduced stroke and increased stiffness to improve dynamic performance and reduce cost. It also relaxes segment-to-segment piston alignment requirements, simplifies fabrication, and extends the effective tilt correction range of the wavefront corrector without increasing actuator stroke.

The use of the n-λ mode of operation of segmented mirrors makes it practical to develop atmospheric compensation systems with very large apertures. Normally, large output apertures require large actuator stroke. For aberrations with a Kolmogorov spectrum, the required stroke goes as the aperture diameter to the five thirds power, ($D^{5/3}$). However, the n-λ mode of the segmented mirror allows the required stroke to remain constant at ± l/2 independent of aperture size, see Figure 5.

4. ACTUATION OF THE SEGMENTS

The segmented mirror uses a tubular piezo-electric actuator with three degrees of freedom per segment, providing each segment with independent control of piston, tip, and tilt. The actuators are made from a ceramic material which exhibits the piezo-electric effect. When an electric field is applied across a piezo-electric material the resultant dislocation of charge centers causes the material to change shape. For the tabulator actuators used a voltage applied between the electrodes on the interior and exterior surfaces of the tube causes a change in the length. The change is a relatively small fraction of the materials dimension and is roughly proportional to the applied voltage. The effect is virtually instantaneous and response time is predominantly limited by the drive electronics and resonances in the actuator and support structure. The exterior electrode is divided into three electrically isolated domains each covering most of a 120° sector that extends the length of the tube. Different combinations of voltage between the three electrodes and the common interior electrode affect the changes in piston, tip, and tilt desired.

5. DYNAMIC PERFORMANCE OF SEGMENTED MIRRORS

The design of the TTC adaptive optics system call for the segmented mirror to be used in an open loop mode. Once the appropriate correction has been determined, the drive signal to the segmented mirror is updated and the segmented mirror moves to that position. No positional feedback is needed to linearize the mirrors response, it will move directly to the commanded position. Operation of the segmented mirror in an open loop mode can significantly simplify system design, particularly for a pulsed laser system. However, it stresses the performance of the actuators and the mounting of the segments to the actuators. To operate effectively in this mode the actuators length must change linearly with applied voltage, and the piston, tip, and tilt movements of the segment must be a linear sum of the three actuator lengths. The segmented mirror has demonstrated open loop positioning performance more than adequate for atmospheric compensation applications. The linearity that makes it possible to operate open loop can greatly enhance closed loop performance as well.

Segmented mirrors have excellent dynamic properties. Because each segment can move independently of all the others there is no actuator preloading or cross coupling between segments. The step response for an individual segment is shown in Figure 6, and the overall segmented mirrors' step response and open loop accuracy is shown in Figure 7. Response times better than 100 μs suggests that this segmented mirror has a potential for closed loop bandwidths on the order of 10 kHz and 5 kHz advanced systems are in use. In closed loop control systems higher loop bandwidth can translate directly to increased loop-gain and reduced loop tracking errors.

6. FABRICATION OF SEGMENTS AND COATINGS

The segmented mirror is assembled from a large number of figured and coated segments. Consequently there is complete flexibility in the choice of materials and procedures used in segment fabrication and coating. Segments can be made that have the best possible figure, finish, and coating present technology can provide. Particular system parameters will dictate what materials and size are optimal for an application. The segments may be prepared using any procedures an optical shop might want to use. Their small size enables a shop to polish and coat them in several low risk batches and makes it possible to obtain segments from multiple vendors. Inferior parts may be rejected at a low value-added stage of the fabrication and so insure production of a high quality segmented mirror.

Coatings used on segmented mirrors may be produced using techniques which are inherently superior those that can be applied to large aperture monolithic deformable mirrors. Reasonable choices for segment substrate materials place no restrictions on the use of high vacuum or elevated temperatures. Coaters can deposit any of the currently available materials in any environment they choose. By comparison, present technology monolithic deformable mirrors are coated near the last stages of assembly. Outgassing and temperature limits on non-optical materials present limitations on temperatures and vacuum that reduce overall coating quality.

Temperature is one of the most important variables controlled during the deposition of a high energy coating. Higher temperatures generally yield a better coating provided the substrate is not damaged by the heat. Coating quality is best when the chamber temperature is above the melting point of the elemental material being deposited. Many coatings are deposited at temperatures around 225° C for optimum overall performance. However, PZT actuators present in the chamber during monolithic deformable mirror coating may depolarize at temperatures as low as 115-120° C. Elevation to temperatures beyond this will substantially diminish an actuators piezoelectric sensitivity. Low temperature coating techniques applicable to monolithic deformable mirrors tend to perform poorly and are applied with greater difficulty. Sputtering techniques may be used at lower temperatures, however deformable mirrors require the coatings to be applied uniformly over larger areas. It becomes increasingly difficult to monitor the entire surface and deposit material uniformly with larger apertures.

With segmented mirrors, a substrate such as silicon can be heated to very high temperatures with ultra high vacuum. At these temperatures the coatings are harder, more uniform, have lower density of scatter centers, less absorption, and better adhesion to the substrate. This has many advantages for the system including maximizing damage threshold capabilities, minimizing cooling requirements, easier cleaning and improved durability.

7. SEGMENTED MIRROR MODULES

The TTC segmented mirrors is assembled from modules containing complete sets of segments and actuators in an n x n group (see Figure 8). TTC has produced working modules from 4 x 4 to 14 x 14 segments and used as many as 44 modules in one segmented array. By forming the segmented mirror from modules, all the potential problems with establishing and maintaining segment to segment gaps and alignment are resolved in fabrication and need not be dealt with in operation in addition, as shown in Figure 8, individual segments and actuators are repairable.

The modules are assembled after segment coating using a procedure that maintains the figure and provides excellent segment-to-segment alignment. The procedure permanently establishes the segment-to-segment gap size, and the nominal segment tip, tilt, and piston. The residual tip and tilt errors are less than three waves (HeNe 6328Å) per segment, and the residual piston error is on the order of 0.5 μm rms.

To facilitate integration of several modules into a segmented mirror each has three independent fine pitched screw adjustors which can be used to give independent control of module tip, tilt, and piston. These adjustors are used during installation to bring the whole module to gross alignment and rarely need attention again. These adjustors have been used successfully to reduce module-to-module piston differences to < 2 μm.

8. SEGMENTED MIRRORS FOR USE WITH WHITE-LIGHT

Systems using very broadband radiation or "white-light" can not make use of the n-λ mode. These systems require absolute phasing of the segments — the segments must be positioned to the correct wavefront without n-λ steps. The piston range required for atmospheric correction now must be completely met by the stroke of segmented mirror actuators, this typically being on the order of several microns. To compensate for the residual piston errors from fabrication some additional actuator stroke must be included, in the amount of about 2 μm (see Figure 9). When long stroke actuators are used, segmented mirror systems are well suited to operation with white light. It is possible to absolutely phase the individual segments to make a piece-wise continuous mirror. These mirrors' have optical performance analogous to their deformable counterparts.

To operate the segmented mirror in a white-light mode of operation, a device is needed to measure the residual absolute piston errors from fabrication so that the appropriate corrections can be applied. To meet the system figure requirement the device should have a measurement accuracy of better than λ/20. It should also unambiguously measure phase over a range greater than the peak to peak fabrication error of the modules, or about 3 μm OPD.

An interferometer which uses two laser wavelengths can effectively create a long 'synthetic-wavelength' by using the difference in the measurement of interferometric phases of the two lasers. For any given pair of wavelengths λ_1 and λ_2 there exists a distance λ_s such that

$$\lambda_s = \frac{\lambda_1 \lambda_2}{\lambda_1 - \lambda_2} .$$

Within the range of one λ_s the difference in measured phase for λ_1 and λ_2 changes linearly with distance and is monotonic. Consequently it is possible to simulate an interferometer of wavelength λ_s from measurements made with λ_1 and λ_2. An interferometer system suitable for two wavelengths operation is shown in Figure 10.

With a helium-neon laser and krypton-ion laser it is practical to generate several synthetic wavelengths. With the HeNe 6328Å line synthetic wavelengths of 3.30 μ, 5.57 μ, 9.82 μ, and 28.6 μ are available by using the Kr[1] at 5309Å, 5682Å, 6764Å, and 6471Å respectively. Any of these synthetic wavelengths should be adequate to unambiguously identify the absolute phase difference between segments of a segmented mirror. This makes it possible to absolutely phase the segments and operate the segmented mirror in a white-light mode, perfectly simulating a continuous mirror and completely eliminating n-λ steps.

9. COOLING OF SEGMENTED MIRRORS

Segmented mirrors lend themselves directly to cooling for high power applications. The segmentation of the reflective surface insures that the influence of thermally induced expansion is isolated to changes in individual segment figure. Each segment can be connected directly to the cooling-fluid intake manifold, and the fluid channel to, and through each segment can be made very short for low static pressure and flow induced jitter. The relatively small size of each segment, and their uniform size and placement on the segmented mirror is a major benefit to cooling. It insures that the reflective surface of the segmented mirror as a whole will receive very uniform cooling.

Thermo Technologies has demonstrated cooled segmented mirrors with absorption rates of 13 W/cm^2 (8 kW/cm^2 incident) with no figure distortion and bandwidths of 3 kHz.

Main beam energy lost through the gaps of the segmented mirror can be safely absorbed by cooling FINS in the segment support structure of the modules. In CW systems using closed loop control, changes in the shape of the support structure due to the thermal loading can be completely compensated by the segmented mirror. Cooling of the support structure is relatively straight-forward for typical gap areas, and does not create any appreciable jitter.

10. ASTRONOMICAL SYSTEM APPLICATIONS

Segmented mirrors, when integrated with appropriate wavefront sensors, figure seensors and control electronics, are well suited for astronomical systems. Figure 11 shows a simplified optical schematic for how an astronomical telescope could incorporate a segmented adaptive optic system.

Fig. 1. 512 segment, 22 cm aperture advanced segmented adaptive optic.

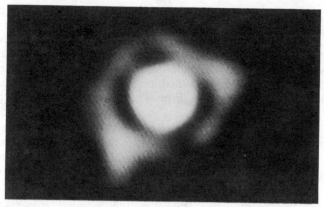

Fig. 2. Segmented mirror correction of Kolmogorov aberration. The segmented mirror had 496 segments and the aberration strength has a coherence length, r_o, equal to one segment diameter. The spot shown has a Strehl of 0.60.

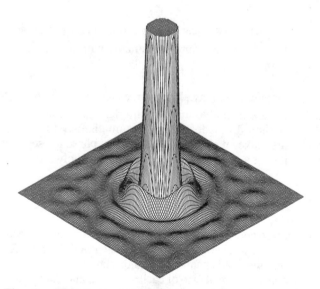

Fig. 3. PSF for a 101 segmented mirror. This plot shows the far-field spot pattern or point spread function for a round segmented mirror formed from 101 square segments, and includes the effects of a 2% gap area. The flat area at the top of the peak is an artifact from the truncation and re-scaling of the plot data, done to enhance some of the smaller features. The peak height of the plot is roughly five times that of the truncated peak.

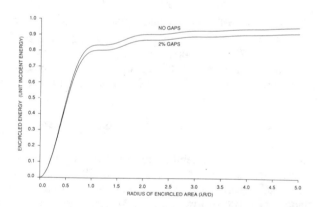

Fig. 4. Encircled energy vs. radius for a 101 segmented mirror. This plot shows the encircled energy in far-field spot of a round segmented mirror formed from 101 square segments. The upper curve represents an ideal 101 segment mirror, absolutely flat, and no gaps. The lower curve represents the same conditions, except with 2% overall gap area distributed evenly around the segments. The curve for the "no gap" condition asymptotically approaches 1.0; the curve for 2% gaps asymptotically approaches 0.98, but approaches it slowly over the next few thousand ordinal units. This plot helps to indicate that the gaps affect only a loss of power from the central lobe of the far-field.

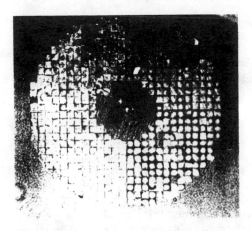

FIGURE SENSOR NULL

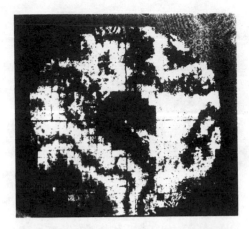

PHASE PLATE ABERRATION

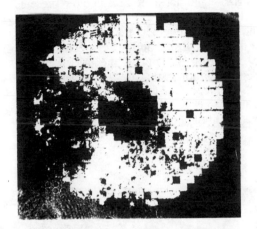

SMALL SHEAR CORRECTION

SMALL AND LARGE SHEAR CORRECTION

Fig. 5. Correction at 353 nm with advanced segmented mirror.

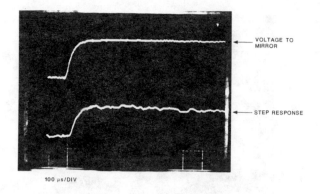

VOLTAGE TO MIRROR

STEP RESPONSE

100 µs/DIV

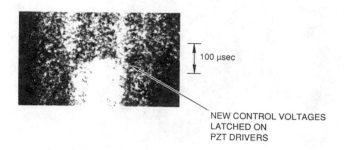

100 µsec

NEW CONTROL VOLTAGES
LATCHED ON
PZT DRIVERS

Fig. 6. Mirror segment actuator step response. This is typical data taken for over fifty segments of the 496 segment mirror. The data was taken with a high bandwidth heterodyne interferometer and represents mean segment piston.

Fig. 7. Dynamic response of the whole segmented mirror. An anamorphic lens system was used to image the segmented mirrors far-field spot on the slit of a streak camera. The horizontal dimension of the photo represents spatial data along the slit, the vertical dimension represents time. Taken together, the photo shows the time history of the far-field spot during a correction. Note that once the correction is applied the mirror moves directly and settles within about 100 µs. A segmented mirror with 496 segments was used here in an open loop control mode to correct a Kolmogorov aberration, the correction has a Strehl of about 0.60.

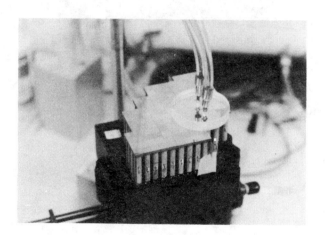

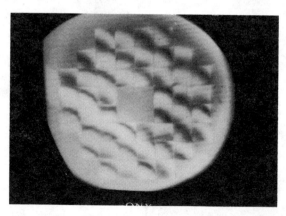

Fig. 8. Segmented mirror module. The 128 segment module shown is mounted on a 14 x 14 array block. An individual segment is being repaired with the standard repair station.

Fig. 9. Pseudo-white light interferogram of a segmented mirror module. The module fabrication technique causes the segments to lie within about 0.5 µm rms of the same absolute piston as demonstrated by this white light interferogram. The residual piston, tip and tilt errors of fabrication have been corrected by applying suitable voltages to the actuators of each segment. Interferograms taken with broadband light sources lose fringe contrast for piston differences on the order of the coherence length of the source. Given the 30 nm filter bandwidth used in this case, all fringe contrast will be lost for piston differences of about 17 µm or more. The generally uniform contrast along each fringe lines indicates that the segments are all within about ± 0.5 µm rms/par. (Note: Apparent segment curvature is beam train aberration.)

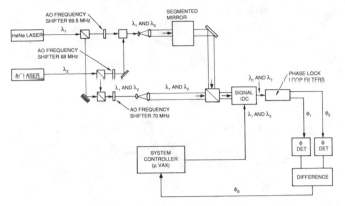

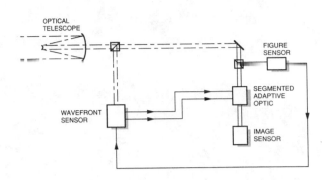

Fig. 10. Two color figure sensor. Shown is a schematic layout for a two wavelength interferometer capable of making synthetic wavelength phase measurements on segmented mirrors.

Fig. 11. Astronomical adaptive optic system.

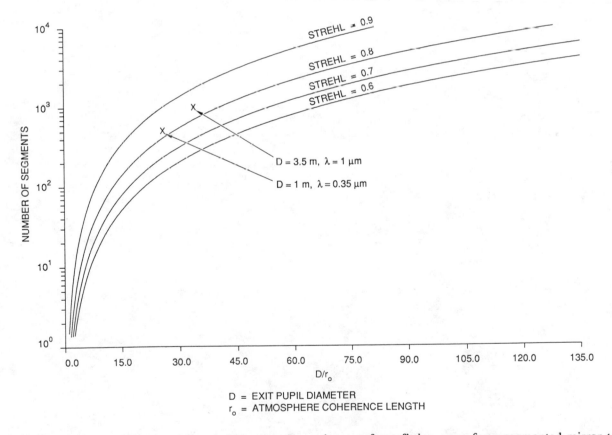

D = EXIT PUPIL DIAMETER
r_o = ATMOSPHERE COHERENCE LENGTH

Selection guide for number of segments. This plot shows the wavefront fitting error for a segmented mirror to an aberration with a Kolmogorov spectrum. To find the number of segments needed for a given aperture, compute the ration D/r_o for desired system exit pupil diameter D and atmospheric coherence length r_o. Starting from this point on the ordinal axis of the plot, move up to the appropriate line of constant Strehl ratio budgeted for the wavefront fitting error. From the line move left to the abscissa and read the number of segments.

SESSION 2

New Techniques for Ground-Based Astronomy

Chair
Fritz Merkle
European Southern Observatory (FRG)

New technologies in the VLT program

Daniel Enard

European Southern Observatory,
Karl-Schwarzschild-Str. 2, D-8046 Garching bei München, FRG

ABSTRACT

The Very Large Telescope program (VLT) is based on an array of four 8 m telescopes which can work in individual or combined modes.

This program will, and has already initiated the development of a number of new technologies in a wide variety of domains. Some of them are listed here below.

- Development of thin zero expansion glass mirrors.
- Development of metal mirror technology.
- Active support of deformable mirrors.
- Replication of optical surfaces.
- Wide band optical coatings.
- Very large brushless torque motors.
- Adaptive optical systems.

1. INTRODUCTION

The need for larger telescopes

Astronomy is now entering a new turning point in the long history of the development of instrumentation. The gradual evolution of astronomical detectors from the human eye to photographic plates and then to photoelectric detectors has now reached the stage in which high resolution two-dimensional detectors with nearly 100 per cent efficiency are either available or will soon be available for all spectral wavelengths from the optical ultraviolet to the deep infrared. Coating technology which makes it possible to limit the light losses on optical surfaces is also rapidly advancing. Nearly perfect coatings are available throughout the infrared and in the optical region. It will soon no longer be possible to upgrade the efficiency of existing telescopes by relatively inexpensive improvements in detector or instrumentation technology. Additional sensitivity will then be gained only by increasing the aperture.

The need for new technologies

Astronomers have always been limited in their ambitions by two factors. One was the technology available which they often had to develop themselves, the other was funding. Both were and still are closely associated in the sense that a reduction of cost is generally the result of a technological breakthrough.

A cost extrapolation law often used in the 60's and 70's assumed the cost of a telescope to be proportional to the primary mirror diameter with an exponent 2.7.

This law has been shown to have some validity for designs extrapolated from the Palomar 5 m telescope, i.e. for an equatorial mount and an F/ratio of the primary mirror close to F/3.

Using this law to evaluate the cost of very large apertures would lead to numbers, which would definitely kill any hope to go much beyond a few meters aperture. It is therefore clear that very large telescopes will be made possible only if their cost can be maintained at a reasonable level. This necessitates the development of new concepts and technologies.

These developments are furthermore made necessary by the need to improve the performance and the observational efficiency.

While 20 years ago, it was believed that the quality of images received at the ground level, what is called "seeing", would hardly be better than 1 arcsec, it is now definitely established that, at good sites, images of 0.5 arcsec or even better can be obtained a reasonable proportion of the time.

The practical efficiency of a telescope, i.e. its ability to concentrate a maximum of energy in the smallest area is as much dependent of its collecting area as on its imaging performance. It is therefore essential to increase the overall imaging performance of the telescope, i.e. its optical quality as well as its tracking accuracy.

It is also essential to use the best seeing periods for the most demanding scientific programs. This is only possible if the telescope and its instrumentation can be flexibly scheduled and remotely controlled. This puts severe requirements on the reliability and maintainability and requires to conceive telescopes as fully integrated machines operated like scientific satellites. Indeed, the basic advantage of ground observing, i.e. its flexibility and the possibility to quickly modify and up-grade instruments to take advantage of new developments must be kept, which does not simplify the task of the designer.

Trends for the new generation of telescopes

The goals mentioned above, the decrease of cost and the improvement of performance can only be met by making the telescopes more compact, lighter, less sensitive to their environment and to use increasingly sophisticated control techniques, the idea being to replace mechanical stability, which leads to heavy and expensive systems by closed loop servo systems.

This is above all relevant with the technology of the primary mirror. In conventional telescopes, the primary mirrors have a moderate relative aperture and are made out of massive pieces of glass supported in many points by counterweights in order to compensate for gravity load variations. New generation mirrors will be faster with F/ratio of the order of 1.5 to 2 and light.

The main technologies considered are:

a)   The segmented approach: the mirror is made of independent segments controlled in position by highly sensitive sensors and actuators.

b)   The thin meniscus approach: the mirror consists of a thin and flexible shell, the figure of which is controlled by a number of force actuators located at its back. The control of the distribution of forces provides the control of the mirror figure.

c)   Passive or semi passive light and rigid structures. The structures most commonly used are honeycomb and egg crate. Beyond about three to four metres it becomes unavoidable to introduce some active control to compensate residual gravity and thermal effects.

The use of light mirrors decreases considerably their cost as well as that of the telescope structure necessary to support it. Through a better control of the stability of the mechanical structure and mainly by introducing an active control of the telescope tracking, it is possible to integrate more the telescope in its environment and correct for errors generated by the wind such as flexions or vibrations. The classical domes are being replaced by relatively open enclosures, which eliminate the thermal convections, a source of image degradation, and also decrease dramatically the building costs.

		3.6 m 70's	NTT 80's	VLT 90's
OPTICS	%	18.4	30	32
MECHANICS	%	24.6	31.2	34.3
CONTROLS	%	14.4	16.4	18.7
BUILDING	%	42.6	23.4	15
TOTAL	MDM/m^2	7.9	3.2	1.5
COST PER TON OF PRIMARY MIRROR MDM/TON		7.5	4.4	3.3

Tabel 1:   Relative cost breakdown
           for different generations of telescopes

These trends are reflected into table 1 which shows the typical evolution of the telescope costs and of the shares of the main technologies for 3 generations. The 3.6 m is an equatorially mounted telescope built in the early 70's with an F/3 mirror and a conventional dome. The NTT is a 3.5 m telescope with an ALT-AZ mount, an F/2.2 primary mirror and an enclosure rotating with the telescope. The VLT is an array of four 8 m telescopes with ALT-AZ mounts, F/1.8 thin meniscus primaries and a highly simplified enclosure. The cost figures are expressed in millions DM per m² of collecting area. The decrease of the building share is matched by a corresponding increase of the other technologies above all optics and controls. The cost per m² decreases in absolute terms much more drastically than the cost per ton of primary mirror which demonstrates the influence of the mass of the primary mirror on cost. An important part of the decrease of cost between the VLT and the NTT is also due to economies of scale, the VLT having 200 m² of collecting area against 10 m² for the NTT.

2. THE ESO VERY LARGE TELESCOPE PROJECT (VLT)

The effective work on a 16 metres telescope, the "VERY LARGE TELESCOPE" project, began at ESO in 1984. The preliminary studies took about 4 years and the project was finally approved on December 8th, 1987.

More than simply a telescope, the VLT should be considered as a program which includes first of all the development of a number of new basic technologies, the development of instrument packages fully consistent with an automatized and remote control of the whole system as well as the implementation of adaptive optics and interferometric techniques which are major parts of this program.

Mirror technologies which could possibly become available in the next 10 years will not permit to exceed a size of 8 to 10 metres. Larger apertures can therefore only be obtained from the combination of several mirrors. The 16 m aperture of the ESO VLT results from the combination of four 8 m mirrors. Rather than to mount the 4 mirrors in the same structure, it has been decided to build an array of four independend 8 m telescopes and to recombine the beams at an external fixed location.

This provides a considerable flexibility for the construction and operation of the telescopes and leaves the possibility to use the array in an interferometric mode. Interferometric techniques have been mainly developed for radio astronomy and are yet in the infancy for the optical range. Much progress is however expected in the next decade and interferometry could become a major mode of operation of the VLT in the years 2000.

The 8 m telescopes are designed to operate with a minimum protection against wind in order to minimise the cost of the enclosure and to optimise the thermal environment of the telescope thus eliminating the local air turbulence, which often degrade the image quality in traditional domes. Fig. 1 shows a model of the VLT with a linear configuration. The enclosure is based on a new concept briefly described in the chapter.

The active primary mirrors

The primary mirrors of the VLT are thin shells of 8.2 m diameter and 175 mm thickness. They are made of Zerodur, a glass ceramics with a quasi zero thermal expansion produced by Schott (FRG).

The approach used so far for producing Zerodur mirror blanks was based on the casting of a massive blocks to be subsequently machined. This would be uneconomical, if possible at all, for pieces as large as those needed for the VLT. A new technology developed by Schott will be used instead. It consists of spinning a concave mould after the liquid glass has been poured in, until the top surface matches the radius of curvature of the mould. The rotation is stopped when the viscosity of the glass is sufficient for the glass to retain its shape. A mass of glass only slightly superior to that of the finished blank is cast. It is about 3 times less than for the conventional technique and reduces considerably the cost and time for machining (Fig. 2).

In parallel, a metal technology is being developed as an alternative. Metal and in particular aluminium can replace glass. Its main drawback is its thermal expansion which is largely compensated by its high thermal conductivity, which avoids local deformation generated by temperature gradients. Large deformations which may still exist are compensated by the active support which is anyway necessary for a thin meniscus whether it is made of glass or not. Several technologies for producing an aluminium mirror blank of large dimension are being tested. One of them is the fusing of forged aluminium plates with electron beam welding. The other one called build-up welding consists of a continuous process of welding by which the piece is "formed" by addition of a high number of welding seams.

The essential feature of the VLT primary mirror technology is its active control. The principle has been often described and is shown by Fig. 3. A wavefront sensor is locked on a bright star located within the unvignetted field of view of the telescope and provides the wavefront error map to a computer, which determines the modification of forces to be applied on the active supports of the mirror to correct its shape. In the same way the centering and focus errors of the optical system are measured and corrected with the secondary mirror. The bandwidth of this active system is small (0.1 to 1 Hz) because only deformations due to gravity and temperature variations, and to some extent to wind, are corrected.

The axial support system of each primary mirror is made of 150 discrete supports. Each has a passive stage consisting of an hydraulic pad and an active stage consisting of an electro mechanical force actuator. The hydraulic pads are connected together in 3 sectors of 120° and form the equivalent of a wiffle-tree. This system takes up the normal gravity load and adjusts itself automatically to gravity load variations when the telescope moves in elevation. The active stage provides the correction forces which control the mirror figure.

The main advantages of an active system are to maintain optimum performance of the telescope but also to reduce the cost and leadtime for the mirror figuring and polishing. Effectively, tolerances for low spatial frequency errors and, in particular, astigmatism which is the most sensitive mode, can be greatly relaxed compared with a conventional passive mirror.

The active secondary mirrors

Telescope optics is very sensitive to the relative centering of the primary and secondary mirrors. The secondary mirror has in addition lateral and axial motions to perform initial centering and focus. In the NTT and the VLT the secondary mirror lateral and axial motions will be permanently under the control of the active optics system, so that perfect focus and centering will be achieved.

In addition, because of the tough requirements on tracking performance, especially for the IR for which images at the limit of diffraction can be obtained with the VLT, it is necessary to correct for fast tracking errors with the secondary mirror.

The principle used with the VLT is shown by Fig. 4. It is based on a magnetic bearing used as a 2-dimensional actuator. This bearing drives the mirror support which through 3 flexion bars can slightly rotate around the mirror vertex. This system requires a very sophisticated control system in order to achieve a 15 Hz bandwidth and a final tracking accuracy better than 0.05 arcsec required to take advantage of the best seeing conditions.

The mirror itself, which is about 1.2 m in diameter, will be lightweighted and its surface obtained through a replication of a concave master surface. Replication of high quality optical surfaces has been realised for diameters of about 500 mm. The technology has to be extended beyond 1 m to be fully exploited by the VLT.

Substrates considered so far are lightweighted Zerodur or Beryllium. The latter is very attractive because of its outstanding mechanical properties and low density. A high quality Beryllium mirror of the size required by the VLT has not yet been realised however.

The same device used for active tracking can also be used for chopping in the IR. Chopping consists of alternating very rapidly the telescope pointing from the object being observed to a sky position which is used to substract the sky background radiation from the object. The VLT secondary mirrors will be capable to chop at 5 Hz and one arcminute amplitude in a square wave mode.

Mechanical structure, drives and encoders

The mechanical structure of the VLT unit telescopes is a highly optimised frame work (Fig. 5). The total moving mass is 230 tons, i.e. 10 times the mass of the primary mirror. In more conventional telescope structures this ratio is about 20.

The VLT may use direct drives instead of the conventional gear wheel and pignon solution. A direct drive solution uses large brushless torque motors located directly on the telescope axis. The moment is transferred to the structure without any contact, hence no friction and a better performance.

For the elevation axis, 2 motors about 2.4 m in diameter will be located directly on the shafts.

For the azimuth axis, a large segmented motor about 10 m diameter will be associated to the azimuth hydrostatic bearing.

Encoders will be either existing strip optical encoders of large diameter providing a very high resolution or laser gyrometers. Gyrolasers would provide, from a reference position, such as the vertical of the telescope tube, the velocity which by integration would give the position. Existing gyrolasers do not provide the necessary accuracy. It is, however, possible to develop larger systems which would be adequate for controlling the motion of a telescope. If such an approach succeeds, it would have numerous applications in a variety of domains such as machine tools.

The inflatable dome concept

As discussed before it is necessary to cut down the cost of the building and also to allow a ventilation of the telescope whilst protecting it of strong winds.

A concept of inflatable dome satisfying those two requirements is being developed. Conventional inflatable constructions used for protecting antennas or sport grounds are based on a single plastic fabric maintained in shape by an internal overpressure which is also used to compensate the wind pressure. A similar principle is used for the inflatable dome, but because the dome must open frequently and also for insulation and reliability reasons, the plastic cover is a double skin construction arranged in separately inflated ribs and is supported by a rigid steel structure made of hoops articulated on two diametrically opposed shafts.

A demonstration prototype has been built and erected at the ESO observatory in Chile, and is being tested.

Fig. 6 shows the principle of the inflatable dome concept and Fig. 7 shows the prototype installed in Chile.

Adaptive optics and interferometry

It is one of the fundamental advantage of an array to offer the possibility to combine the telescope beams in a phased mode with which the spatial resolution of a single telescope can be increased by more than one order of magnitude.

Up to now, this phased or interferometric combination has been realised for very small apertures and relatively short base lines. The problem of a phased combination of the VLT is immense. It necessitates firstly to phase the individual telescope apertures with an adaptive system (see J.M. Beckers' paper at this conference), then to compensate the variation of path length between telescopes with optical delay lines and to correct for fast phase variations generated by the atmosphere as well as by the limited stability of the telescopes and their auxiliary optical components. The stability goal is of the order of the wavelength and a large number of optical components are necessary to combine the four telescopes. The approach is to have most of the components passively stable and to control the stability of the outcoming beams with a few dynamically controlled elements.

This technology is obviously still in the infancy. However, the basic system components exist or can be developed.

Providing the necessary means are mobilised, interferometry with large apertures could become the major breakthrough of this century in astronomical observation and would undoubtedly lead to fascinating as well as unexpected discoveries.

It is one of the major goal of the VLT.

3. CONCLUSION

The VLT represents therefore alltogether a catalysor for the development of new technologies with far reaching applications as much as by itself a new technology for astronomical observation.

Figure 1. Model of the Very Large Telescope. The 16 m aperture is obtained through the combination of four 8 m telescopes.

Figure 2. A 4 metres spin cast mirror. This mirror
is half the diameter required for each of the four
unit telescopes of the VLT. It has been produced by
Schott as a demonstration of the technology proposed
for the VLT.

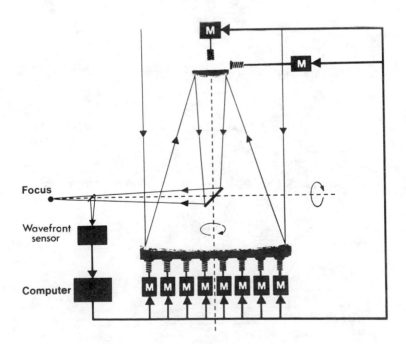

Figure 3. Scheme of the active optics system. Wavefront
errors are determined in quasi real time, from the
analysis of the image of a reference star. After processing
the forces applied to the primary mirror and the position
of the secondary mirror are modified in order to correct
the telescope optics.

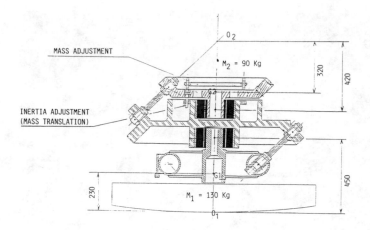

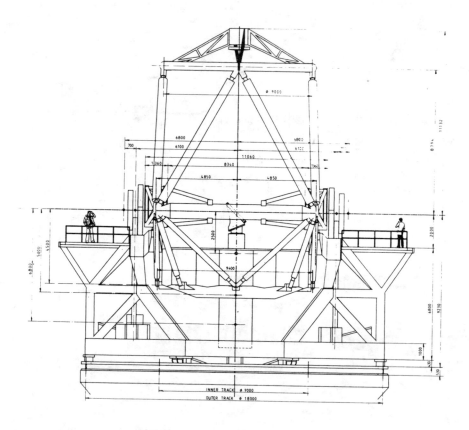

Figure 4. Scheme of the active secondary mirror. The mirror is supported with three flexion bars centered on the mirror vertex. A magnetic bearing is used as a two-dimensional actuator to control the mirror angular position. A similar system is used to control a counter mass which acts as a dynamic damper.

Figure 5. Mechanical structure of the 8 m unit telescopes.

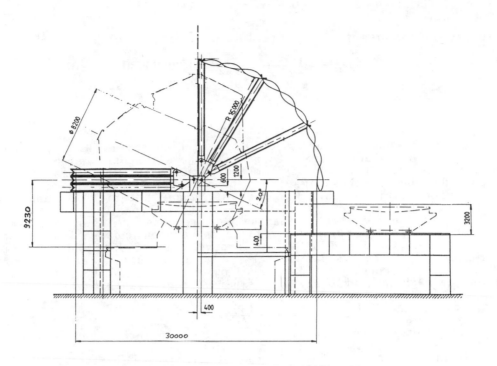

Figure 6. Scheme of an inflatable dome, a possible concept for the enclosure of the VLT unit telescopes.

Figure 7. Experimental 15 m diameter inflatable dome erected at La Silla. A slight overpressure is sufficient to oppose the most extreme wind loads. An articulated steel structure consisting of hoops is used to maintain the shape of the envelope during opening and closing.

A video-polarimeter for metrology, field inspection and telescopic observations.

Audouin Dollfus, Thierry Fauconnier

Observatoire de Paris, 92195 Meudon, France.

ABSTRACT

A Video-Polarimeter enables imaging of a field exclusively with the light which is polarized. A polarization selector isolates at will the six Stokes parameters. A CCD detector array feeds the images on a video system and on a memory. An interactive image processor computes combinations of these images to produce final images reproducing the scene in degree of circular polarization, in degree of linear polarization and in the azimuth of the linear polarization.

Application for bidimensional polarization measurements in laboratory are illustrated. The Video-Polarimeter allows also open air field inspection and enables detection of artificial objects added in the field of view. Through a telescope, the instrument produces polarization images of astrophysical objects such as planetary surfaces. Adapted to a monochromatic solar telescope, the design allows analysis of the photospheric active centers by producing magnetic, velocity and temperature gradient images.

I - PRINCIPLE

I.1. The Video-Polarimeter. The instrument "Video-Polarimeter" produces images of a scene exclusively with the component of its light which is polarized. It displays images of the degree of linear polarization, the degree of circular polarization, and the azimuth of linear polarization. The instrument was designed at Observatoire de Paris (Dollfus et al., 1989).

A scene which is made of unpolarized light appears as a uniform grey field. Features in the scene which produce a light circularly polarized appear superimposed, added or substracted, depending of the sense of the circularity, and with a contrast proportional to the amount of circular polarization.

At will, the instrument displays also the scene in linear polarization, with light hued features where the linear polarization is parallel to a reference azimuth, and dark hued where the polarization is normal to this direction. The same type of result can be also obtained but with the reference azimuth at +45°.

Combination of these two last images produces a field with luminance proportional to the degree of linear polarization, irrespectively of its azimuths. Another combination translates the field into the azimuths of the linear polarization.

These images are produced on a video-screen, almost in real time; they can be stored for further analysis and computer processing. They are quantitative; the degree of polarization can be measured for each pixel with an accuracy of 0.4%, or better when adjacent pixels are merged.

Other works along these lines have been those by Walraven (1981) and by Prosch et al., (1983).

I.2. The Stokes parameters. A light flux is usually a mixture of light with a fraction which is unpolarized, a fraction which is polarized circularly and a fraction which is linearly polarized in an azimuth θ. these properties are traditionally described by the Stokes vector

in which, over the field of x, y of the instrument :

I(x,y) is the total flux in the area x, y,

$$S = \begin{pmatrix} I \\ Q \\ U \\ V \end{pmatrix}$$

+Q(x,y) is the flux produced by the light which is linearly polarized in a direction parallel (+) or perpendicular (-) to a reference azimuth.

+U(x,y) is the same, for a direction at +45° of the reference azimuth.

+V(x,y) is the flux produced by the light which is circularly polarized with a rotation trigonometric (+) or inverse (-).

When the polarization is produced by scattering or reflection processes, the azimuth of reference is usually taken perpendicular to the directions of the incident and of the emergent beams. We assume $I = E_O + E_p$ in which E_p is the flux of light which is polarized, and E_O is the flux of unpolarized light. We have $I = E_O + Q + U + V$.

1.3. Polarization imagery construction.

The instrument records successively or sequentially six images, respectively designated $R(+Q)$, $R(-Q)$, $R(+U)$, $R(-U)$, $R(+V)$ and $R(-V)$. The image $R(+Q)$, for example, behaves as if it was taken through a polarizer selecting the light linearly polarized along the azimuth of reference $\theta = 0°$, and transmit the flux $R(+Q) = Q + \frac{1}{2}(E_O + U + V)$. The image $R(-Q)$ behaves as through a polarizer at $90°$, with the flux $+Q$ not transmitted and $R(-Q) = \frac{1}{2}(E_O + U + V)$. Immediately memorized, these two images $R(+Q)$ and $R(-Q)$ are then combined by a real-time processing device. The difference gives Q, the addition gives I, the ratio produces Q/I which is the image of the field in degree of linear polarization for the azimuths taken as reference. The same is true for the images $R(+U)$ and $R(-U)$ which display the field in degree of U/I and for $R(+V)$ and $R(-V)$ which produce images in degree of circular polarization V/I.

The three images Q/I, U/I and V/I held all the information about the polarization all over the field analysed. However, it is often expedient for interpretation to display the result in another set of parameters which are :

- $P(x,y)$, the degree of linear polarization, irrespectively of the azimuth,
- $\theta(x,y)$, the azimuth,
- $e(x,y)$, the degree of circular polarization.

The third image $e(x,y)$ is the same as V/I. The two others are produced by combining the two images Q/I and U/I to compute :

$$P(x,y) = [(Q/I)^2 + (U/I)^2]^{\frac{1}{2}}$$
$$\theta(y,y) = \frac{1}{2} \text{ arctg } U/Q$$

2 - POLARIZATION SELECTOR

In front of the objective lens which images the field on the detector, there is a fixed polarizer sheet P transmitting the light at a reference position angle $0°$. Ahead, there is a fixed quarter-wave retardation plate $(\lambda/4)_O$ with axis at $+45°$. Then, two quarter-wave plates $(\lambda/4)_1$ and $(\lambda/4)_2$ are added. Their axes are initially set at $\alpha_1 = \alpha_2 = 0°$ and they can be rotated around the beam axis by steps of exactly $45.0°$. When the front plate $(\lambda/4)_1$ is incremented by $+45°$, the over plate $(\lambda/4)_2$ is mechanically steped by $-45°$, at the same time, but for each even step of the front plate only.

During a complete cycle of eight increments R_i, the front plate occupies successively eight positions at $+45°$ each other from $0°$ to $+360°$, the second plate occupies four positions at $-45°$ each other from $0°$ to $-180°$. The configurations which are selected are given in the following table :

Position	1	2	3	4	5	6	7	8
α_1	0	$+\Pi/4$	$+\Pi/2$	$+3\Pi/4$	Π	$5\Pi/4$	$3\Pi/2$	$7\Pi/4$
α_2	0	0	$-\Pi+4$	$-\Pi/4$	$-\Pi/2$	$-\Pi/2$	$-3\Pi/4$	$-3\Pi/4$
Selection	$R(+V_O)$	$R(+Q_O)$	$R(+Q_O)$	$R(-V_O)$	$R(+V_O)$	$R(-U_O)$	$R(-Q_O)$	$R(-V_O)$

These configurations have been demonstrated with a Poincaré sphere analysis by Dollfus (1985). They can be computed by a Mueller matrix development which produces :

$$R_i = -\sin 2\alpha_2 [Q_O \cos^2 2\alpha_1 + U_O \sin 2\alpha_1 \cos 2\alpha_1 - V_O \sin 2\alpha_1] + \cos 2\alpha_2 [Q_O \sin 2\alpha_1 \cos 2\alpha_1 + U_O \sin^2 2\alpha_1 + V_O \cos 2\alpha_1]$$

Finally the following imaging substractions produce the required Stokes parameters

$$(R_3 - R_7) \rightarrow 2Q_O \qquad (R_2 - R_6) \rightarrow 2U_O \qquad (R_1 - R_4) \rightarrow 2V_O$$

Alternatively, the parameter $2V_O$ can be isolated by one of the three other combinations $(R5 - R4)$, $(R5 - R8)$ or $(R1 - R8)$.

If the phase retardation of the quarter wave plates departs slightly from the correct value $\varphi(\lambda) = \Pi/4$ to produce $\varphi(\lambda) = \Pi/4 + \epsilon(\lambda)$, then a spurious signal is introduced and, when selecting for example Q_O, we collect instead :

$$Q'_O = \frac{Q_O + \epsilon V_O}{1 - \epsilon V_O}$$

V is injected in the signal and the resulting "cross-talk" could be serious when Q_O is small and V_O large. If $\varphi = 1°$, the spurious signal which is introduced is $1.54 \times 10^{-2} V_O$.

In order to minimize this effect, the three quarter wave plates are achromatic components of the Beckers type, made of a quartz plate cemented with a synthetic magnesium fluorid MgF plate. The radio between the two thicknesses is 1.16. The residual wavelength dependence of the birefringence and other details are found in Beckers (1972).

Assuming now correct retardation for the quarter wave plates, but position angles α_1 or α_2 departing slightly from their true orientations which are exact multiple of 45°, then $\alpha_1 = m\Pi/4 + \beta_1$ and $\alpha_2 = n\Pi/4 + \beta_2$ and similar computation produces :

$$Q'_O = \frac{Q_O + 2\beta_2 U_O}{1 - 2\beta_1 U_O}$$

U_O is now injected in the signal. If $\alpha = 1°$, a cross-talk of $3\times10^{-2} U_O$ is introduced.

A mechanical design reduces this effect to a negligible value. The two rotating retardation plates are held each in a eight position Genova-cross mounting, which gives mechanically fixed positions angles at exactly 45° with the relevant mechanical accuracy. A proper gearing associate the driving shafts of the two Genova-crosses, with a relative rotation rate of $+\alpha$ and $-\alpha/2$. The driving motor operates the gear to produce a step rotation of 45° in less than 100 millisec.; then, the two plates rest at their exact new position until the drive shaft makes a new revolution to initiate a second 45° step. The motion is such that the second plate is operated exactly at the same time and in the opposite direction, once every two movements in the first plate. The principle of the double Genova-cross mechanism is outlined in Fig. 1. Each of the six combinations $R(\pm Q_O)$, $R(\pm U_O)$ and $R(\pm V_O)$ can be individually selected at will, or they can be sequentially driven at a maximum rate of several positions each second.

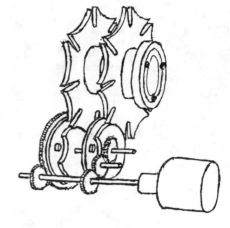

Figure 1

3 - DETECTOR

The camera IS-400 manufactured by the company I2S is equipped with a detector CCD Thomson THX 7861, with 576 x 384 pixels of 23 x 23 $(\mu m)^2$ size covering a surface of 6.624mm (vertical) x 8.832 mm (horizontal). The response is 18mV/lux with a saturation at 27 lux and a signal/noise ratio of 2500.

The CCD THX 7861 is controlled by a CCIR standard board. The need for video-polarimetry implies the positioning of the different images within the accuracy of a same pixel. For this purpose, the camera is genlocked to the digitalizer board.

In addition to the classical TV display, the camera can be used with an integration mode enabling a maximum integration time of around 30 min., limited by the thermal dark current. The detector is held in a vacuum chamber and cooled by a Peltier effect cryogenic design, decreasing the temperature by 45°C below the room temperature. The operator assigns an exposure time and control the scene evolution in a video-monitor in which, after each integration, the image is immediately replaced by the new up-dated image. Images can be kept, at will or sequentially, and placed on record.

4 - PROCESSING

The camera feeds the device sketched in the block diagram of Fig. 2.

4.1. The digitalizer-display. The digitalizer-display block includes three boards linked by a VME bus. The VIDEO board digitalizes the camera signal into 8 bits and introduces a tabulated correction for the slight departure to linearity of the camera signal output. The IMEM board can memorize images each 1/25 sec. The CDISP board produces a 625 lines CCIR video-signal, and displays the images on a video screen, either in black and white, or false colors, through relevant look-up tables.

4.2. The memory. A 6MO Random Access Memory enables quick storage of images in less than 0.5 sec. The addition of three boards RAM Microsys 2MO produces the storage capacity of 32 images, 192 KO each.

The capacity for one of these images is used for pre-programmed computation tables:
- 256 O are assigned to a degree 4 polynomial function for correction of the video signal linearity - 64 KO are assigned to the determination of the azimuth of the linear polarization

by a tabulated function arctg of a 16 bits number (the ratio of 2 images U/Q) - 64 KO are used for the tabulated determination of the degree of linear polarization, which is the square root of a 16 bits number (the combination of images $(Q/I)^2 + (U/I)^2$).

4.3. The image processing device. The micro computer includes a 68000 CPU board, a 512 KO RAM and two drives for 5 1/4 inches floppy disks of 1.2 MO, held by bus VME.

The software, in C and Assembler languages, enables to record images in TV or in integration mode, reads and displays images, stores them in RAM or in floppy disk, adapts contrast of false color, shows a pixel intensity, operate translations or zooming and format reductions, displays images side by side, computes arithmetical operation between images.

The software enables also specific sequences of orders which operate the polarization selector, records the relevant images, combines them to compute the degrees of polarization Q/I, U/I or V/I and then P and θ, and to display the corresponding images.

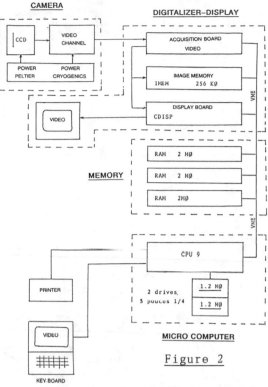

Figure 2

5 - TEST

5.1. Sensitivity. For each pixel, the threshold of polarization detection is related to the light intensity by the variation 1/N, in which N is the digitized light level. For the maximum intensity allowed by the 8 bits, this threshold is 1/256=0.39%. When using the programmed computation of the micro-processor, one bit is used for the sign, the operation is run with 7 bits, the threshold in polarization detectability is 1/128=0.78% at the intensity corresponding to 128, and then remains the same for higher intensities.

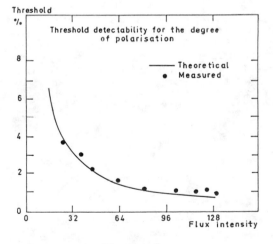

Figure 3

The figure 3 compares this theorctical threshold with the sensitivity directly measured by producing increasing small polarization on the light flux, until detection.

This sensitivity can be increased at the expense of the angular resolution by merging m adjacent pixels, with a gain $1/\sqrt{m}$, and at the expense of the duration of the observation by combining n consecutive sequences of images, with a gain $1/\sqrt{n}$.

5.2. Cross-talk between the polarization components.

The following table reports the signal recorded for all the components of polarization, when a 100% polarization is assigned to one of these components. The assigned component is recorded with an efficiency of 97%. The others exhibit, in this extreme condition, residual signals of around 4.5% which never exceed 7%.

State of polarization assigned	Signal measured (%)		
	Q/I	U/I	V/I
+Q/I = 100%	+97	-7	+3
-Q/I = 100	-97	+5	-4
+U/I = 100	+6	+97	-5
-U/I = 100	-2	-97	+5

5.3. Response to the polarization components. For increasing values of the component of polarization Q/I, positive or negative, the signal measured responds linearly, all over the range from -70% to +70° as shown in the figure 4. The same is true for U/I and V/I. The values of P did not depart from linearity but have a slope 1.07 (figure 5). The response for θ is also linear but with a slope of 1.09 (fig. 6).

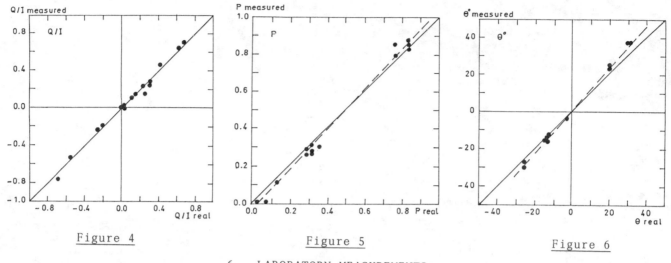

Figure 4   Figure 5   Figure 6

6 - LABORATORY MEASUREMENTS

An example of two dimensional polarization measurements in the laboratory is illustrated by the fig. 7 refering to the birefringent induced by stress in a plexiglas rod of 9x9mm² square section and 110mm length, under a weight of 500gr. The background is a uniform field of light linearly polarized at 45°.

The instrument produces 5 images respectively for Q/I, U/I, V/I, P and θ, which describe completely the state of polarization all over the field. They are reproduced in black and white in the fig. 7. False color provides additional help for the interpretation. Measurements along a vertical section near the middle of the rod are given. Averaging 5 aligned pixels produces an accuracy of 0.4×10^{-2}. The curves for Q/I and U/I are expressed in units of 10^{-2}. Q/I varies linearly along the vertical section, being exactly 0 at the median point. U/I reaches a maximum value of 94.7×10^{-2} at the median point and decreases symmetrically to reach 85.3×10^{-2} near the upper and lower faces. V/I has larger variations, exactly linear, with a degree of -15×10^{-2} at the median point. P behaves like U/I, with a maximum value of 95×10^{-2}. The azimuth θ of the linear polarization rotates progressively from -1.6° to +1.6°.

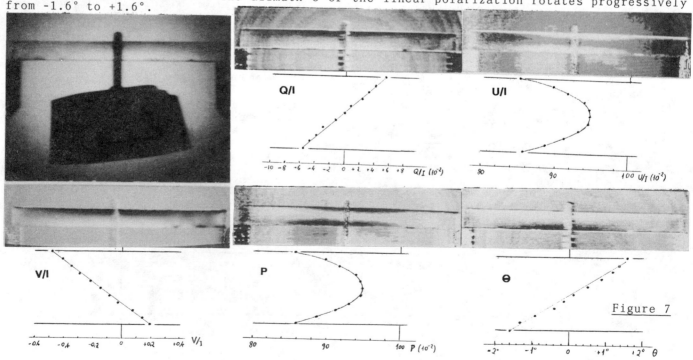

Figure 7

7 - FIELD INSPECTION

7.1. In the portrait of fig. 8, the image at top is an ordinary picture but, at bottom, the field is imaged exclusively with the light which have acquired a linear polarization under reflection. The left side of the face, protected against the direct beam of light, reflects only the ambient light from the room and produces few polarization. The side of the face at right is directly illuminated; the shiny parts of the skin, nose, sheek and forehead, produce a strong linear polarization (recorded as dark). The wet parts of the face, the lips, the eyes, polarized also significantly. The brow moved between the images recording, and a black and white double edge is produced.

7.2. In the sequence of images reproduced in the fig. 9, the field is occupied by a tree, a car, a metallic fence, the pavement of a road and, in the background, the city of Paris and a cloudless sky. The sun is near the horizon and illuminates the scene from the right; its direction is taken as the azimuth reference. The image Q/I is essentially a response to the scattering by direct illumination; the sky and the windows of the car exhibit a high degree of linear polarization perpendicular to the direction of the sun (dark hued in fig. Q/I). The part of the trunk which is in shadow produces a higher polarization, because its illumination results from multiple scattering essentially in the horizontal plane. The same is true for the front of the car. The buildings of the city (hard to see in the direct image I) and the pavement of the road appear by their low polarization (light hued). The metallic car produces almost no polarization (white in the figure).

The linear polarization U/I, which is at 45°, is essentially produced by multiple scattering from outside the scattering plane. It is small everywhere (light hued in fig. U/I), except on the part of the trunk which is in shadow, because of a significant sideway multiple scattering effect, and in the windows of the car because of a strong vitrous reflection of the skylight.

The circular polarization V/I, which is also a result of multiple scattering, appears only in the shadowed part of the trunk. The car disappears completely.

The image P displays linear polarization as light hued features, with unpolarized light dark. The field behaves essentially like a negative of the image Q/I, because of the dominent effect of the direct illumination. The deviations of the azimuth of the linear polarization are spectacular (fig. θ).

Figure 8

Figure 9

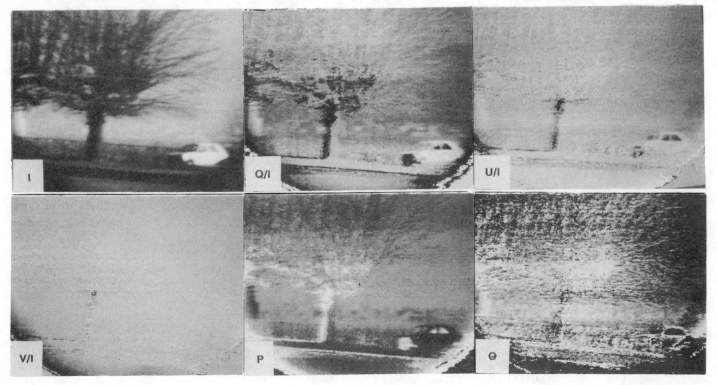

8 - TELESCOPIC OBSERVATIONS

At the focus of a telescope, the video-polarimeter produces images of astronomical objects in their polarized lights. Of special interest are the Solar System bodies which polarized by reflection the unpolarized solar light.

8.1. The bodies which negligible atmosphere produce a polarization by the combined effects of reflections, refractions, absorptions, diffractions at the surface and by their multiple effects between the surface irregularities.

In the figure 10, we analyse an area of the lunar surface near the west limb, at the focus of the 100cm telescope of Meudon observatory. On February 10, 1989, the phase angle was 118°. The direct image at top shows Mare Undarum near the center, crater Firmicus at bottom, crater Apollonius at right. These craters and the Mare are flooded with a dark material. In the linearly polarized image Q/I, these dark surfaces appear with a high polarization (light hued) and their superimposition over the terrae surface is evidenced. Other types of terrains are exhibited; between Mare Undarum and Apollonius, there is an elongated patch slightly brighter in the I image, darker and sharp edged in the Q/I image. This type of terrain appears also on other places, namely between Firmicus and Apollonius.

For rough solid surfaces made of small grains, such as the lunar surface, there is a classical relationship between the value Pmax of the maximum polarization produced and the albedo A, which is Pmax x A = k. The coefficient k is related to grain size. In the present case, Q/I almost corresponds to Pmax and the image I approximates an albedo image A. Accordingly, the product of these two images, which is Q, should display a uniform grey field, except for significant grain size local variations. Such is almost the case of the image Q of fig. 10 at bottom, proving that the dark flooding material and the brighter crustal surfaces have constructed a same micro texture at their surfaces, despite their great difference in albedo and composition (respectively basaltic and anorthositic). However, in addition to small spurious effect at the edges of craters due to the decrease of illumination at slopes, a dozen of small dark patches are exhibited in the Q image essentially at the bottom of small craters or at the edges of flodded areas. Here, the microtexture of the surface must be modified (smaller grains ?).

8.2. Jupiter is surrounded by a dense and opaque atmosphere. The planet is observed, in the figure 11, on November 6, 1988 at 21h40m UT, under a small phase angle of 3.7° for which the polarization by direct scattering is negligible. The image in P displays the linear polarization produced by multiple scattering in the gaseous and cloudy components of the jovian atmosphere. There is a strong polarization over the two polar areas, slightly more extended around the north pole (at bottom). The Q/I, U/I and θ images, not reproduced, indicate that the linear polarization is oriented almost perpendicular to the limb. At $\lambda = 600$mn, this polarization reaches $(47 \pm 2) \times 10^{-3}$ near the south pole and $(45 \pm 2) \times 10^{-3}$ near the north pole. These properties indicate a gaseous atmosphere almost free of aerosols around the two poles. At lower latitudes, the limit is rather sharp, the polarization reaches at once an uniform and very small value of $(-0.5 \pm 0.6) \times 10^{-3}$ produced by the layer of crystal clouds. The belts produce a slightly higher polarization, with $(6 \pm 3) \times 10^{-3}$.

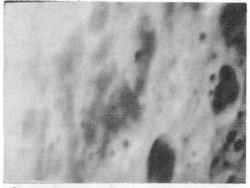

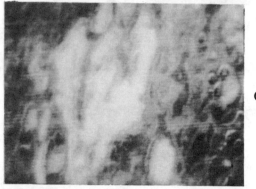

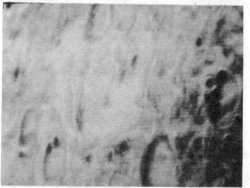

The lunar surface - Figure 10.

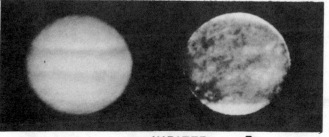

I **JUPITER** P Fig.11

8.3. The solid surface of planet Mars appears at the telescope through a thin and transparent atmosphere which does not perturb significantly the polarization produced by the ground. But local clouds or veils occur, they are highly polarized and can be directly imaged over the almost uniformly polarized surface, with the video-polarimeter.

The figure 12 refers to planet Mars on January 22, 1989. The globe is at great distance to the earth and its angular diameter does not exceed 7.6 arcsec. At 17h42m, the areographic longitude of the sub-earth point is 120°, the dark feature Mare Sirenum lies on the upper right. The southern hemisphere is entirely occupied by the wide and light hued planum Amazonis. Under a phase angle of 40.2°, the planetary surface produces usually a polarization of $+17 \times 10^{-3}$. Measurements around the disk center on the image Q/I (see figure) give $(18 \pm 1) \times 10^{-3}$. The orbital longitude $L_S = 247°$ corresponds to the late winter for the northern hemisphere and the artic region is overcast with a seasonal cloud, the winter polar hood. Although hardly detected in the direct image I, the hood appears white in the Q/I restitution (with North at bottom). Its degree of polarization reaches $(+37 \pm 4) \times 10^{-3}$. There is also

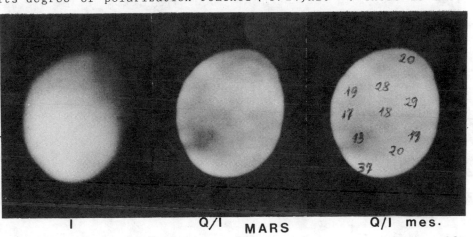

. Figure 12

a faint haze scarfing the south temperate latitudes, which exceed the polarization of the planetary surface by 10×10^{-3}. This thin mist is completely indetectable in the direct image and even by visual inspection with the eyepiece and the telescope. Undetected also is the unusually low polarization at the bottom left of the disk, which produces a dark patch in the image Q/I and a degree of polarization of $(+13 \pm 2) \times 10^{-3}$. This atmospheric disturbence could possibly be produced by dust grains suspended in the atmosphere.

I   Q/I   MARS   Q/I mes.

9 - SOLAR PHYSICS

The video-polarimeter was also adapted to our solar telescope equipped with a monochromatic birefringent filter, the instrument FPSS of Meudon Observatory (Dollfus et al., 1985). The polarization selector is placed in front of the filter. Images of the solar surface are obtained with the light of essentially the bottom of a spectral line, or each of the two wings, or with the nearby continuum. Using the polarization selector, these images are taken successively with the different Stokes polarization components of the incident light. They are then associated each other, in order to produce new sets of images mapping over the solar surface specific physical parameters, such as the line width, the temperature gradient, the motion along the line of sight and the magnetization (Dollfus et al., 1986).

The fig. 13 refers to an active center observed with the radiation Hα of hydrogen on June 14, 1988. A small spot near disk center is associated with a thin dark filament and a bright plage. The image VEL at bottom records the motion of the hydrogen atoms along the line of sight (radial velocity). Dark features characterize upward motion and indicate an overall altitude rise for the small filaments and other parallel features. Near the bottom left, there is a stronger filament intersecting the corner in the Hα images. All this area displays also an upward motion.

ACKNOWLEDGEMENTS - This research was conducted at Observatoire de Paris, Astrophysical Section at Meudon, France, under contract DRET 85/077, with the contributions of MM. Michel Dreux, Patrick Boumier, Thierry Pouchol and Olivier Croin.

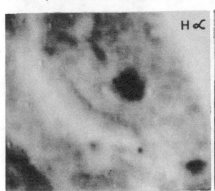
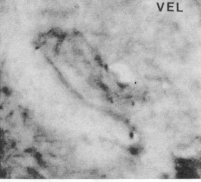

Figure 13

Hα VEL

REFERENCES

Beckers J.M. (1971). Applied Optics. 10, 973
Dollfus A., (1985). NASA Conf. Pub. n° 2374, 192-201.
Dollfus A., Colson R., Crussaire D., Launay F., (1985). Astron. Astrophys. 151, 235-253.
Dollfus A., Crussaire D., Pernot E., Lioure A. (1986), R.C. Acad. Sci. Paris 303, sér. II, 153-158.
Dollfus A., Fauconnier T., Dreux M., Pouchol T., Croin O. (1989). C.R. Acad. Sci. Paris 308, série II, 19-24.
Prosch T., Hennings D., Raschke E. (1983), Applied Optics 22, n° 9, 1360-1363.
Walraven R. (1981), Optical Engeen. 20, n° 1, 14-18.

Wide spectral range F/2.3 prime focus spherical corrector for 3.5 m Ritchey-Chretien telescope

M.Magnani, S.Pieri, A.Romoli

Officine Galileo via A.Einstein 35, 50013 Campi Bisenzio Florence ITALY

ABSTRACT

This paper deals with the design of a three spherical lenses corrector, able to produce wide flat field at the prime focus with focus ratio F/2.2 - 3.5m of a R-C telescope. The system is corrected over a spectral range extending from 300nm to 1100 nm. The corrector has the following characteristics:
reduced size of the optics; all spherical surfaces; resolution better than 1 arcsec within 30 arcmin flat field ; possibility to extend the field up to 1 degree with reduced resolution.
The image quality of the corrector is shown by means of Spot Diagrams, Point Spread Function and Encircled Energy Function for different off - axis values and spectral ranges.
The paper also includes an analysis of possible alignment errors performed by means of computed interferograms.

1. INTRODUCTION

The Authors studied the feasibility of a prime focus corrector for the " GALILEO " R - C telescope, which will be provided of an active primary mirror similar to ESO-NTT telescope (Barbieri 1988) - (1). This design was developed for, and in collaboration with, the Italian Astronomical Community and supervised by the Osservatorio Astronomico di Padova.
The Galileo telescope required an extended field of view in order to accomodate, in the focal plane, a large size CCD detector, an active optics sensor and a TV guiding camera. Therefore the prime focus system has been designed to adapt an optical channel for the wavefront sensor, according to the Shack - Hartmann (S - H) test procedure and a second separate channel for the telescope guiding.
The first requirements for the system were as follows:

- max. size of optics : 700 mm diameter,1000 mm length
- field of view subtended by the CCD detector : about 12 arcmin
- max. field of view : more than 30 arcmin
- max. circle diameter containig the 90% of spot energy : 0.5 arcsec in the CCD field of view
- spectral range : form 300 nm to 1100 nm

The focal length of the aspherical primary mirror is 7700 mm with F# 2.2

After a first trade off study, the choice fell on a design solution with 3 refractive elements.

2. LAY-OUT OF CORRECTOR

The corrector is a set of three silica spherical shaped elements. The basic configuration is derived from the classical Sampson and Wynne triplet (2), (3). The most interesting aspects of this solution are the reduced size and the advantage coming from the use of spherical surfaces. [fig. 1]
The optical characteristics of the prime focus system are as follows:

- focal length : 8300 mm
- field of view for the CCD detector : 11' 20"
- max. field of view : 1 degree.

2.1. S-H test and telescope guiding

The optical beam for the S-H test and telescope guiding is extracted at the distance of 15 arcmin from the principal axis, by means of a folding mirror. Successive splitting is operated between the testing and guiding optical beams.

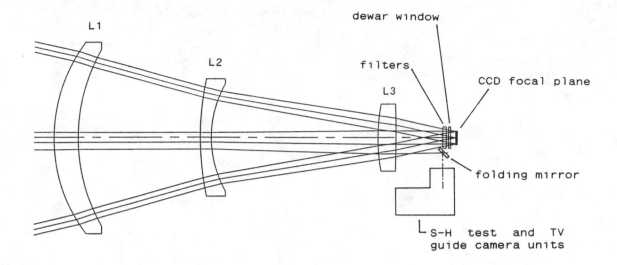

Fig. 1   Lay-out of corrector

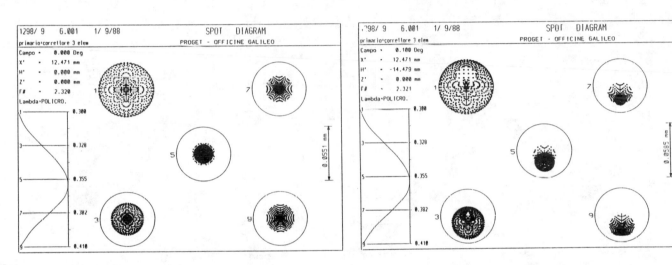

Fig. 2   Spot Diagram for U response curve

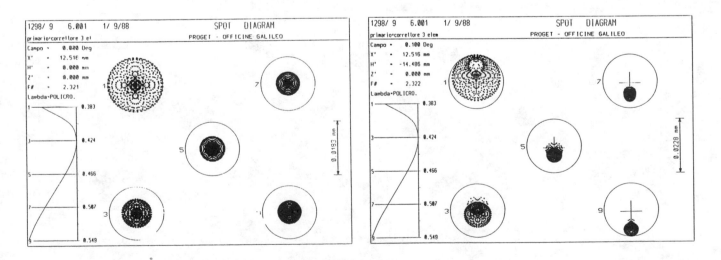

Fig. 3   Spot Diagram for B response curve

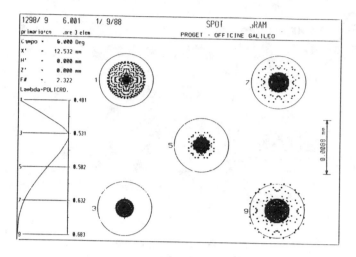
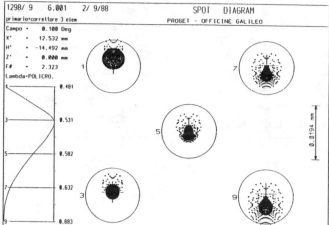

Fig. 4   Spot Diagram for V response curve

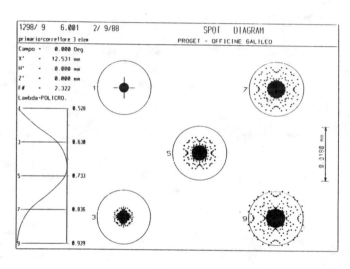
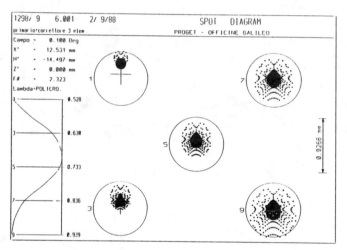

Fig. 5   Spot Diagram for R response curve

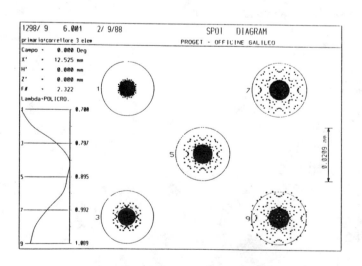
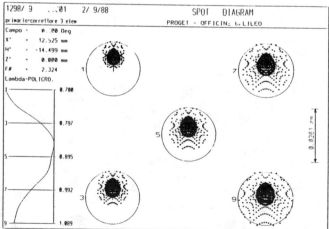

Fig. 6   Spot diagram for I response curve

3. IMAGE QUALITY

The system was designed and analized using the optical design computer program package PROGET (*).The analysis takes count of the typical atmospheric transmission values on the considered spectral band and of the typical spectral photometric responses of UBVRI system.

Figures from [2] to [6] show the Spot Diagrams for the UBVRI spectral bandes.Each picture shows the Spot Diagrams at five wavelength inside the considered spectral band on axis and at 0.1 deg. Figures from [7] to [9]show the Diffraction Encircled Energy Function, on axis and for two off-axis values in the V response curve domain.

Table [1] shows the circle diameter values (in arcsec) containing the 90% and 70% of spot energy for UBVRI bands, for some fovs within 0.50 deg. from axis.
As shown in the table (BFL column) the change of the response curve produces a variation of the focus . The defocus compensation may be performed by means of filters thickness calibration.

Table 1
Encircled Energy as a function of field of view

band	BFL shift from V band	Fields of view									
		axis		0.07°		0.14°		0.20°		0.50°	
		90%	70%	90%	70%	90%	70%	90%	70%	90%	70%
U	-0.061	0.68	0.41	0.71	0.44	0.76	0.52	0.86	0.63	1.69	1.42
B	-0.016	0.32	0.20	0.34	0.22	0.43	0.34	0.62	0.46	1.57	1.27
V	-	0.18	0.08	0.21	0.11	0.31	0.20	0.47	0.31	1.39	1.12
R	-1e-3	0.23	0.13	0.26	0.15	0.35	0.21	0.48	0.31	1.54	1.23
I	-7e-3	0.30	0.18	0.34	0.20	0.40	0.25	0.62	0.36	1.59	1.27

4. MANUFACTURING TOLERANCES AND INTERFEROMETRIC ANALYSIS OF ALIGNMENT ERRORS

The manufacturing error analysis of the corrector shows that a spherical error of 0.5 fringes and an astigmatic error of 0.1 fringes is allowable for each surface, in order to obtain an acceptable image quality. The tilt errors allowable for each surface are within 10 arcsec.The variation of the system parameters (i.e. radii, thicknesses, opto - mechanical interdistance) causes the focal plane position changement, and so focusing adjustment will be required. This adjustment may be done moving the assembly of L2 and L3 elements [fig. 1].

The quality image loss analysis was performed by means of computer simulated interferograms particularly for the effects of tilts and transversal displacement of each element.
Fig. [10] shows as reference the simulated axial interferogram and the wavefront shape of the prime focus system without alignment errors.The test is computed in single pass, at 632.8nm wavelength (He - Ne laser).

4.1. Transversal displacement and tilt analysis

Tilt analysys is done for 1 and 3 arcmin tilt angles and tranversal displacement analysis for 0.1 and 0.5 mm,both for the complete corrector and for each individual element.The results of the above analysis are summarized in table [2], expressed in terms of fraction of lambda.

(*) PROGET is an Optical Design Computer Program developed by OFFICINE GALILEO S.p.A.

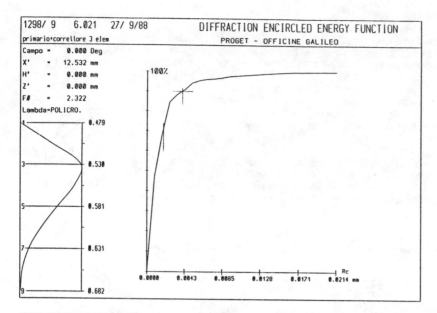

Fig. 7

Encircled Energy Function
on axis

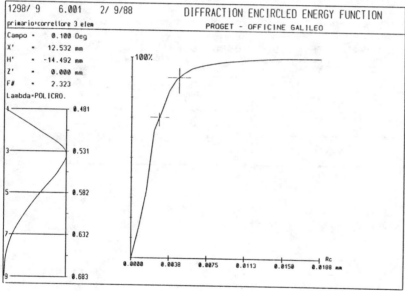

Fig. 8

Encircled Energy Function
at 0.10 degree

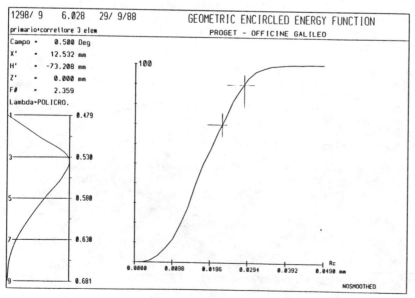

Fig. 9

Encircled Energy Function
at 0.50 degree

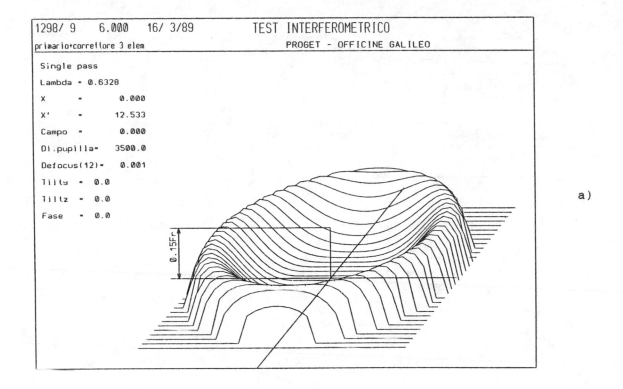

```
1298/ 9    6.000    16/ 3/89        TEST INTERFEROMETRICO
primario+correttore 3 elem              PROGET - OFFICINE GALILEO

Single pass
Lambda = 0.6328
X       =       0.000
X'      =      12.533
Campo   =       0.000
Di.pupilla=    3500.0
Defocus(12)=    0.001
Tilty  =  0.0
Tiltz  =  0.0
Fase   =  0.0
```

0.15Fr

a)

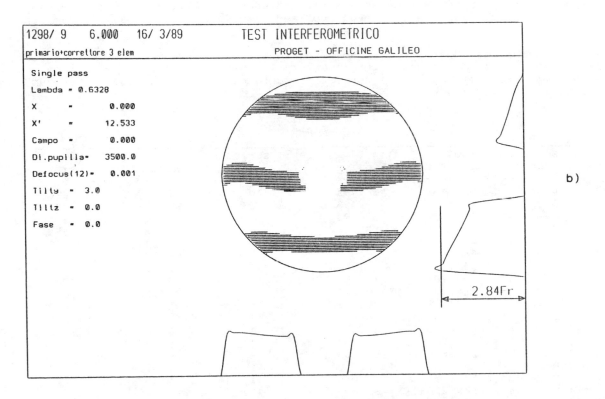

```
1298/ 9    6.000    16/ 3/89        TEST INTERFEROMETRICO
primario+correttore 3 elem              PROGET - OFFICINE GALILEO

Single pass
Lambda = 0.6328
X       =       0.000
X'      =      12.533
Campo   =       0.000
Di.pupilla=    3500.0
Defocus(12)=    0.001
Tilty  =  3.0
Tiltz  =  0.0
Fase   =  0.0
```

2.84Fr

b)

Fig. 10   Prime Focus System without
               alignment errors :

               a) axial OPD. b) axial interferogram
                   (1 FR = 1 Lambda)

Table 2

wavefront error lambda=632.8 nm for	transversal displacement		tilt	
	dy=0.1	dy=0.5	w=1'	w=3'
complete corrector	0.48	1.98	0.42	1.04
L1 element	0.23	0.52	0.29	0.57
L2 element	0.30	0.95	0.38	0.88
L3 element	0.26	0.68	0.25	0.43

Fig. [11] shows the effect of a 0.5 mm transversal displacement, of the complete corrector.
Fig. [12] shows the effect of a 3 arcmin tilt angle of the complete corrector. The not negligeable value of wavefront errors, caused by small displacements and tilts, suggests to consider to provide individual adjustment for each element of the system.(4)

5. GHOST ANALYSIS

The ghost fenomena reduction is an important goal of the prime focus system design. This because there are no coatings which efficently cover spectral ranges so large as needed.

Axial ghost analysis shows the substantial absence of ghost fenomena coming from the corrector optical surfaces. Whereas not negligeable ghost comes from the flat surfaces of the filters and dewar window.

Table [3] shows the ghost effects caused by couples of optical surfaces in terms of spourius spot diameter (mm) and light intensity (arbitrary units) on the focal plane. Surfaces from 3 to 8 belong to the corrector, surfaces 9 - 10 to the filters and surfaces 11 - 12 to the dewar window.

Table 3

surfaces pair		Spot diameter	light intensity		surfaces pair		Spot diameter	light intensity
4	3	516.168	24.435		10	4	490.580	41.229
5	3	603.711	9.493		10	5	247.248	200.387
5	4	527.328	28.903		10	6	391.603	79.881
6	3	574.380	3.657		10	7	58.529	3575.986
6	4	444.404	62.027		10	8	103.218	1149.812
6	5	561.707	20.633		10	9	4.670	0.561e+6
7	3	364.944	91.978		11	3	545.175	7.637
7	4	198.704	310.256		11	4	499.535	39.764
7	5	26.190	17859.025		11	5	245.233	203.695
7	6	205.338	290.533		11	6	402.009	75.799
8	3	514.144	8.587		11	7	57.633	3687.986
8	4	453.339	59.606		11	8	108.165	1047.030
8	5	340.304	105.780		11	9	8.984	0.151e+6
8	6	227.686	236.299		11	10	4.314	0.658e+6
8	7	96.161	1324.756		12	3	550.077	7.502
9	3	531.156	8.046		12	4	505.888	38.771
9	4	579.226	36.512		12	5	243.878	205.964
9	5	249.449	196.866		12	6	409.175	73.167
9	6	380.550	84.589		12	7	57.030	3766.471
9	7	59.506	3459.563		12	8	111.515	985.078
9	8	97.865	1279.032		12	9	11.902	86470.492
10	3	538.307	7.834		12	10	7.232	0.234e+6
					12	11	2.919	1.437e+6

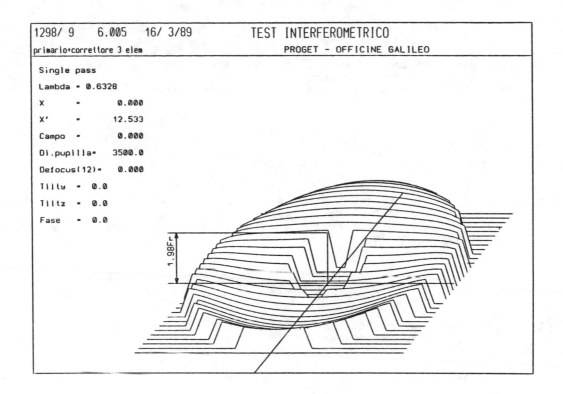

```
1298/ 9    6.005   16/ 3/89        TEST INTERFEROMETRICO
primario+correttore 3 elem              PROGET - OFFICINE GALILEO

  Single pass

  Lambda = 0.6328

  X       =      0.000

  X'      =     12.533

  Campo   =      0.000

  Di.pupilla=  3500.0

  Defocus(12)=   0.000

  Tilty  =  0.0

  Tiltz  =  0.0

  Fase   =  0.0
```

Fig. 11   OPD with 0.5 mm Transversal Displacement
               of the complete Corrector

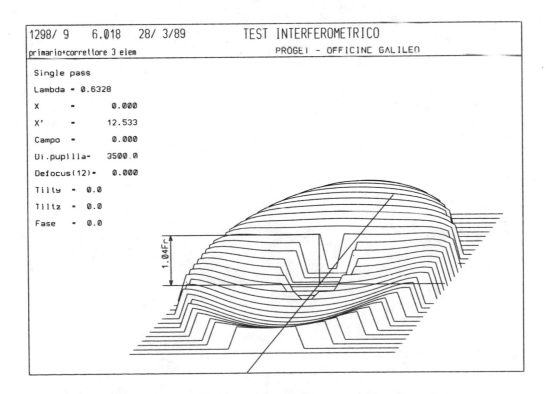

```
1298/ 9    6.018   28/ 3/89        TEST INTERFEROMETRICO
primario+correttore 3 elem              PROGET - OFFICINE GALILEO

  Single pass

  Lambda = 0.6328

  X       =      0.000

  X'      =     12.533

  Campo   =      0.000

  Di.pupilla=  3500.0

  Defocus(12)=   0.000

  Tilty  =  0.0

  Tiltz  =  0.0

  Fase   =  0.0
```

Fig. 12   OPD with 3 arcmin Tilt-angle
               of the complete Corrector

6. CONCLUSIONS

The choice of an only spherical solution involves a small derating in the optical performances, compared with the first requirements.
The corrector satisfies completely the resolution requirements in the BVR and I ranges,but for the U band the spot diameter, at the 90% of energy is about 0.7 arcsec, instead of the required 0.5 arcsec.
Introducing aspherical surfaces in the triplet, the optical power of elements may be decreased consequently decreasing the chromatic aberration, which is the first cause of this derating.

7. ACKNOWLEDGMENTS

The authors wish to thank prof. C. Barbieri, prof. P. Rafanelli of Osservatorio Astronomico di Padova - Dipartimento di Astronomia dell' Universita' di Padova and prof. P. Conconi of Osservatorio Astronomico di Brera - Milano, for their contribution in developing the feasibility analysis of the system.

8. REFERENCES

1.   BARBIERI C., "The Galileo Project", presented at the JNLT Conference, Tokyo Nov.,1988.
2.   SAMPSON R. A., 1913 Mon. Not. R. astr. Soc., 73, 524.
3.   WYNNE C. G., 1968 Astrophys.J., 152, 675.
4.   HOPKINS R. E.," Some Thougts on Lens Mounting ", Opt. Eng. 15(5), 428, 430.
             Sep-Oct 1976.

High spatial and temporal resolution imaging with the RANICON

Mark Clampin

Center for Astrophysical Sciences, Department of Physics and Astronomy
The Johns Hopkins University, Baltimore MD 21218

Francesco Paresce[1]
Space Telescope Science Institute,
3700 San Martin Drive, Baltimore MD 21218

ABSTRACT

An advanced two dimensional photon counting system employing a Resistive Anode Image Converter (RANICON) has been recently developed and tested at the STScI for use on ground based telescopes. It can presently obtain two dimensional images over a 25 mm diameter active area with 35 - 40 μm FWHM overall spatial resolution and $\leq$ms time resolution. The entire near UV, optical and near IR range can be covered with the use of bialkali, S-20 and GaAs photocathodes at overall sensitivities of 10 - 20 %. Its basic operating characteristics and results of recent field trials will be presented and discussed with special emphasis on its applications to time resolved imaging.

1. INTRODUCTION

The RANICON is an optical photon counting detector based on the microchannel plate (MCP) detector discussed by Lampton and Paresce (1974) for UV astronomy. At the Space Telescope Science Institute (STScI) we have developed an optical version of the RANICON for applications in ground-based Astronomy. This detector is of the same basic design as the improved UV detector discussed by Firmani et al. (1982). Development of RANICON detectors at STScI has centered on obtaining high resolution and improving the overall photon counting efficiency of these devices. The most recent design, the advanced RANICON, has yielded the best resolution obtained so far with a RANICON, combined with improved sensitivity. We discuss recent work on this detector and also report the first results from our evaluation of a GaAs photocathode RANICON having excellent red response.

2. DETECTOR DESIGN

In figure 1 we show a schematic of the advanced RANICON detector highlighting the main elements of the design. Photoelectrons are produced by a 25 mm active area S20 photocathode deposited on the back surface of a 5mm thick silica glass window. The photoelectrons are accelerated across a 300 μm gap by a 1 kvmm^{-1} field where they are incident upon a microchannel plate stack consisting of 5 plates (length:diameter = 40:1) arranged in a 'V + Z' configuration. This arrangement acts as a form of baffle which minimizes ion feedback damage to the photocathode and also produces the modal electron gains of 5 x 10^7 required for photon counting performance. The event charge clouds which exit from the MCP stack are encoded by a resistive anode which determines the event centroid from the ratio of charge at each corner of

---

[1] affiliated with the Astrophysics Division, Space Science Department of ESA.

the anode. The resistive anode is a circular-arc-terminated (CAT) design (Lampton and Carlson 1979), and provides a geometrically linear image providing the preamplifier rise time is longer than the anode's time constant.

Four preamplifiers, connected to the resistive anode, feed the shaped anode signals to the signal processing unit. This unit digitizes the signals and inputs them to two fast divider chips which calculate the two 12 bit addresses corresponding to the X and Y event location calculated from the relationships

$$X = a + b \ /(a+b+c+d) \ \text{and} \ Y = a + d \ /(a+b+c+d), \tag{1}$$

where a,b,c and d are the charge pulses from each corner of the Resistive anode. These operations are controlled by a circuit which discriminates on the basis of pulse amplitude and triggers the conversion to digital when it detects the pulse peak. The signal processing system is interfaced to a 80286 based PC computer which increments the events in a 1024 x 1024 video memory, allowing real time display of integrations. Data storage consists of hard disk and a high capacity 2Gb video tape unit for time resolved applications. The 25 mm active area may be mapped to image formats of 512^2, 1024^2 or 2048^2 pixels.

The STScI RANICON is especially notable for the absence of a barrier film on the first MCP in the 'V + Z' stack. The film usually acts as a physical barrier to prevent ions escaping from the MCP stack and being accelerated back towards the photocathode. Unfortunately, the protective film also attenuates the incident photoelectron flux by up to 75 % and so its removal is desirable. Furthermore, a smaller photocathode to MCP gap is permissible if there is no film and so spatial resolution can be improved since radial spreading of the photoelectrons in this gap is a major contribution to the overall detector resolution (Clampin et al. 1988).

The usual choice of a RANICON photocathode is the multialkali S20, or a bialkali. Both these photocathodes have a blue spectral response, with the multialkali having an "extended-red" response, providing some red sensitivity out to ∼800 nm. Recently the first RANICON with a negative electron affinity GaAs photocathode has been evaluated by us (Clampin and Paresce; 1989a, 1989b). The GaAs photocathode RANICON, known as the Red-RANICON, typically has a uniform responsive quantum efficiency (RQE) of ∼20 % from 600 - 900 nm. The sharp cutoffs in sensitivity outside this range are due to the GaAs band gap at the long wavelength and the transmission of the photocathode at the short wavelength. Figure 2 shows a comparison between the alkali photocathodes and the GaAs photocathode. It can be clearly seen that the near-IR response of GaAs is far superior to that of the "extended-red" photocathode.

While the Red-RANICON design is essentially the same as that shown in figure 1, there are a few differences imposed by the choice of photocathode. A barrier film covering the input MCP is essential for GaAs photocathodes, to hermetically seal the photocathode from the MCP stack environment and to provide ion feedback protection. This is because the GaAs photocathode rapidly loses sensitivity if the Cs-O monolayer which activates the photocathode (Clampin and Paresce 1989b) is contaminated by outgassing from the MCPs. In the prototype device we have evaluated the photocathode-MCP gap was 1000 μm, however, it is expected that this will be reduced to 750 μ in the production models.

3. DETECTOR PERFORMANCE

The 'V + Z' MCP stack in the advanced RANICON typically yields gains of the order of 5 x 10^7, which are required to obtain high spatial resolution from the detector. In figure 3 we show a pulse height distribution (PHD) illustrating the narrow (∼90 - 100% FWHM), quasi-Gaussian distribution required for photon counting. A narrow distribution is also desirable for good matching to the signal processing electronics, since the range of pulse amplitudes to be digitized by the analog-to-digital convertors is diminished. For the 'V + Z' MCP stack it appears to be the case that an improved PHD is obtained when there is no barrier film on the input MCP. RANICON detectors having the barrier film typically have PHDs with a resolution of 120 - 150 % FWHM (Clampin et al 1988).

The spatial resolution of the advanced RANICON is typically 35 - 40 μm FWHM. This figure degrades to ∼50 μm towards blue wavelengths ($\leq$400 nm) as the positional uncertainty due to lateral drift of photoelectrons, across the photocathode to MCP gap, is wavelength dependent for multialkali photocathodes. In figure 4 we show an image of a USAF resolution chart, obtained with the advanced RANICON using a 2048^2 image format (14 μm pixel). The 16 lpmm^{-1} pattern is just resolvable. In the case of the Red-RANICON a spatial resolution of 85 μm FWHM was obtained with a prototype detector, however, a reduction in the MCP to photocathode gap from 1000 μm to 750 μ should improve the resolution to 40 μm. The resolution of the red-RANICON is not subject to chromatic effects, yielding uniform resolution from 600 - 900 nm.

The time resolution of the RANICON system is currently limited by the baseline restoration circuit, a paralyzable circuit in the signal processing electronics having a dead time of 6 μs. This circuit ensures that the detection of a pulse peak is not biassed by the decaying tail of the previous event. Work is currently in progress to change to a non-paralyzable circuit which will improve the peak count rate and, thus, the time resolution at very high count rates ($\geq$200 kHz).

While the detector has no readout noise, there is dark noise which varies with the type of photocathode. The blue sensitive bialkali photocathode is relatively quiet, with typically $\simeq$ 100 counts sec^{-1} over a 25 mm active area. The multialkali S20 photocathodes require cooling to −20°C to achieve $\leq$100 counts sec^{-1} over the 25 mm active area, while the new GaAs photocathode RANICON requires cooling to −35°C - −40°C to get the dark count to $\leq$100 counts sec^{-1} over the same active area. Operating with dark counts of ∼ 100 counts sec^{-1} the dark noise is negligible except for very long integration times.

In figure 2 we show the responsive quantum efficiency (RQE) curves for the different types of photocathode. Overall quantum efficiency is lower than these figures since there are losses associated with the MCP stack. The main loss results from the barrier film, if present, which can reduce sensitivity by up to 75 %. When the barrier film is not used, as with the advanced RANICON, losses are mainly a result of photoelectrons which do not enter a channel. For the advanced RANICON overall efficiency is typically 60 - 70 % of the photocathode RQE. In the case of a GaAs photocathode where the barrier film is essential, photoelectron attenuation by the film may be minimized by a potential of 800 - 1000 volts across the photocathode to MCP gap.

Dynamic range performance of the RANICON detectors is currently determined by the MCP stack and the signal processing electronics. The performance of the MCP stack is image dependent, with small point sources having a higher saturation level than a uniform flat field source. The maximum count rate over the whole 25mm active area is of the order of 1 Mhz, while for a point source illumination it is of the order of 10 counts sec^{-1}. The maximum total count rate which can be processed by the signal processing electronics is currently of the order of 100 kHz, and is set by the baseline restoration requirements.

Recently, trials have been conducted with the RANICON at the McGraw-Hill observatory on an echelle spectrograph and in direct imaging mode using the 2.5 m telescope. In figure 5 we show an echelle spectrum of a standard star. Photon counting detectors remain competitive with CCDs in this application when long integrations combined with large wavelength coverage are required. Figure 6 shows the globular cluster NGC5024 in the light of Hβ and illustrates the large field coverage obtained with the RANICON. Figures 7 and 8 are images obtained for a program to study the dynamics and morphology of planetary nebulae and show narrowband images of NGC6058 and of NGC6445 respectively.

4. ASTRONOMICAL APPLICATIONS

The RANICON has applications in both imaging and spectroscopy where large fields and the absence of readout noise or cosmic ray events is beneficial. The increasing availability of low noise CCDs and the expected arrival of large format devices make it hard for the photon counting detectors to compete with these devices. The timing capability of photon counting detectors is, however, unique and cannot be matched by CCDs without a very considerable degradation in performance. The ability to time-tag each photon event makes spectroscopic and imaging observations of objects having short periods, such as cataclysmic variables and pulsars, possible.

The rapidly growing field of high resolution astronomy, where most observations require excellent time resolution, is an another example. The demand for diffraction-limited imaging from large telescopes ($\sim$4 m) and the next generation of very large telescopes ($\sim$ 8 - 10 m) has led to many new applications for photon counting detectors.

A relatively simple technique is to use integrations time of $\sim$20 ms which can be recentered and added to correct for residual telescope tracking errors and image motion due to wavefront tilt. Additional selection of the individual frames can be used to isolate periods of relatively good seeing. For larger telescopes ($\geq$1.5 m) little gain is achieved since the telescope aperture (D) is not well matched to the "seeing-cell" size (r_o). Good matching may be achieved by sub-dividing the telescope pupil into apertures with optimum matching ($D/r_o \simeq 3 - 5$) and individually processing the image from each aperture (Lelievre et al. 1988). Such techniques can also be extended to yield complementary long slit spectra having the same spatial resolution as the image.

The high sensitivity of the Red-RANICON is ideal for speckle imaging where new techniques (Baier et al. 1988) for imaging and spectroscopy are allowing faint extragalactic objects to be studied for the first time with near diffraction-limited resolution. Nakajima et al. (1989) have recently demonstrated the use of RANICONs to obtain diffraction-limited images by applying the method of phase closure to images obtained through non-redundant aperture masks. Long baseline interferometers comprising two or more telescopes also require high speed photon counters to image interference fringes (Labeyrie et al. 1986). Very high resolution will be obtained with long baseline arrays of large telescopes such as the ESO 8 m telescope array project (Merkle 1988).

5. CONCLUSIONS

The timing capability of the photon counting detectors will, increasingly, be the main criteria governing the use of these instruments for astronomical applications. With spatial resolution of $\sim$40 μm FWHM, geometric linearity, up to 2048^2 pixels, temporal resolution of $\sim$ 10 μm and an overall photon counting efficiency of the order of 60 - 70% of the photocathode RQE, the

RANICON is an excellent choice for many of these applications. Furthermore, few photon counting detectors currently offer the red response afforded by the Red-RANICON. Future developments in NEA photocathodes should allow extension of the red response to 1.1 μm with the use of other III-IV photocathode materials, while the use of high electric fields (field assist) should ultimately yield spectral response out to ~1.6 μm

ACKNOWLEDGEMENTS

We wish to thank ITT for the loan of a Red-RANICON and for useful discussions regarding the detector and photocathode fabrication. We also wish to thank J. Crocker and M. Rafal for engineering assistance and A. Sen and C. Cox for assistance with the data acquisition hardware. We wish to thank H. S. Stockman and R. Giacconi for their continuing support of RANICON detector development at the Space Telescope Science Institute through the Director's Discretionary research fund.

REFERENCES

G. Baier, J. Eckert, K. H. Hofmann, W. Mauder, D. Schertl, H. Weghorn and G. Weigelt, **"Speckle Masking"** , NOAO-ESO Conf. on High-Resolution Imaging by Interferometry" Garching, March 1988, **I** , 151. (1988).

M. Clampin, J. Crocker, F. Paresce and M. Rafal, **"Optical RANICON detectors for photon counting imaging. I"**, Rev. Sci. Inst. **59**, 1269.

M. Clampin and F. Paresce, **"Photon counting imaging with a GaAs photocathode: Evaluation of the Red-RANICON for astronomical imaging"**, Astron. Astro. *in press* (1989).

M. Clampin and F. Paresce, **"Spatial resolution characteristics of a GaAs RANICON "**, Rev. Sci. Inst. *in press* (1989).

C. Firmani, E. Ruiz, C. W. Carlson, M. Lampton and F. Paresce, **"High-resolution imaging with a two-dimensional resistive anode photon counter"**, Rev. Sci. Inst. **53**, 570 (1982).

Labeyrie, A., Schumacher, G., Dugue, M., Thom, C., Bourlon, P., Foy F., Bonneau D. and R. Foy, **Fringes obtained with the large "boules" interferometer at CERGA"**, Astron. Astro. **162**, 359 (1986).

M. Lampton and F. Paresce, **" The RANICON: A resistive anode image convertor"**, Rev. Sci. Inst. **45**, 1098 (1974).

M. Lampton and C. Carlson, **"Low-distortion resistive anodes for two-dimensional position-sensitive MCP systems"**, Rev. Sci. Inst. **50**, 1093 (1979).

G. Lelievre, J. L. Nieto, D. Salmon, A. Llebaria, E. Thouvenot, J. Boulesteix, E. Le Coarer and J. Arnaud, **"Very high resolution imaging using sub-pupil apertures, recentering and selection of short exposures"**, Astron. Astro. **200**, 301 (1988).

F. Merkle, **"Synthetic aperture imaging with the European Very Large Telescope"**, J.O.S.A **5**, 904 (1988).

T. Nakajima, S. Kulkarni, P. Gorham, A. Getz, G. Neugebauer, J. B. Oke, T. A. Prince and A. C. Readhead, **"Diffraction-limited imaging II: Optical aperture synthesis imaging of binary stars"**, Ast. J. **97** 1510 (1989).

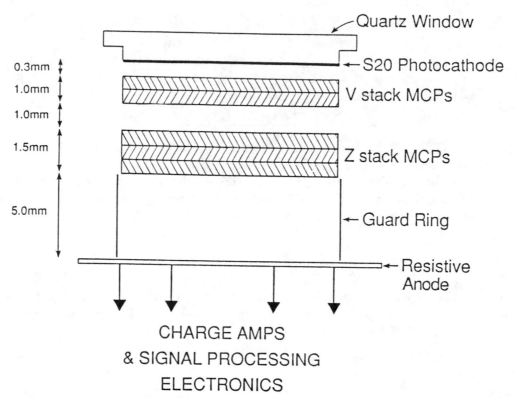

Figure 1: Schematic showing the design of the advanced RANICON detector.

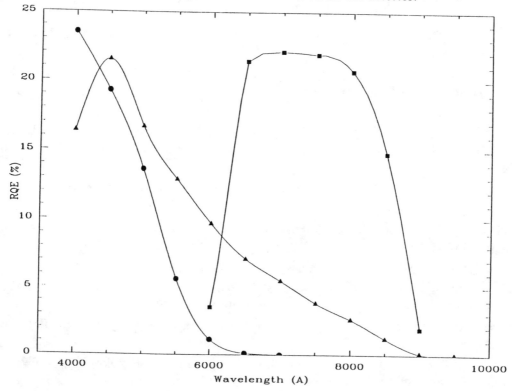

Figure 2: Responsive quantum efficiency (RQE) curves for measured for RANICON detectors with bialkali, S20 and GaAs photocathodes.

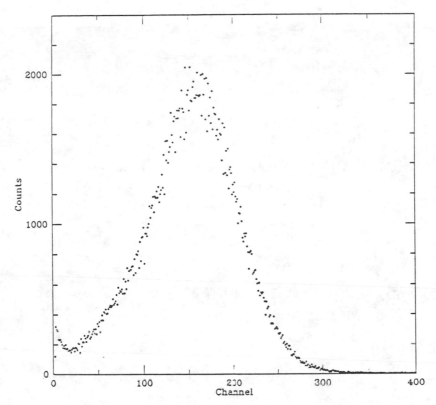

Figure 3: 'V + Z' microchannel plate stack pulse height distribution obtained with advanced RANICON detector.

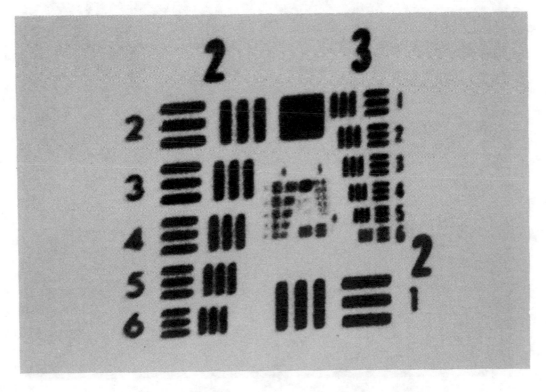

Figure 4: Image of the USAF resolution chart obtained with a 2048^2 pixel format.

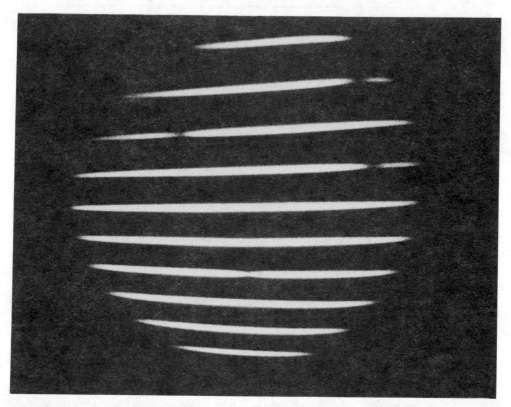

Figure 5: Echelle spectrum of a B star HR6629.

Figure 6: Zoomed image of the core of NGC5024, a globular cluster, showing the central 2-5 arcminutes of a 5 arcminute field.

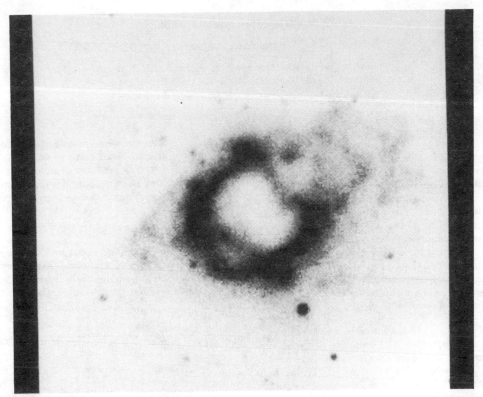

Figure 7: Narrowband Hα image of NGC6445.

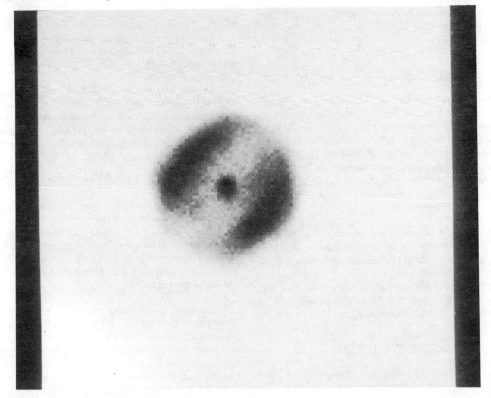

Figure 8: Narrowband [O III image of NGC 6058.

When telescopes start to walk...

Dietmar E.K. Plathner

Institut de Radioastronomie Millimétrique (I.R.A.M.)
Domaine Universitaire, 38406 St. Martin d'Hères, France

ABSTRACT

A system study has been started to elaborate and define methods of moving optical telescopes of the 2-m class continuously during astronomical observations. When operating several such telescopes together in an interferometer configuration, this mobility permits us to suppress costly delay lines and may also yield faster and better coverage of the u,v plane. The motion of the telescopes is however subject to the strict requirements of mechanical and thermal stability necessary for interferometric work. This implies stiff and vibration-free structures as well as metrology systems for speed and position control. The metrology systems may present a particular bottleneck as they have to measure distances up to several hundred metres with a precision of a fraction of a micron.

All these considerations lead to a solution in which a telescope transporter unit would be equipped with two sets of tripod supports. They are alternately placed on counterparts in the ground and can move the telescope in x and y directions. During their operating cycle, the tripod supports are rigidly connected to the foundations, thus providing the pedestal of the telescope with the required stiffness for astronomical and interferometric observations. Overall speed and position control is derived from locally-installed, short distance measuring systems.

1. INTRODUCTION

Visible and infrared interferometry has been proposed with mobile telescopes for better and faster (u,v) coverage and for simplifying the instrumentation by suppressing the delay lines which are otherwise necessary (Labeyrie et al., 1988[1]; Vivekanand, Morris, Downes, 1988[2]). The telescopes would be of the 2 to 3-m class, which represents in itself a powerful astronomical tool. The distances to be covered by the mobile telescopes are typically several hundred metres with tolerances for speed and position even smaller than for "ordinary" stationary instruments.

As a consequence, if one wants to find engineering solutions which might meet the limitations set by observations in the interferometric mode, it is obvious that the whole support system (telescope and transporter) of the necessary optics must be chosen and designed according to the most advanced technology regarding stiffness and vibrations. Such a system has to be complimented by a powerful metrology equipment with resolutions matching the overall interferometre specifications.

2. SYSTEM REQUIREMENTS

A first approach to specifying system requirements was done by Bourlon (1988) [3] for a platform interferometer. In the initial phase, the interferometer should have two or more two-metre class telescopes, movable on a horizontal platform. Maximum extension of the platform should be 300 m. The position of the telescopes on the platform must be known with differing precisions, depending on the state of the observing. In general, the uncertainty on the optical path-length difference (OPD) can be as follows:

±2 mm	after one week (in case of a shutdown)
±0.5 mm	after 12 hours (start of daily observations)
±0.3 mm	after 2 hours (change of configuration)
±0.1 mm	after 15 min. (blind measurements)
±0.02 mm	after 5 min. (change from reference source to object)

These errors can also be regarded as the low frequency drifts.

Higher frequency fluctuations or vibrations are exposure time dependent which itself is a function of the wavelength, the required contrast and the atmospheric behaviour. Without consideration of the atmosphere above the telescopes, the vibration tolerances are:

Exposure time	r.m.s. fluctuations of optical path
20 ms	15 nm
50 ms	25 nm
300 ms	110 nm
800 ms	250 nm
1850 ms	500 nm
4200 ms	1000 nm

The telescopes' motions should be possible at a rate of 30 mm/s for slewing to a given position and for tracking, the maximum speed would be 11 mm/s.

The maximum wind speed tolerated during obervation is limited to 7 m/s with occasional excursions to 10 m/s and slight degradation of telescope performance. The telescope has the typical specifications of an instrument for optical and infrared observations, should deliver a coherent beam of 50 mm diameter and should be built for outdoor use (Plathner, 1988[4]).

3. FEASIBILITY CONSIDERATIONS

The following feasibility considerations presume the optics problems are solved, and that the question is now how to start the telescopes to "walk". This means only items like liaison to the ground, displacement mechanisms, metrology and environmental conditions are of interest, for a transporter unit which can move a telescope horizontally in a way that the optical path tolerances given above can be respected.

The most obvious way to do this would be to use a transporter with wheels running on rails or on a flat surface. But wheels might not be sufficiently vibration-free, and one could replace them by air cushions. A third version is a transporter equipped with legs which can be orientated in all directions and could even be used on any terrain without special preparation — let us call it a "spider". Finally, version 4 is a more technical variant of the spider where the complex leg systems are replaced by linearly moving x-y displacement units.

Version 1:

The transporter with wheels runs either on rails or on a flat, smooth surface. Both require serious alignment and the trans-

Table 3.1   Feasibility Considerations

No.	Item	Version 1	Version 2	Version 3	Version 4
1	Good stiffness of ground connections	6	1	7	10
2	Reliability of metrology system	5	1	7	9
3	Needs no long-distance metrology system	1	1	5	10
4	Needs simple foundations	3	1	10	8
5	Needs no special ground preparation	3	1	10	8
6	Easy to move in x and y direction	3	10	7	10
7	Independent of thermal variations	3	8	10	10
8	Does not need great alignment effort (as for rails for instance)	2	1	9	9
9	Does not need complex drive systems	6	1	4	9
10	Accepts a power sypply by cable	7	1	1	1
11	Accepts high weights (from telescope)	8	2	5	9
12	All construction elements are available	5	5	5	10
13	Is not influenced by dust	1	5	10	9
		53	38	90	112

porter needs permanent control of elevation and tilt in addition to the horizontal position and speed survey. This implies a powerful metrology system permanently in operation. As wheels might slip on the support, their rotation cannot serve to monitor the position of the carriage: a long-distance measuring system is necessary which is for the time being not available with the precision required, at least for distances over several tens or even hundreds of metres. The risk that wheels might slip is increased as wheels can only be preloaded by gravity when running on a flat surface and their contact to the support might be endangered by dust particles. The poor ground connection is also a limitation for the vibrational stiffness of the transporter. On the other hand, if one uses rails and pre-loaded wheels, it becomes impossible to move in two dimensions horizontally, the dust problem remains and thermal distortions might become a problem.

Version 2:

Air cushions to replace the wheels would solve the dust problems. However, there are enormous obstacles to overcome to provide this transporter version with sufficient rigidity, weight capacity and propulsion power. Such a solution combines the special requirements of a telescope in space with the difficulties of a ground-based instrument.

Version 3:

The spider is an elegant approach to get the telescope to walk. One could think of two sets of three robot arms, underneath the transporters body, which can be articulated in all directions and are alternately touching the ground or of a same number of tripod legs with linear actuators in each arm of the tripod as proposed by Labeyrie[5]. A good stiffness for the ground connection can only be obtained, however, when the supporting area is prepared, which means that one looses the advantages of an all-terrain vehicle. Due to the motion in space of the feet at the end of the legs speed and position control becomes very complex, requiring a correspondingly complex metrology system. It is furthermore probably necessary to provide the transporter with a long distance measuring device. The spider transporter might also be limited in its weight acceptance, but permits free motion on an x-y plane and does not suffer from dust. Backlash in the complex "leg" trains might cause problems.

Version 4:

This solution is based on machine tool requirements. There are again two sets of three "legs". The motion in space of the feet is created by linear z-slides moving in x, y and z direction respectively. They are equipped with preloaded, directly driven

friction drives. The linear motion over typically 500 mm can be very precisely controlled and monitored by laser interferometer systems. Elevation above ground and verticallity is maintained by a correct alignment of the (short) linear slides and corrected during load transfer by the measuring system. The long distance positioning control is replaced by accumulation of the data from the local laser interferometers and calibration at the starting point. The system "walks" on equally spaced support points fixed to simple pile foundations in the ground. This leads to good rigidity of the liaison to the ground and low sensitivity to dust.

A tentative judgement on the pros and cons of the four versions is summarized in Table 3.1 where feasibility considerations are listed. Value points have been attributed (1 means worst suited; 10 means completely meeting the requirement).

Versions 3 and 4 are obviously quite superior to versions 1 and 2 with some advantage for version 4. It is therefore this version which was considered in more detail and which will now be briefly described further.

4. DESCRIPTION OF THE SYSTEM

The sytem to move the telescopes during observation is composed of three items: foundations in the ground, the transporter and the metrology equipment.

As we want to displace the telescopes over distances up to several hundred metres, foundations may become rather costly. The "walking" facility of the transporter however permits us to simplify the ground supports. It is proposed to pour concrete pile foundations of 100 to 150 mm diameter on the corners of a grid 1 m on a side. Such pile foundations are known to damp vibrations in the vertical direction, and to be very stiff in the horizontal plane (Richart and Woods, 1970[6]). A typical arrangement is shown in Fig. 4.1.

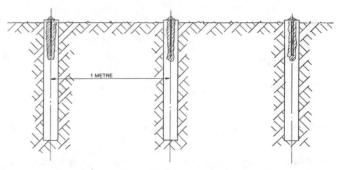

1 METRE

Figure 4.1.   Pile foundations

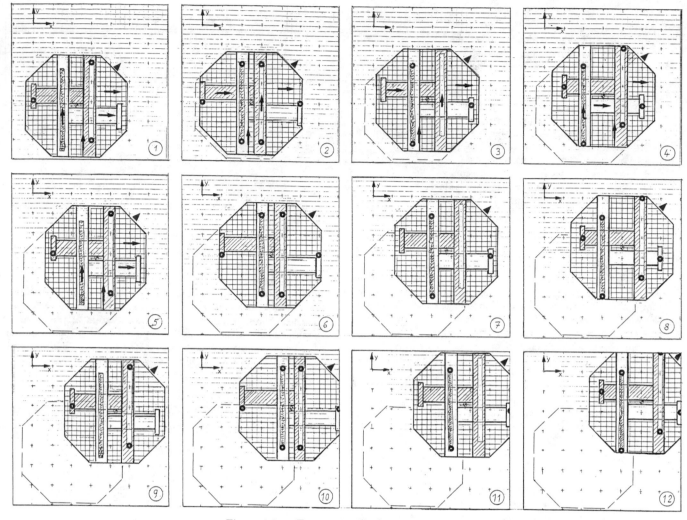

Figure 4.2.   Transporter displacement scheme

The concrete foundations are on top equipped with stainless steel supports which interlock with the feet of a transporter when it passes. There is no special precision required to place the support points, as the transporter feet will correct for deviations.

For its "walking" facility, the transporter is equipped with two sets of three legs. With one set of legs on the support points the telescope is correctly supported. Seen from the small platform of the transporter which is carrying the telescope on top, the legs can be moved in the x and y direction by half the distance between two support points on the ground. It is thus possible to bring the second set of legs into contact with the support points when the first one has come to the end of its stroke. A typical displacement scheme is shown in Fig. 4.2 indicating a 45° motion from the lower left corner to the upper right. To stabilize the platform of the transporter on a horizontal plane, the feet underneath the legs can be fine adjusted in the vertical direction.

All linear motions in Cartesian coordinate directions are built as preloaded, backlash-free roller systems with low levels of friction. The drive motors are directly connected. The electric power to supply the motors and the electronics comes from a battery stack which is on board of the transporter.

The metrology equipment as the third element of the telescope displacement device is mainly composed of laser interferometers. For each set of legs a laser source is split into four beams. Two of the beams are used to monitor the x-displacement of the transporter, the third indicates the y-stroke and the fourth keeps a constant height level (z-component) between the transporters' platform and an unloaded support point in the ground. To define the position of the transporter structure fully in space, two high precision clinometers level the platform about the x and y axes. A schematic set-up of the metrology equipment is shown in Fig. 4.3.

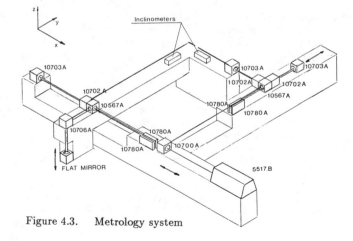

Figure 4.3.   Metrology system

To use this high resolution, locally installed metrology equipment also for the long distance control, the two sets of metrology systems are operated with a small phase shift with respect to the duty cycle of the legs. This means that the second metrology system takes over shortly before the changeover from the first to the second leg system occurs. By accumulation of the laser interferometer outputs a precise long distance measurement is possible. The sequence of the duty cycles of the legs and the measuring system is indicated in Fig. 4.4.

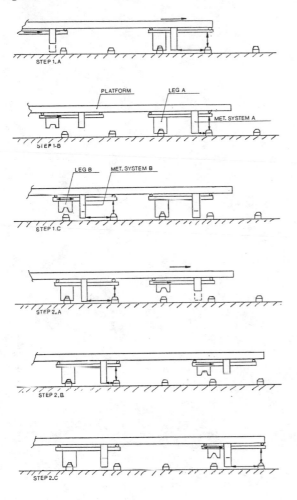

Figure 4.4.   Sequence of duty cycle

5. CONCLUSIONS

If a horizontal motion of interferometer telescopes is desired to suppress delay lines and to obtain a faster and better u,v plane coverage, it is important to create at any moment of observation a rigid ground connection to meet the vibrational requirements imposed by this kind of work. The proposed transporter is always with one of its two leg systems interlocked with the corresponding support points on the foundations and its drive units are backlash-free and of high stiffness. The installed metrology system provides sufficient resolution and covers both the short distance range and the long distance displacements.

6. ACKNOWLEDGEMENTS

This paper is based on a design study requested by the Institut National des Sciences de l'Univers, Paris.

7. REFERENCES

1. A. Labeyrie et al., "Steps Towards an Optical Very Large Array", Proc. of NOAO-ESO Conference on "High-Resolution Imaging by Interferometry", (1988).

2. M. Vivekanand, D. Morris, D. Downes, "Continuously Moving Telescopes for Optical Interferometry", Astron. Astrophys. 203, 195 (1988).

3. Ph. Bourlon, "Specifications for the Platform Interferometer", CERGA, F-06460 St. Vallier de Thiey (1988).

4. D. Plathner, "A New Mount for Mobile Telescopes in an Optical Interferometer", Proc. of the NOAO-ESO Conference on "High-Resolution Imaging by Interferometry" (1988).

5. A. Labeyrie, Private Communications (1988).

6. F.E. Richart Jr., R.D. Woods, Vibrations of Soils and Foundations, Prentice-Hall Inc., Englewood Cliffs, New Jersey (1970).

SESSION 3

New Technologies for Space Astronomy

Chair
Fritz Merkle
European Southern Observatory (FRG)

HARDI: A high angular resolution deployable interferometer for space

Pierre Y. Bely *
Space Telescope Science Institute, Baltimore, Maryland, 21218

Christopher Burrows*
Space Telescope Science Institute, Baltimore, Maryland, 21218

François Roddier
Institute for Astronomy, Honolulu, Hi, USA.

Gerd Weigelt
Max Planck Institut für Radioastronomie, Bonn, FRG

Abstract

We describe here a proposed orbiting interferometer covering the UV, visible and near IR spectral ranges. With a 6-meter baseline and a collecting area equivalent to about a 1.4 meter diameter full aperture, this instrument will offer significant improvements in resolution over the Hubble Space Telescope, and complement the new generation of ground-based interferometers with much better limiting magnitude and spectral coverage. On the other hand, it has been designed as a considerably less ambitious project (one launch) than other current proposals. We believe that this concept is feasible given current technological capabilities, yet would serve to prove the concepts necessary for the much larger systems that must eventually be flown.

The interferometer is of the Fizeau type. It therefore has a much larger field (for guiding) and better UV throughput (only 4 surfaces) than phased arrays. Optimized aperture configurations and ideas for the cophasing and coalignment systems are presented. The interferometer would be placed in a geosynchronous or 6-pm sunsynchronous orbit to minimize thermal and mechanical disturbances and to maximize observing efficiency.

1. Introduction

Observational optical astronomy is always scientifically driven to develop telescopes with fainter limiting magnitudes and higher resolution. However, it is clear that these two goals cannot be pursued simultaneously anymore. Larger ground-based telescopes have much greater collecting area but provide little improvement in resolution unless extremely demanding techniques are used. Space-based telescopes of traditional configuration such as the Hubble Space Telescope (HST) give great improvement in resolution (being diffraction limited), and a consequent improvement in limiting magnitude, but further improvements are limited by launch constraints. It is probably going to be impossible to launch a filled aperture telescope that gives an order of magnitude improvement in resolution over HST for the forseeable future.

To achieve still higher resolution, interferometers are the answer. On the ground, baselines can be very large, but the atmosphere restricts integration time and therefore limiting magnitude. A space-based interferometer, on the other hand, is not limited by integration time and thus could reach much fainter objects. Furthermore, a space interferometer, although likely to be limited in

---

*   Affiliated to the Astrophysics Division, Space Science Department, European Space Agency.

baseline initially, gets improved resolution from operation in the UV (near the Lyman continuum, a space interferometer will have about 4 times the resolution obtained from the ground in the U band with the same baseline).

Many concepts for space-based interferometers have been proposed, but they are generally of major proportions, with baselines of 15 meters or more that will require extensive technological development. We believe that the technical feasibility of space interferometry must be demonstrated before projects of this magnitude can be initiated. A smaller interferometer with a baseline on the order of 6 meters, would be less ambitious than the current generation of proposals and might consequently limit somewhat the science on which they are based. On the other hand, it would be much lower in cost, risk and development time, and would serve as a stepping stone to the larger projects. The validation in space of enabling technologies in areas such as deployment, active optics, laser metrology, vibration suppression, high accuracy guiding and pointing, would be a major technological spinoff from such a project. Such validation is essential if the larger proposed projects are to be demonstrably feasible.

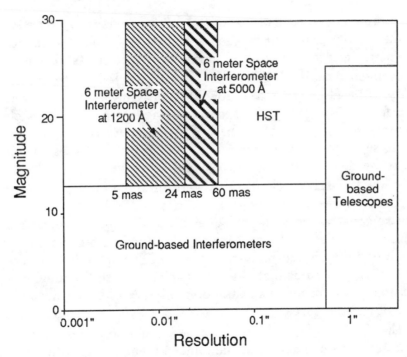

Figure 1. Domain of the proposed interferometer (hatched area) compared to that of existing or proposed instruments.

As shown in Figure 1, even an interferometer of such a moderate size would offer important advances over both HST and ground-based interferometers, especially if it can be operated in the UV. For example, this would allow bright quasars, Seyfert galaxies, or stellar chromospheres at Lyman alpha to be imaged at several times the resolution of HST. For several scientific areas, the resolution of HST is just marginally inadequate (e.g. imaging the narrow emission line region in a variety of QSOs). Clearly also, it will often be necessary to pursue the study of discoveries made with HST and the new large ground-based facilities at higher resolution

We present here a first attempt at defining the main characteristics of an instrument corresponding to this rationale. We call this instrument "HARDI", for High Angular Resolution Deployable Interferometer. We also describe the various configurations and technological options that we plan to examine in detail as part of our ongoing preliminary study of the instrument.

2. Aperture configuration

The optimal aperture configuration of an interferometer depends on a number of factors such as scientific goals, complexity of the observed objects, synthesized point spread function, deconvolution, speckle or phase closure techniques, practical constraints etc... In order to determine the best configuration for our proposed instrument and scientific applications, we plan to do a comparative study of three typical configurations. The three aperture configurations, labelled Type I, II, and III, have an outer diameter of 6 meters and are very diluted with less than 6% filling factor.

Type I is composed of six 40cm-diameter mirrors on six arms and a 1m diameter mirror on axis (5.4% fill factor). The aperture configuration is highly redundant with the intention of supplying a high signal to noise ratio[1,2].

Type II is a pupil function proposed by Cornwell[3]. It contains nine 40 cm diameter mirrors arranged on a circle with a 2.8 meter radius (4% fill factor). Its advantage is excellent instantaneous u-v plane coverage which could have applications in the observation of ephemeral phenomena or microvariabilities.

Type III offers complete coverage of the u-v plane by aperture synthesis. It is composed of six 60cm-mirrors (6% fill factor) arranged in such a fashion as to lead to a quasi uniform u-v plane coverage when the entire telescope is rotated half a turn around its optical axis.

Type III has not been described elsewhere to our knowledge. In it, the mirror locations are such that the density of baselines increases roughly linearly with the separation. The idea is that the object spectrum for any system with unresolved bright components is close to flat. Therefore, one want approximately equal coverage of the u-v plane out to the diffraction limit in order to get the same signal to noise ratio at each frequency. As longer baselines sweep a greater area when rotated, there need to be more of them to give equal coverage.

A number of optimal Type III configurations were obtained for various numbers of sub-apertures and different sub-aperture sizes using the Monte Carlo method with more than 10 000 trials each. The subapertures were constrained to lie at equal distance from the optical axis, so that they can be fabricated by replication. Each sub-aperture was divided in 10x10cm elements and the moduli of the elementary baselines were binned in 10cm intervals. The optimization criteria was to minimize the rms of the spread of the modulus distribution with respect to the ideal linear function. We have selected a configuration with six 60cm in diameter mirrors as being a good compromise between the number and size of subapertures.

Figure 2 shows the three configurations described above together with their corresponding u-v plane coverage and point spread function in the image plane. We are planning to conduct computer simulations and laboratory experiments to evaluate these configurations as a function of the type of object to be resolved and the point spread function deconvolution algorithm.

3. Optical design

Interferometers used in optical astronomy are generally of the Michelson type. This design suffers from a lack of field[4] and poor throughput especially in the UV due to the large number of relay mirrors required. Our proposed instrument is of the thinned aperture or Fizeau type (Figure 3). This interferometer configuration uses a smaller number of reflecting surfaces and offers a sufficient field of view to permit guiding using offaxis "bright" stars.

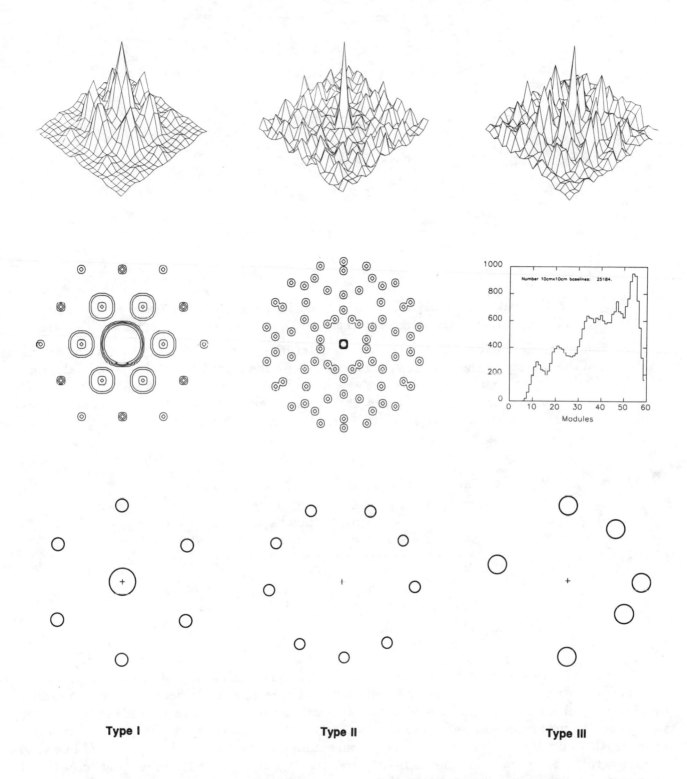

Type I   **Type II**   **Type III**

Figure 2. The three aperture configurations under study (bottom) shown with their u-v plane coverage (middle) and the point spread function (top). For Type III which is rotated around its axis during observations, the histogram of the baseline modules is shown instead of the two-dimensional u-v plane.

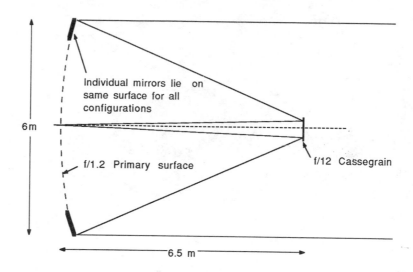

Figure 3. Schematic optical diagram of the proposed interferometer. The Fizeau configuration is preferred over the Michelson type because of its larger field and smaller number of reflecting surfaces.

The final numerical aperture of the system is determined by the necessity to match the angular resolution of the system to the detector's pixel size. Using the Nyquist criterion, the final numerical aperture of the system must be $F/D = 2p/\lambda$, where F is final focal length of the system, D the overall aperture diameter, p the pixel size and λ the operating wavelength. Table 1 gives the minimum numerical aperture of the system as a function of the wavelength for current typical pixel sizes.

Table 1.

Wavelength (μm)	Resolution (milli-arcsec)	Detector pixel size (μm)	F/ratio for optimal match
1.0	42	50	100
0.6	25	15	50
0.24	10	15	125
0.12	5	15	250

Since a fast primary surface is essential to minimize the overall length of the telescope, obtaining such slow beams directly would lead to an impractical Cassegrain magnification. This is examplified by Figure 4 which shows the influence of the Cassegrain numerical aperture and that of the primary surface on the major optical parameters of the system. The tradeoffs are complex and will require an in-depth study, but for the purpose of our conceptual study an f/1.2 primary and f/12 Cassegrain appeared to be reasonable combination. Optical relays will be used for reimaging onto the three detectors (UV, visible and near-IR) with the appropriate scale. These relays should be coated to minimize reflecting losses in each of the wavelength bands.

The Cassegrain combination will be of the Ritchey-Chretien design to produce a large enough field of view. A total field of at least 10 arcminutes in diameter is required to give a good probability

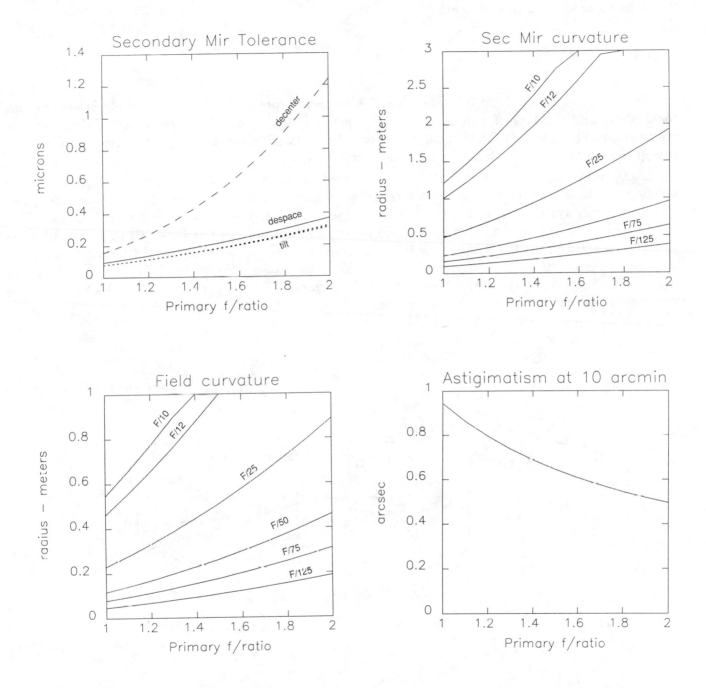

Figure 4. Effect of the primary mirror surface and final beam numerical aperture on the secondary mirror positioning tolerances, secondary mirror curvature, field curvature, and astigmatism. Only the secondary mirror curvature and field curvature are dependant on the final beam numerical aperture, the secondary mirror position tolerance and astigmatism are not, at least to the first order. All effects are shown for 1200Å and assuming a Ritchey-Chretien combination. The value for the secondary mirror tilt tolerance is given in displacement at the edge of the mirror.

of finding a pitch-yaw guide star in the 14th magnitude range. We would expect roll control to be achieved using fixed head star trackers. As in the case of the science field, reimaging will be required to produce a proper scale.

4. Cophasing and coaligning system

In view of the very tight tolerances on the respective position of the optical elements and the focal plane and the lack of external shielding, one cannot rely on the dimensional stability of the structure, either passively (with insulation), or actively (with structural heaters). An active system is required to "freeze" the image during the exposures.

Our proposed active optics system is composed of actuators on the primary mirrors and the secondary mirror servoed to a laser metrology system controlling the internal optical path lengths. This metrology system, using a Dyson[5] interferometer, is described schematically in Figure 5 . The active optics system is bootstrapped by observing a bright star in the focal plane and coaligning and cophasing each primary aperture in successive pairs. Each primary would be depointable to remove its contribution from the focal plane. This is desirable to allow for failures on orbit in any event. The metrology system is then activated to "lock in" the optical pathlengths between the various optical elements and the focal plane.

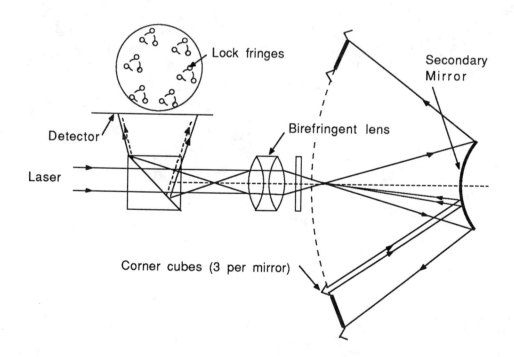

Figure 5. Coaligning and cophasing system. A Dyson interferometer setup is used to the maintain the optical path lengths in the system using retroreflectors mounted at the periphery of the primary mirrors.

In addition to serve to cophase the interferometer, the active optics system will also be integrated in the pointing control system of the spacecraft. The pointing system will be composed of two layers. A traditional spacecraft attitude control based on gyroscopes and star trackers will be used for slewing and coarse pointing. The fine pointing (guiding) will be done by using the active optics system to steer the optical beam based on the information supplied by a guide star in the field.

5. Spacecraft general design and orbit

As shown on Figure 6, the supporting structure is composed of a central tower and six articulated arms. These arms are braced with telescopic members which extend for deployment and confer axial rigidity to the structure. Once open, the moments of inertia around the three axes are nearly equal, thus minimizing the attitude control requirements.

Figure 6. Artist view of the proposed interferometer during deployment.

The entire interferometer assembly is protected from the sun by a sun shade located on the rear of the spacecraft. There are no side baffles. This leads to a considerable simplification of the spacecraft structure, but the price to pay is that the pointing has to be limited to about 45 degrees from the anti-sun direction. The solar arrays are attached to the sun shade to avoid the low frequency excitations that a steerable system would create.

The entire telescope structure and optics will be passively cooled by radiation against the sky to allow near IR observation. Preliminary calculations indicate that a temperature on the order of 100° K may be attainable.

As for the orbit, we are conducting an in-depth study to determine which of the possible earth orbit would be the most favorable for the proposed instrument. Factors such as thermal and mechanical disturbances, sky coverage, radiation level, observing efficiency, baffling, communication etc.. are being considered. So far the main contenders appear to be the 6pm sunsychronous and geosynchronous orbits which offer significant advantages over low earth orbit.

The overall mass of the spacecraft is estimated at 3 tons which is compatible with the payload capacity to sunsychronous or geosynchronous orbit of medium-sized launchers such as Ariane 4.

6. Conclusion

We have outlined here our approach to going beyond the resolution of HST. It seems to us that a space interferometer is eventually going to be a necessary next step. Even with a modest baseline the scientific drivers are enormous. The concept we are developing forms the basis for a cost effective first attempt in this direction.

References:
1. F. Roddier, "Redundant v.s. non-redundant beam recombination in aperture synthesis with coherent optical arrays", JOSA A, 4, 1396 (1987).
2. T. Reinheimer, F. Fleischmann, F. Grieger, and G. Weigelt, "Speckle masking with coherent arrays", Proc. ESO Conf. "High-resolution imaging by interferomentry", Garching, p. 581,(1988).
3. T.J. Cornwell, "A novel principle for optimization of the instantaneous Fourier plane coverage of interferommetric arrays", IEEE Trans. Ant. Prop., 36, 8, 1165 (1988).
4. J. E. Harvey, "Performance characteristics of phased array and thinned aperture optical telescopes", Proc. SPIE 751, 62 (1987).
5. J. Dyson, "Common-path interferometer for testing purposes", JOSA, 47, 386 (1957).

Aperture synthesis in space

M. Faucherre[1], A. H. Greenaway[2], F. Merkle[3], J. E. Noordam[4], M. A. C. Perryman[5]
P. Rousel[5], F. Vakili[6], S. Volonte[7] and G. Weigelt[8]

1 Institut d'Astrophysique Spatiale/LPSP, N° 10, 91371 Verrieres-le-Buisson Cedex, France.
2 RSRE, St Andrews Road, Malvern, Worcs WR14 3PS, UK.
3 ESO, Karl-Scwarzschild-Strasse 2, 8046 Garching-bei-Muchen, Federal Republic of Germany.
4 NRFA, Postbus 2, 7990 AA Dwingeloo, Netherlands.
5 ESA-ESTEC, Postbus 299, 2200 AG Noordwijk, Netherlands.
6 CERGA, Observatoire de Caussols, 06460 St Vallier de Thiey, France.
7 ESA Headquarters, 8-10 rue Mario nikis, 75738 Paris Cedex, France.
8 Max-Planck-Institut fur Radioastronomie, Auf dem Hugel 69, D5300 Bonn 1,
Federal Republic of Germany.

ABSTRACT

Optical aperture synthesis (OAS) may be used to obtain images of much higher resolution than "seeing"-limited observations presently made from the ground. The principles of OAS are essentially those used in radio astronomy and may be applied to space-based or to ground-based observations. The greater spatial resolution obtained would facilitate the imaging of stellar envelopes around Be stars, the study of the internal dynamics of active galaxies, etc. The application of aperture synthesis techniques in space, at visible and at ultra-violet wavelengths, should permit imaging of much fainter sources than would be possible from a terrestrial telescope array. Infra-red observations are best made from the ground.

A summary of the conclusion reached by the Space Interferometry Study Team set up by ESA will be presented. A short description of the important parameters relevant to a space mission (attitude control, orbit, structural dynamics, etc) and a comparison to terrestrial atmospheric conditions will be given. Possible instrument configurations will be described and it will be shown that a large field of view may be achieved, so that the instrument may be calibrated on bright stars whilst observing faint sources.

Mission concepts for a "monostructure" $\sim$30 metres in size will be examined and a possible strategy for Space Interferometry in the next 20 years considered.

1. INTRODUCTION

In June 1987 the European Space Agency sponsored[1] a "Workshop on optical interferometry in space". The summary and recommendations of this workshop form a perfect introduction to this paper and are reprinted below by kind permission of ESA.

"The long-term ESA strategy for optical interferometry in space will open a radically new domain in astronomy, namely, the discovery of planetary systems and the optical imaging of star surfaces, ionised and heated clouds, gravitational lenses, and active galactic nuclei and jets at milli- and micro-arc sec resolution.

"Such a long-term goal, which may someday use an interferometer on the moon, can only be achieved in steps; ground-based optical interferometers, severely limited by the earth's atmosphere, should be followed by an initial space mission of modest size, to be launched before the end of the century.

"The scientific aim of this mission should be to exploit some of the unique possibilities of space interferometry, such as ultraviolet spectral-line imaging of kilometric-size structures on the sun, imaging of stars fainter than a V-magnitude 14-15 (the practical limit on the ground) using short baselines (less than 20 metres), or mapping with longer baselines the broad-line region in bright extragalactic sources. Even a mission of limited scope will have considerable impact on astrometry. In the infrared (5-20 microns), the probability of new discoveries is very high. However, since the atmospheric coherence area is larger in the infrared than in the visible, and since the requirements for cooling of IR detectors in space are severe, the more urgent task for the near future is the development of a vigorous ground-based effort at wavelength 2 to 20 microns.

"The ability to maintain internal phase coherence over sufficiently long periods (minutes to hours) is fundamental in the design of a space interferometer. This might be done either with the observed source itself or with offset reference stars. Adequate sensitivity and imaging quality can be achieved only if this technologically challenging technique can be realised.

"Two mission concepts emerge from the meeting: a single-structure array (up to about 20m in size), or a cluster of free-flying coupled telescopes. Both concepts are possibly compatible with the space station.

"Resolution requirements call for milli-arcsec or better at 100nm initially, which would be at least ten times better than the Space Telescope. The longer-term aim would be to reach micro-arcsec resolution. To obtain images of high dynamic range at wavelengths of 100-1000nm, it is desirable to have up to 10 telescopes of size 0.3 to 1.0 metres.

"The two concepts require specific technologies. For example, an array mounted on a single structure calls for fibre optics, inertial compensation for the flexing of the structure, and possibly inflatable or deployable modules. An array composed of free flying satellites requires smooth propulsion and accurate ranging. A mission-oriented technological programme is essential, and will benefit from on-going studies made at ESA for other purposes. The workshop panel members unanimously recommend that a mission-oriented study group be established, which could propose a well-identified science objective and select the associated mission concept, stimulate development of the appropriate technologies and ensure optimal interfacing with on-going and essential ground-based programmes. They also recommend that contacts be pursued with other agencies to achieve international collaboration in this initial mission, to avoid duplication of effort and to ensure maximum mission return".

In response to the above recommendation the Space Interferometry Study Team (SIST) was set up, the membership of which corresponds to the authorship of this paper. The terms of reference for SIST broadly follow the recommendation quoted above, and the fifth meeting of this group is being held co-incident with this conference. This contribution, and its companion paper, are intended to give a brief outline of the progress made by SIST, prior to submission of the final report some time before the end of this year.

2. SPACE INTERFEROMETRY - BRIEF HISTORICAL SURVEY

A full survey of proposals for spacecraft interferometry would be beyond the scope of this paper, but a non-exhaustive survey is given in table 1 in order to illustrate both the fecundity of proposals and the underlying themes. More details may be found in references 1-4.

Table 1 - Historical survey

Year Proposal Comments

1979 FLUTE   - one dimensional, rigid tube; sectional assembly for baseline extension; two telescopes sliding within tube for baseline variation, access to faint sources by using offset guiding on bright star; full "optical" bandpass to be used after dispersion.

1979 COSMIC - one, later two, dimensional rigid structure; sectional assembly for baseline extension; at least six telescopes in fixed positions; direct, "white light" imaging; initial optical alignment on bright source, thereafter only minor corrections to optical path differences (opd) errors over long time scales.

1980 TRIO   - two (later many) telescopes in independent, free flying satellites; dispersed fringes for two telescope version; spectral format under consideration for 2-d version; all telescopes equidistant from beam combining satellite; number of telescopes to be augmented over extended period; solar sail propulsion to minimise fuel requirement; positioning at Lagrange point L5 for uniform gravity field; optical configuration stabilised using laser radar; beam transport using waveguides considered in 1984.

1980 SAMSI   - two telescopes in independent, free flying satellites, (later three tethered satellites with spiral orbits); beam combining satellite and telescopes in 3 low earth orbits with shallow inclination (to sweep 1-d baselines); ion engines for fine positioning of telescopes.

1984 POINTS - dual, near-orthogonal, two telescope interferometers in articulated, semi-rigid, tubes with 2m baselines, specific design for ultra high precision astrometry; internal optical configuration to be monitored by lasers, using near common path, "full-aperture metrology"; channelled spectrum operation.

1984 OASIS   - three-fold symmetric deployable, "floppy" structure; 15 (later 9) telescopes; beam transport by mirrors and free space (later by waveguides); use of optical delay lines (or waveguides) for opd equalisation; partially redundant (self calibrating) configuration; intention to use radio aperture synthesis type algorithms; optical configuration monitored by observing offset bright star, with "real time" corrections in hardware or software.

1984 ISIS   - 1 or 2 dimensional, semi-rigid structure; optical configuration stabilised to within coherence length only; highly redundant telescope configuration favoured; data analysis to be as for terrestrial "speckle" imaging, integration times to be matched to achieved stability; reference stars used only for "speckle holography".

1987 BSE   - two telescopes on small (5m) baseline; only bright (mag $\lesssim$ 13) double stars to be observed; broad spectral range by dispersed fringes or Fourier transform spectrometry; deployment in low orbit from shuttle; opd equalisation relaxed (several waves).

1987 SUN   - 4 telescopes in 1-d array on small (2m) space station attached payload; only solar coronal loops to be studied in UV; stabilisation of opd using IR signal from most distant telescopes. Other opds by dead reckoning (later pairwise "white light" interference in visible between all telescopes).

1988 FLOAT   - several telescopes mounted within a single structure; beam transport using single mode optical waveguides; opd stabilisation mainly be inertia (optics not physically attached to structure).

This list is not complete and, moreover, most of the proposals mentioned above have undergone an evolution of their design and have, to some degree, interacted and overlapped. Conceptual differences are collected in table 2.

Table 2 - Conceptual differences

free flyers (3 or more co-operating satellites)	vs	single structures with many telescopes.
stable optical configuration with only minor opd adjustments required	vs	"floppy" structures requiring real time opd correction in hardware and/or software.
free space beam propagation	vs	beam transport using single mode fibres.
two-dimensional apertures	vs	one dimensional apertures.
dispersed fringe systems	vs	"white light" operation.
non-redundant pupil format	vs	partially, or fully redundant pupil.
low earth orbit	vs	high orbit, at least geostationary.
input pupil geometry matches output pupil geometry (Fizeau)	vs	input pupil geometry and output pupil geometry are dissimilar (Michelson).

In the absence of financial or practical constraints one would always select the left hand concept from the above list. There are, however, constraints that may make the concept in the right hand column more attractive. Each of the above will be considered in turn and an explanation given, where appropriate, why SIST believes that the balance of advantages tips in favour of the "inferior" concept.

3.   STRATEGIES FOR SPACECRAFT INTERFEROMETRY

At visible frequencies the atmosphere induces time-dependent distortions which cause severe image degradation. Typically, the point spread function of a large astronomical telescope has a detailed speckle structure that changes on a short (0.01sec) time scale. The long time average of these speckles yields images with angular resolutions equivalent to that obtainable from a diffraction-limited telescope of about 10cm diameter (ie $\sim$ the correlation length of the distorted wavefront). Interferometric techniques exist that permit one to recover the diffraction-limited performance of terrestrial astronomical instruments, but the sensitivity of such techniques is dependent on the number of detected photons per "coherence cell" per "coherence time". The practical consequence of this is to effectively limit the usefulness of such techniques to observations on very bright sources. Since the atmospherically induced distortions are very angle dependent, there are not enough bright stars to permit one to use them to calibrate the instrument whilst observing faint sources.

Clearly one may launch telescopes whose size exceeds the atmospheric correlation length, but the largest size available is limited by launch vehicle considerations. To exceed the angular resolution available from HST one must use segmented optics. The same interferometric techniques that are used from the ground may then be applied to compensate for defects in such segmented instruments, but the sensitivity will be limited by the number of detected photons per segment per "coherence time". The latter will be limited by vibrations and/or other instrument instabilities and thus the potential for synthetic aperture optics in space is limited by the instrumental stability that may be achieved. Since there is no significant dependence of these instabilities on the angle of observation, one may calibrate a space instrument on a bright star, provided that the instrument has sufficient sensitivity and sufficient field of view to "nearly always" include a reference star.

3.1 Multiple satellites or single structure?

The multiple satellite solution has the greatest flexibility of any interferometer concept in terms of baseline extension and configuration. Additionally, there seems little doubt that the kilometric class baselines required to achieve micro arcsec resolution at visible frequencies are most unlikely to be achieved using single satellites. Thus the highest angular resolution range identified in the introduction will only be achieved from a lunar observatory or from an interferometer consisting of a cluster of free flying satellites. The prospects of lunar interferometry seem rather distant and at present it is difficult to see how ESA could identify a short to medium term mission that would advance prospects in this area at a greater pace than the experience presently being gained from the terrestrial interferometer projects currently in hand or under study (see references 1,3,5,6).

Since each satellite requires propulsion and guidance, the multiple satellite solution is likely to be expensive. Further, loss of positional control on a single satellite could pose a hazard to the remainder of the instrument, use of short baselines may also be difficult. A "starter" project proposed by Labeyrie[7] would permit baselines up to 100m in geostationary orbit, the instrument could be scaled to longer baselines simply by deployment in a higher orbit. However, although there is experience in positioning two satellites to centimetric precision at short range (ie, docking) there is no experience in station-keeping to this precision over long ranges for long periods of time and with a minimum of three satellites (two telescopes, one beam combining station). Although it might be thought that the fuel requirements for such station-keeping would limit mission lifetime, Labeyrie has shown that solar sails should be able to provide sufficient thrust for this function. Use of an extended three dimensional deployment of the satellites ("lens-like arrays") may be used to relax the positioning requirements and would give the instrument a better field of view, but may cause difficulties when re-pointing the instrument (see below). Because there is no extended structure associated with the array, one must either position all satellites to within about 100nm or one must include a short delay line for each telescope, probably within the beam combining satellite. The travel of the delay lines will then determine the station-keeping accuracy required, and will be used to compensate relative errors in station-keeping and to correct undamped vibrations on the optical components.

More problematic is the re-pointing of the whole array. To keep the optical path lengths equal requires a precise positioning of all the satellites in three dimensions. To re-point over small regions of sky, movement of just the beam combining satellite would suffice but to point at a new region of sky may require considerable expenditure of fuel, or considerable time (solar sails), or both. This will reduce the number of sources that may be studied during the mission lifetime.

Single structures restrict the array configuration both in form and extent, but present a platform that may be used for delay lines (thus facilitating rapid re-pointing over moderate angles) and the whole structure may be readily re-pointed over large angles. Use of a structure avoids problems of drift between several satellites, but introduces equivalent problems due to thermal expansion and raises the need to consider mode damping within the satellite. Whilst it seems likely that space structures of more than 100m are possible, it seems unlikely that structures approaching kilometric size will ever be used for interferometry.

Bearing in mind the requirements to reach high angular resolutions, the interferometric mode of the VLT and other terrestrial projects, SIST are of the opinion that any space interferometer project (even if only of modest physical size) should be "technologically extendable to baselines in excess of 100m". Thus, whilst the structural form of a mission of such baseline need not be addressed in a prototype mission, such a prototype should not rely on features which may not be valid in an instrument scaled up to > 100m size. In this context it is felt that concepts that cannot be so scaled up should be given consideration in terms of the science that they can deliver, but not in terms of a step on the "learning curve" to long baseline space interferometry. SIST notes that both multi-satellite and single structure designs should be extendable to 100m missions and considers both worthy of further study. However, SIST also feels that the multi-satellite solution is likely to be more expensive and thus that a single structure is a better candidate for a first mission in the near future.

3.2   "Rigid" or "floppy" structures?

Clearly, any complication in the control system required in a satellite is to be deprecated, and "rigid" structures requiring no continuous or regular optical path length control are, therefore, more attractive than concepts in which such control is intrinsic. However, one must consider how certain one can be that such rigidity may be achieved.

The fundamental modes of a large structure will have low frequencies, but the optical sub-structures will have higher natural frequencies and one must be careful not to excite these. One would generally expect that the mode damping in a "floppy" structure would be better than in a "rigid" structure, but one might also expect that the amplitude of low frequency distortions of the whole structure would be larger in the "floppy" case. Studies at JPL have indicated that single truss structures can be quite stable over short time scales, although all structures will be subject to thermal effects likely to cause large, but predictable and relatively long time scale, movements. For deployable structures, the behaviour of joints and hinges seems difficult to model at the required precision. The use of inflatable structures appears to be an attractive alternative. In optical interferometry the critical parameter is the time interval over which unmonitored/unmodelled opd variations do not exceed 0.1λ, say, and thus both the amplitude and frequency of distortions are of interest. Naturally, concepts designed to work with a "semi-rigid" or "floppy" structure will perform at least as well if the structure proves to be more stable than expected, whilst concepts designed to work with a "rigid" structure may not work effectively if the structure should prove less stable than predicted. For this reason it is felt that concepts utilising single structures should include either passive (ie software) correction of opd errors or active correction (ie servo driven delay lines). In terms of cost and reliability it is preferable that software corrections are employed, since these may be dispensed with more easily and do not represent single-point failure problems during a mission lifetime. In this context it is noted that if the number of delay lines used is equal to the number of telescopes in the array, one could tolerate the failure of a single unit with no significant operational consequences, and two or three units with consequences for the pointing control that must be achieved. Hardware or software corrections can be applied to correct deformations or vibrations and these may be monitored using internal metrology (POINTS), although the minimisation of such problems by using the inertial isolation of optical sub-assemblies within a structure (FLOAT) may be attractive.

3.3   "Free space & mirrors" or waveguide beam transport?

There is presently a lack of single mode fibres at short wavelengths although, according to one manufacturer at least, this is "merely" a question of cost (new materials would be required for $\lambda < 250$nm). In this situation, the use of fibres would appear to preclude operation in the important UV range, which is not accessible from terrestrial sites and gives the highest angular resolution for a given baseline.

The essential requirement of an interferometric beam transport system is that the optical beams are delivered in a condition in which interference takes place and is of high quality. In practice, this means that the beam transport should prevserve the relative strengths (to at least 70% accuracy) and relative polarisation states (to at least 25° of input polarisation state) of any beam input at the telescopes of the array and that over the measurement interval the beam transport should not change the relative phases by more than, say, $\lambda/8$. Each of the above figures represents a degradation of signal quality by about 10% and in formulating an overall system error budget one would need to aim for performances an order of magnitude better than these.

The losses and polarisation changes on reflection are fairly well understood and for UV wavelengths losses due to multiple reflections may be severe. For an optical train with many reflections there are many surfaces to be controlled, which presents a demanding, if understood, problem. The useful field of view obtained with such a reflective system is also understood although, as shown in a companion paper[8], this may become rather small.

Use of single mode waveguides (SM fibres) potentially reduces the number of parameters over which control must be maintained to achieve satisfactory interference between the beams[9]. SM fibres are designed for a given wavelength, λ_c, and will be single mode for this and for longer wavelengths. For $\lambda > \lambda_c$ the guided mode penetrates further into the fibre cladding and in consequence losses are higher and are sensitive to bending of the fibre. Over fibre lengths required in interferometry, it seems likely that losses will be acceptable in the range λ_c to $2\lambda_c$. SM fibres are very lossy for modes other than the one for which they are designed and the resultant "stripping" of other modes acts as a beam conditioner, which is useful for interferometry. This "mode stripping" is partly responsible for the coupling losses. The eigenmode for SM fibres is an axial beam of gaussian-like profile and the airy disc from a well corrected lens couples quite efficiently to this. In the mid visible a SM fibre core has a diameter of 3–5μm. Losses increase if the propagation direction and position of the input beam are not well aligned to the axis of the fibre core and efficient coupling requires a positional precision better than 1.2μm, with an angular alignment better than 1°. There is a possibility to use fibre horns (tapers) to achieve some tradeoff between these requirements, but the chromatic properties of such horns must be carefully considered. Fibre cores tend to attract dust particles and a dust particle on a 30μm horn is less severe than the same particle on a 3μm fibre core, however, graded-index lenses could also be used to ease cleanliness problems.

For interferometric purposes the fibres must have identical optical path length and identical birefringence if achromatic performance is to be achieved. The optical path lengths within fibres can be controlled via temperature and via strain, however, propagation within fibres is dispersive (as are the thermo-optic and strain-optic coefficients).

A temperature change of 1°K over 1m of fibre length will typically produce a change of 100 radians at the fibre output. This change is larger than would be produced by expansion of the fibre length because the thermo-optic coefficient is substantially larger than the expansion coefficient. Over the many metres of fibre in an interferometer the fibre packaging would need to accurately control temperature. This appears to be feasible and control by heating wires or conductive coatings on the fibres looks practical.

Whereas phase changes induced by temperature changes have a cylindrical symmetry about the fibre axis, those induced by strains do not and accurate predictions of the effects requires better knowledge of material properties, eg Pockels coefficients, than are readily available for fibre materials. SM fibres exhibit extrinsic and intrinsic birefringence. In the case of circular core fibres, stress induced birefringence causes perturbations to the polarisation state of the guided mode and results in an unstable polarisation state at the fibre output. It is generally difficult to keep such externally induced birefringence sufficiently small and fibres with high birefringence due to deliberately induced stress are employed. The advantage of such fibres is that they propagate two eigenmodes with well defined linear polarisation, which do not cross couple unless the fibre is excessively stressed. The propagation constant is different for the two polarisation modes and as a result they "beat", giving rise to an elliptically polarised output. Balancing these effects at a single wavelength may be done with established techniques; to produce achromatic fibre phase modulators for path length control appears to be feasible, but needs further development and must be achieved simultaneously with polarisation control.

In conclusion, the stabilisation of broad band fibre interferometres containing metres of fibre requires the accurate balancing of several large effects, over a range of wavelengths. Use of short fibre lengths for field-splitting may be more straightforward. If the data collection is in dispersed mode the balancing need not be perfect, but ideally any imbalance should be accurately modelled.

Use of a single fibre restricts the instrument field of view to the eigenmode of the fibre projected back onto the sky through the telescope. In this respect, use of optical fibres makes optical interferometry look very much like its radio counterpart, with the backprojected eigenmode being the "primary beam". This field of view may be smaller than that of a mirror based transport system, although the advantage to mirror systems may reduce or reverse for longer baselines.

Despite their obvious attractions, SIST feel that it is too early to make decision in favour of fibres over mirror based beam transport. However, progress in this area is rapid and it is felt that work on both systems should continue for the present.

3.4 Two-or one-dimensional aperture arrays?

Two-dimensional telescope arrays have the advantage that they have potential for producing two-dimensional "snapshot" images, which are useful when observing short time-scale phenomena. One-dimensional arrays can only produce "snapshots" of one-dimensional projections and two-dimensional images must be synthesised a posteriori from these projections.

SIST believes that the emphasis on interferometry must be directed to eventual production of two-dimensional images and that access to short time-scale phenomena, thus the "snapshot" potential, is important. This does not mean that one-dimensional structures are not suitable as a first interferometric mission, but does mean that there should be nothing intrinsic to the mission that would prevent the concept being extended to a two-dimensional mission at some future date. However, a one-dimensional mission would, by its nature, not scale directly to a larger two-dimensional project. It is thus felt that, unless the cost advantage of a one-dimensional mission is critical, a two dimensional first mission should be preferred. For similar reasons, it is suggested that a first mission should ideally consist of a minimum of three telescopes.

3.5 Dispersed or "white-light" fringes?

Use of dispersed fringes offers two significant advantages in the interferometric context. Firstly, the increased spectral resolution gives one access to a larger total bandpass whilst preserving a reasonable coherence length (thus relaxed tolerances on path length equalisation) and secondly, it provides the access to information about the source structure at a range of wavelengths which, as Labeyrie[10] pointed out, becomes more important at higher spatial resolutions.

Spectral dispersion generally indicates greater demands being made on the detection system (in terms of detector format or read-out rate). If dispersive elements giving a continuous spectrum are used it will probably be necessary to ensure that interference fringes are oriented normal to the direction of dispersion. For a two-dimensional array this will reduce the effective instrument field of view. Alternatives would be to use channelled spectrum images; to obtain the spectral information along the time axis by Fourier transform spectrometry; or making a narrow band image that is scanned (using a Fabry-Perot etalon, for example).

Direct formation of "white light" images requires very accurate path length equalisation. The potential difficulty to scale such requirements up to larger missions leads SIST to conclude that a first mission should not depend on direct formation of such "white light" images.

3.6 What level of input pupil redundancy?

Non-redundant telescope arrays are widely used in radio astronomy and have the advantage that they yield the maximum possible spatial frequency coverage for any array. However, non-redundant arrays do not guarantee a unique image reconstruction[11], at least in snapshot mode. Further it has been claimed that not only may partial redundancy be used to obtain a model independent solution, but also to improve the dynamic range[12] achieved. Weigelt[13] has stressed the sensitivity gain from highly redundant arrays when observing close to the instrument sensitivity limit. However, there is still debate concerning these points and SIST considers that these issues are not of sufficiently fundamental importance that they should in any way be permitted to drive mission considerations.

3.7 Low or high orbits?

Use of low earth orbit has significant advantage in terms of mission cost and in terms of manned involvement for construction or refurbishment in the context of space station. Space station is considered as a rather hostile environment for space interferometry because of pointing stability, thermal shocks on entering/leaving the earth's shadow and environmental cleanliness. It is noted that some smaller missions with very specific objectives might function in such an environment, but SIST do not consider LEO suitable for a mission to prototype a future long-baseline mission. Highly elliptical, eg Molynia type, orbits may be satisfactory for a first mission.

3.8 Fizeau or Michelson interferometry?

Fizeau interferometry preserves the relative geometry of the collector array in the interferometer output pupil, Michelson interferometry does not. This difference leads to several conclusions which will be summarised here, the detailed reasoning being given in a companion paper[8]. The Fizeau concept is superior in several respects, in that the beam combination may be achieved with few reflections (good UV transmission), and the effective field of view may be much larger (arc minutes) than in the Michelson case (arc seconds). Further, if the Fizeau interferometer is arranged using a "lens like" array with long effective focal ratio, the precision required in positioning the optical elements may be relaxed. However, if such an array is scaled up to baselines > 100m, one finds that the large f ratio results in a geometrically unwieldy instrument and that this large f is essential if the tolerances required to maintain the field of view are to be practical. In both Michelson and Fizeau cases a larger baseline leads to an intrinsically small field of view and in order to obtain a field sufficiently large to include a bright star on which to calibrate the instrument in "real time", one must split the field of view. This necessitates the use of differential path length compensation and complicates instrument design, but appears to be the most practical means for achieving baseline extensions beyond about 10m in a single structure.

4. CONCLUSIONS

The interim nature of the conclusions presented here are stressed and criticism is actively solicited.

SIST conclude that ESA should consider further the possibility of an interferometric mission that is of small scale (< 30m) but "technologically extendable" to a future mission with a baseline in excess of 100m. Interferometer proposals that do not have this extendability should only be considered for their scientific merit and not as contributing to the goal of long baseline optical interferometry in space.

The "first step" interferometer should preferably operate with a dispersed spectrum and have sensitivity at the short wavelength end of the "optical" region. Its successful operation should not depend on a structure that <u>has</u> to have more than short term stability at the sub-wavelength level (short defined as less than a second), nor should its operation <u>depend</u> on an arrangement of telescopes that is one-dimensional or consists of less than three telescopes.

Although SIST recognises that work remains to be done in several areas, notably the use of optical fibre beam transport and the implications of this for UV transmission and broadband operation, it is felt that a modest mission based on Michelson interferometry and assuming a "floppy" or "semi rigid" structure is most likely to be suited to these requirements.

Since single satellite missions are unlikely to reach the very long baselines that will ultimately be required, SIST concludes that studies directed to a longer term goal of multiple satellite or lunar interferometry should be pursued, but should not be considered for a first mission.

5. ACKNOWLEDGEMENTS

SIST are grateful to ESA for their help and encouragement in this study, and to the staff of ESTEC and various sub-contractors for presentations in several key areas. Correspondence with J. Jones is acknowledged. AHG and JEN are grateful to acknowledge receipt of NATO grant 723/84.

6. REFERENCES

1.   "ESA Workshop on Optical Interferometry in Space", Granada, Spain, 16-18 June 1987, ESA SP-273.
2.   "Colloquium on Kilometric Optical Arrays in Space", Cargese, Corsica, 23-25 October 1984, ESA SP-226.
3.   "Optical and Infrared Telescopes for the 1990s", Tucson, Arizona, 7-12 January 1980, Ed A. Hewitt, KPNO, 1980.
4.   "Workshop on High Angular Resolution Optical Interferometry from Space", Baltimore, 13 June 1984, Bull A.A.S.16, (1984), pp747-837.
5.   "Interferometric Imaging in Astronomy", Oracle, Arizona, 12-15 January 1987, Ed J. W. Goad, NOAO, 1987.
6.   "High-resolution Imaging by Interferometry", Garching bei Muenchen, FGR, 15-18 March 1988, Ed F. Merkle, ESO Proceedings No 29.
7.   A. Labeyrie, in ref 1, post-deadline papers.
8.   M. Faucherre and F. Merkle, these proceedings.
9.   P. Connes et al, in reference 2, pp49-61.
10. A. Labeyrie, in reference 3, pp786-796.
11. A. H. Greenaway et al, in reference 5, pp153-156.
12. J. E. Noordam and A. G. de Bruyn, Nature 299 (1982) 597-600.
13. G. Weigelt, reference 1, pp69-72.

Aperture Synthesis in Space: Computer Fringe Blocking

Farrokh Vakili

OCA-Calern, 06460 Caussols, France
Astronomisk Institut, 8000 Aarhus C, Denmark

Laurent Koechlin

OCA-Calern, 06460 Caussols, France

ABSTRACT

We discuss ways to remap the exit pupils of a ring-shaped array of optical telescopes, to obtain simultaneous spectral and angular informations about the object under study. Such an array, operated as a long baseline interferometer in space, would attain very large limiting magnitudes in absence of atmospheric turbulence, and open a new imagimg window down to 100 nm wavelengths. We consider this instrument in typical photon-noisy situations, and propose a spatio-temporal technique to integrate the flying fringe pattern recorded by a time-tagged detector at its focal plane. In principle, our method should relaxe the internal stiffness of the array to a few millimeters, making floppy structures or free-flying satellites adequate for very long baseline interferometry in space.

1. INTRODUCTION

Much will be learnt in the coming 20 years from the foreseeable discoveries to be made by the HST, and by the 10 meters class ground-based interferometers like the VLT. But a 50 to 100 meters size space-borne interferometer, comprising a dozen of 1 meter telescopes, will totally change our view of the universe by providing milliarcsecond informations at UV wavelengths, and on objects as faint as the 26th magnitude in the visible. For this reason, space agencies are currently considering optical aperture synthesis as the next major project in their horizon 2000 scientific plans. Besides its huge amount of scientific results, such a project will initiate the technological studies which are necessary for the design of the long term kilometric interferometers made of free flying satellites: probably the only way to attain microsecond angular resolutions on celestial objects.

2. FLOPPY/FREE FLYING VERSUS STIFF

A main question to be adressed when dealing with decametric arrays is, whether the structure supporting a dozen of telescopes should be stiff or floppy (an intermediate step towards a cluster of separate floating satellites). In a stiff structure (e.g. HARDI project by Bely et. al. 1989), the elements of the array -followed by the train of optical components, are maintained at their theoretical locations, within a fraction of the wavelength (.1 micron). A closed loop system, based on a metrological laser and a bright star in the neighbourhood of the science object, would ensure the co-phasing and co-alignement of the array, very similar to a huge HST.

On the other hand, the floppy structure (OASIS project by Noordam et. al. 1987), would relaxe the positioning of elememtary apertures at the extremity of the interferometric arms by compensating the optical path differences (hereafter OPD), using delay lines, grouped at the central/focal station. This is of course different from the free flying project TRIO (Labeyrie 1987), which compensates for the OPD by displacing the satellites themselves, under solar radiation pressure. In both projects, the coherence length is relaxed to a few mm by dispersing the interference fringes. However, OASIS assumes a bright source brought in the interferometric field of view, by means of fiber optics, and used as an external phase reference, making long exposures possible, hence a dramatical increase of the limiting magnitude.

It should be noted at this point, that in a Fizeau type optical set-up as it is envisaged for HARDI, each elementary pupil is an off-axis mirror, which can work at a specific distance from the optical axis of the array. Thus, going to longer baselines needs for additionary off-axis segments, which wouldvery soon limit the maximum baseline. On the contrary, the Michelson optical set-up adopted for TRIO, or similar approaches (Faucherre et. al. 1989), are virtually unlimited to span in baseline. This is of capital importance, and should guide the possible choice of a mean term space interferometric project as a precursor to the future kilometric arrays in space. Now we describe the optical correlator for a

TRIO/OASIS interferometric array, and the way to obtain simultaneous color and angular informations. We then discuss the method for dealing with spectrally dispersed fringes and the computational requirements for its implementation on the space interferometer.

3. PUPIL REMAPPING OF A RING SHAPED ARRAY

Besides its wavelength and turbulence free advantages, space offers the unique possibility to configure an array of telescopes with the "best" geometry. By best we mean the optimal sampling of the objective fourier components, since an interferometer acts as a spatial filter. For obvious reasons, a circular array offers the nice possibility to naturally equalize the optical paths from individual telescopes to the central beam-combining optics. Furthermore, if the telescopes can be moved around the ring, the interferometer can be re-configured to match the desirable spatial filter. This works in favor of free flying satellites. Nevertheless, changing the position of one aperture out of n, affects (n-1) baselines among n(n-1)/2, so a floppy structure with a few movable telescopes can easily fulfill this adaptive filtering criterion.

Related to this consideration, is the question of finding the geometry which provides a desired MTF -or (u,v) plane coverage. During observational runs on a same object, geometries should be found progressively as soon as new images of the object become available after deconvolution process. A method to find these geometries has been developed, basically using an error-reduction algorithm, similar to that of Fienup (1978). It works as followings:

a) Define a desired MTF -alternatively a PSF, which does not correspond to an obvious analytical geometrical solution: namely the input distrubution of the telescopes on a circle

b) Start from a random distribution of the telescopes on the circle.

c) Take the fourier transform of this input pupil, check for the difference between the related PSF and the desired one (integrate this difference over the whole image plane).

d) If larger than a given error, force the modulus of the computed fourier transform to the desired PSF, while leaving the phase free.

e) Fourier transform back to the pupil plane, set all the points out of the circular support to zero, select the n maxima (n=number of telescopes) on the circle. Go to c) until the error criterion is satisfied.

Depending on the desired (u,v) plane coverage, this method may stagnate in local spurious solutions. An additional loop has been added, which shifts the telescope positions around the circle by an arbitrary small angle. The overall algorithm goes through cycles of error-reduction and positional rotations, and works quite fast on a 68000 personnal computer. It has successfully found in a few minutes a "most uniform" (u,v) coverage for the OVLA project (Labeyrie et. al. 1988). Figure 1 shows the results of an optimal arrangement computed for an array of 12 telescopes, respecting an additional non-redundancy criterion on the MTF.

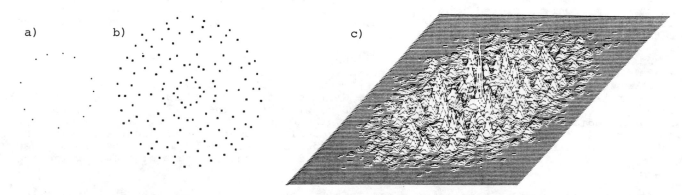

Figure 1. Characteristics of a ring-shaped array of 12 optical telescopes. a) The pupil distribution on a circular array. b) corresponding fourier components in the MTF, e.g. (u,v) plane coverage. c) The intensity distribution or PSF of the array in mono-chromatic light. Plots have been made in arbitrary units: meters for the input aperture, cycles per arcsecond for the middle and normalized flux per marcs square for the right.

It is of capital astrophysical importance to design an interferometric instrument to include spectroscopic possibilities as well. It has been observationally demonstrated (Thom et. al. 1986, Koechlin et. al. 1979), that simultaneous wavelength and angular informations bring new constraints on the physical models which can be built for a number of curious objects such as Be stars. No need to say higher the spectral resolution, the higher angular resolution and vice-versa. A possible approach to form the "spatio-spectral" power spectrum of the object can be extrapolated from the widely used optical design of the stellar interferometers located in southern France (Koechlin and Rabbia 1986, Bosc 1988).

The "trick" lies in directing the n collimated beams from the input pupils towards the centre of the ring, and by slightly tilting them from the radial direction (fig. 2). The beams can be intercepted by field lenses, which form the exit pupils on n flat mirrors. These mirrors are equally spaced on a stright line, and bend the incoming beams at 90 deg with respect to the plane of the circular array. Thus, they can be fed to the slit of a spectrograph which forms a complexe spatio-chromatic interferogram on a 2-dim detector. In this design we re-encode in fact the 2-dim directions along the sky, along a unique axis of the detector, which frees the second one for dispersing the fringes. A 2-dim fourier transform of such an interferogram gives a set of fringe peaks spread in 2 directions: first the dual of the angular direction defined along the sky, and the second the dual of wavelength-hence the OPD. Each fringe peak contains the modulus and argument of the objective power spectrum, degraded by instrumental amplitude and phase effects (figure 3).

The flat mirrors which bent the beams, can occasionally be actuated around 2 angles to correct for misalignements and internal tilts of wavefornts. We must also mention that since the n beams are not combined at the centre of the ring, they undergo a phase shift due to field rotation, which may partially destroy the fringe contrast. However, as far as the radius of the ring remains significantly larger than the size of the central correlator this rotational shift produces negligeable effects. It can be seen from figure 2, that the order in which the exit pupils have been aligned, minimizes this field rotation effect.

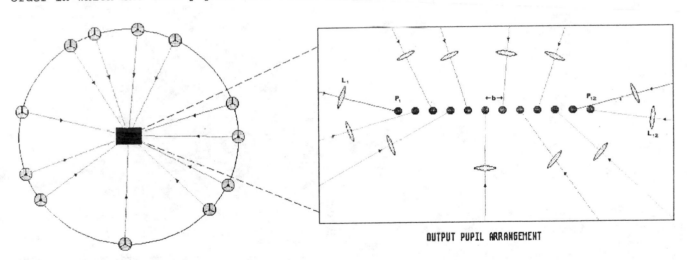

INPUT PUPIL ARRANGEMENT

OUTPUT PUPIL ARRANGEMENT

Figure 2. Input circular pupil remapped as a linearly rearranged exit-pupils. Collimated beams are slightly tilted with respect to the centre of the ring (top-viewed), and reflected perpendicular to its plane (normal to the figure). Output pupils are formed on flat mirrors by field lenses at eqal spacings b. The resulting fringes have periods between λ/b (λ=wavelength) and $\lambda/11b$. The interfrence fringes can be dispersed in the perpendicular direction to the linear array by a classical slit-spectrograh.

Detectors may put a severe limitation on the number of telescopes which can be used in an array, if we want to fulfill the sampling criterion for all fringe patterns present in the polychromatic interferogram (66 for a dozen of telescopes). In most cases it is desirable to record thousands of 1 angstrom spectral channels on the same detector. Present time-tagged photon counting cameras (PAPA, MAMA, etc.), need to be improved by a factor of 4 to offer enough pixels for such broad spectral bands.

For this reason, the Golon rules for non-redundant spacings between pairs of telescopes (also used in radio-interferometry) is not the optimum way to arrange a large number of exit pupils. This can be better understood in terms of missing spacings which occur when the number of pupils to be aligned exceeds 4 (for which the perfect rule of 1,3,2 works).

A missing distance (equivalent to a missing frequency in the frequency domain) causes a loss of an amount of picture elements equal to the number of pixels contained in one period of an immediately higher frequency fringe pattern. An alternative to this dilemma, illustrated in figure 3, is to introduce non-redundant arbitrary OPD's between a number of equally spaced telescopes. Identical exit baselines (between P1 and P2, and P2 and P3 for instance), donnot produce fringe peaks at identical frequencies, because their frequency has been shifted along the OPD axis.

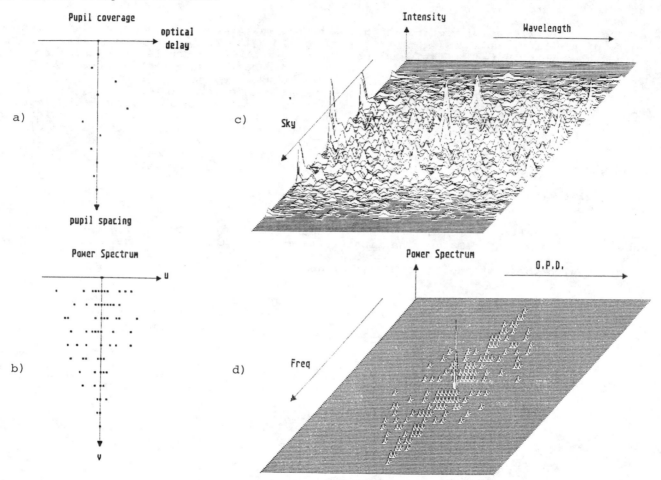

Figure 3. Pupil-space re-encoding to obtain simultaneous color and angular informations in the focal plane of the interferometric array of 12 telescopes. a) Normally aligned exit-pupils in the central station of the array undergo arbitrary phase retardations which would disentangle the corresponding (u,v) points in the MTF b). Thus the intensity distribution c) in the image plane can contain both color and angular information about the science object. The fourier components of the objective power spectrum can directly be recovered from the amplitude and phase of the fringe peaks spread around the central energy peak.

The main drawback of this roundabout is that for a large number of telescopes, offset OPD's accumulate for the lowest frequencies (because the shortest inter-pupil is the distance which repeats the most often). Corresponding fringe peaks may be pushed close to the limit of coherence length, suffering also in amplitude by a factor of Sinc(OPD). Moreover, the geometrical deformations of a floppy structure may temporally make coincide the fringe peaks of a same exit baseline. In practice, if we want to avoid this peak overlaps, we must consider the coherence length reduced by a factor equal to (n-1). For instance, a 1 å spectral resolution at .55 micron would provide a 3 mm coherence length, reduced to less than 300 microns in the case of the 12 telescope array considered in figure 3. It has been argued by Noordam (1988), that this difficulty should disappear, if the spatio-spectral interferograms are recorded by a high temporal resolution camera, and dealt with in a OPD plus fringe rate and acceleration space. We will consider this point in the next section.

4. DEALING WITH POLYCHROMATIC FLYING FRINGES BY 3-DIM FOURIER TRANSFORMS

A floppy structure or a floating cluster of satellites in space are subject to geometrical deformations due to the gravity gradient, thermal effects or attitude oscillations after pointing manoevrings. Even after stabilization, residual OPD variations may corrupt the phase of interfering beams, from which the name "flying fringes", characterizing the time variable aspect of the interferogram, exactly like the familiar speckle interferograms obtained with ground-based large telescopes (see figure 5).

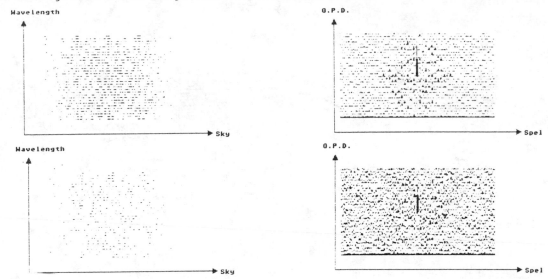

Figure 4. Spatio-spectral interferograms (see fig 3), simulated in photon-noisy situations. Top-left: 2000 photon-events recorded for constant OPD's in the fringe pattern of a 12 telescope array. Top-right: once fourier transformed, one can detect secondary fringe peaks spread around the central energy peak, from the position of which the OPD's can be directly computed. Bottom-left: the same interferogram, but with 200 photon-events. Bottom-right: fringe peaks are at noise level in the 2-dim power spectrum (Spel= spectrum element).

The flying aspect is not a problem by itself, as long as the flux level is high. Then, a very short exposure could freeze the fringe motion, and visibility amplitude and phase extracted from the fourier transform of the 2-dim interferogram (fig. 4). For more realistic and almost always astrophysically interesting sources like quasars, the number of photons during the lifetime of unblurred fringes is too small for correctly estimating the visibility. It is thus desirable to increase the integration time, by "computer blocking" their motion. As first proposed by Koechlin (1984), this can be done by 3-dim fourier transforming the 2-dim interferograms to which a 3rd time coordinate has been added, on which one records the time arrival of infalling photon-events. The principle of this method very similar to the Global Fringe Search of radio-astromomers (Schwab 1984), is schematically shown in figure 6. In this framework, and with micro-second time resolution cameras such as the MAMA detector, OPD variations as high as 10 centimeters per second can be accepted, as long as they remain almost linear. In the followings, we shall concentrate on the extension of this technique to constantly accelerated fringes.

Figure 5. Illustration of the flying fringes for a two-telescope interferometer. These interferograms are not real ones, but how they would be "seen" in the computer memory. They represent a monochromatic fringe pattern which is constantly drifting in time. Left: constant OPD during the integration time. Middle: a medium fringe rate. Right: extreme fringe rate, almost vertical to time axis. If the time resolution where not available, one should cut vertically the interferogram in very short exposures to avoid the decorrelation of the fringes: the exposure time would be decreased proportional to the fringe rate. The S/N would then increase as square root of the number of exposures, whereas if a 2-dim Fourier transform is taken of the spatio-temporal interferogram, photons would remain correlated during the time they drift linearly (for the spatio-spectral fringe patterns this would be a 3-dim fourier transform).

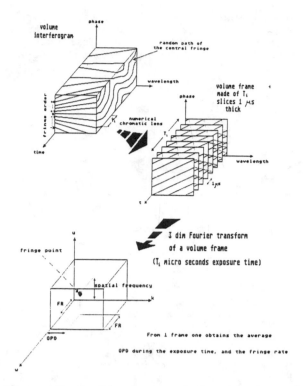

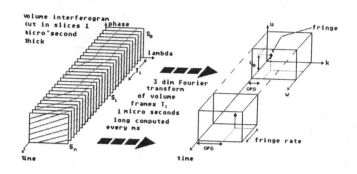

Figure 6. Spatio-temporal fourier transform technique to track flying fringes. Polychromatic interferograms (top-left), are recorded as volume interferograms of angular, color and
time dependant volumes by a micro-second time resolution camera. Volume-exposures, during
T micro-seconds are considered where the fringe drift remains constant (middle-left). The
wavelength-dependant fringe spacing is eventually calibrated and corrected in the computer
memory. Each elememtary volume-exposure is 3-dim fourier transformed, to concentrate the
intensity modulation energy in a fringe-sphere (comparable to a fringe-peak for a 2-dim
fourier transform). The position of this sphere in the volume power spectrum (bottom-left),
gives the fringe frequency, the average OPD and fringe-rate (velocity). In order to follow
continiously the evolution of this sphere, the exposure-volume slides continiously along
the time axis, and 3-dim fourier transforms ideally computed every 1 micro-second.

At extreme fringe velocities of a few cms per second as mentionned before, one would
quickly run out of the coherence length ($\lambda^2/\delta\lambda$ where $\delta\lambda$ is the spectral resolution). But
if a bright source is present in the interferometric field of view, to which the same
processing is applied, the OPD error signal can be directly found and sent to delay lines,
to stick the interferometer around the white fringe. Thus even though the interferometer
is unstable, the fringes can be followed and "blocked in the computer". This is roughly the
philosophy which has been adopted by Noordam (1989) for the OASIS project.

5. COMPUTER IMPLEMENTATION OF FRINGE BLOCKING ALGORITHMS

A constant fringe rate assumption for the flying fringes is a first step to improve
the S/N for measuring more properly the visibilities or for servo-looping the interferometric array in space. Ideally, one would like to globally integrate the fringe signal,
because if possible, the S/N would improve directly with time, instead of the square number
of the short exposures during the same time.

The next step after a constant fringe rate is a constantly accelerated OPD. Such an
acceleration can be calculated in the same way as the fringe rate from the 3-dim power
spectra. More precisely, since the fringe rate is extracted from the position of the fringe
sphere in the volume fourier transform, the acceleration can be found from the position of
an equivalent sphere in a 3-dim interspectrum. This interspectrum is made between the 3-dim
fourier transform of an actual volume exposure, and the fourier transform of the same exposure but one micro-second backwards in time. Such a 3-dim interspectrum corresponds in fact
to the time derivative of the fringe rate, hence the acceleration. From the S/N point of
view, the interspectrum is slightly worse than the power spectrum: it will be proportional to the square root of the geometrical mean of the average number of photons in 2 succe-
sive volume exposures, therefore $\sqrt{2}$ smaller than the S/N for the power spectrum. However,
if effectively computed, it can be used in association with the fringe rate and the OPD,

in an optimal Kalman-Bucy filter to predictively control the delay lines. Whether the knowledge of this acceleration is really useful, and does not complicate the computational requirements, remains to be checked by numerical simulations or directly on those ground-based interferometers with seeing limited apertures, where the situation is much similar to a space interferometer.

More troublesome is the software-hardware implementation of such a numerical technique. For instance, if the detector size is 1000x1000 pixels with 1 micro-second time resolution, and if the power spectrum wants to be computed every 1 milli-second, we must deal with a D=MxNxL=1000x1000x1000 Fourier transform every milli-second. This sounds out of reach, but not unfeasable as it will become clear in the followings.

a) Since the exit-pupil spacings relative to their size are known and fixe in time, the number of fringes per Airy disk, hence the spatial frequencies are well known in one direction of the 3-dim power spectrum. This confines the fourier components to (n-1) subplanes of the 3-dim fourier domain, in which n(n-1)/2 frequencies must be calculated.

b) Volume interferograms are basically empty, because we use a time-tagged detector. More precisely each temporal slice of the volume interferogram contains a unique photon repaired by its' coordinates (X,Y,t). Therefore the 3-dim power spectrum can be expressed as:

$$S(u,k,w) = \sum_M \sum_N \sum_L \exp\{-2i\pi(uX+kY+wt)/D\}\cdot\delta(X,Y,t) \qquad (1)$$

where $\delta(X,Y,t)$ is a Dirac distribution associated to a photon-event. Equation (1) can be re-written as:

$$S(u,k,w) = \sum_L \exp(-2i\pi wt/L)\cdot\{\sum_M \sum_N \exp(-2i\pi(uX+kY)/MxN)\cdot\delta(X,Y,t)\} \qquad (2)$$

Thus the last 2 summations can be performed by adding   sine and cosine coefficients, adressed by X, and indexed from Y. These coefficients can be found in fast ROM's. The last summation for t can be done by classical FFT algorithms, performed by commercially available vector processors. Preliminary estimations of computational requirements (Vakili 1988), show that for a 12 telescope array, a parallel architecture based on such DSP's can perform these calculations in real-time, and prove a computational band-pass of almost 1 kilo-hertz which is probably superior to what can be expected from that of a mechanical delay line.

6. CONCLUSION

Though not proven in real observational situations, the scheme outlined above indicates that floppy structures, or free-flying satellites can be "software rigidised" if the phase fluctuation spectrum does not exceed in amplitude and frequency the computational band-pass estimated in 5. Thus, they donnot represent a "worse" case of a stiff structure based on a Fizeau-type optical set-up, for which cophasing difficulties increase directly proportional to its' size. The sensitivity of the 3-dim method should however be checked in realistic photon-noisy situations. Ground-based observations on double stars, with a bright component and a faint companion such as Mizar, or a Be shell star, correspond quite well to the space conditions, and much experience should be gained, besides the astrophysical throughput.

7. ACKNOWLEDGEMENTS

This paper has been much inspired and stimulated by J.W. Noordam, to whom F. Vakili is greatly indebted. The study was also initiated by S. Volonte, and encouraged by M. Perryman from ESA, to whom we express our acknowledgements.

8. REFERENCES

1) P. Bely, C. Burrows, F. Roddier and G. Weigelt. "A High Angular Resolution Deployable Interferometer", these proceedings.

2) J.E. Noordam, A.H. Greenaway, J.D. Bregman and R.S. LePoole. "OASIS: AMission Concept". ESA Workshop on Optical Interferometry in Space, Granada, Spain, june 1987, ESA SP-273.

3) A. Labeyrie "TRIO and Mini-TRIO", same as ref. 2, post-deadline papers.

4) M. Faucherre, F. Merkle. "Beam Combination in Aperture Synthesis from Space: Field of View", these proceedings.

5) J.R. Fienup. "Reconstruction of an Object from the Modulus of its Fourier Transform". Opt. Lett. 3, 27-29, 1978.

6) A. Labeyrie, G. Lemaitre, C. Thom and F. Vakili. "Steps towards an Optical Very Large Array". NOAO-ESO Conference on "High Resolution Imaging by Interferometry". March 1988, Garching, FRG.

7) C. Thom, P. Granes and F. Vakili, Astron. Astrophys.165, L13-L15, 1986.

8) L. Koechlin, D. Bonneau and F. Vakili. Astron. Astrophys. 80, L13-L14, 1979.

9) L. Koechlin and Y. Rabbia. Astron. Astrophys. 153, 91-98, 1985.

10) I. Bosc. "The New Optical Table of GI2T". same as reference 6).

11) J.E. Noordam. "The Requirements for a Fringe Rate Detector". Internal report to ESA-SIST groupe, 1988.

12) L. Koechlin. "Fringe Drift Compensation in Computer Memory". ESA Colloquium on "Kilometric Optical Arrays in Space". Oct. 1984, Cargese, Corsica, France, ESA SP-226.

13) F.R. Schwab and W.D. Cotton. "Global Fringe Search Techniques for VLBI". Astron. J. Vol. 88, 5, 1983.

14) J.E. Noordam. "Satellite Stabilisation for Optical Interferometry in Space". Internal report to ESA-SIST, April 1989.

15) F. Vakili. "On-line Fringe Tracking with the Space Interferometer". Internal report to SIST-ESA, april 1988.

Imaging capabilities of the Faint Object Camera
on the Space Telescope

Francesco Paresce
Space Telescope Science Institute, Baltimore, MD 21218
and
European Space Agency, Astrophysics Division, Space Science Dept.

The Faint Object Camera built by the European Space Agency for the
Hubble Space Telescope (HST) contains three optical relays capable
of reimaging the HST focal plane with high spatial resolution at
F/48, F-96, and F/288 focal ratios. Recent simulations and ground
calibrations have demonstrated the capability of carrying out high
quality astronomical observations down to 15-20 milliarcsecond
spatial resolution and limiting visual magnitudes of 29-30. In
this paper, the results of these tests and calculations are
presented and discussed in the context of the scientific
capabilities of the mission. Particular emphasis will be placed
on the optical characteristics of the F/288 high resolution
apodizer which promise a revolution in our understanding of the
structure of very faint nebulosity around bright nearby objects
such as planetary systems around young stellar objects and ejecta
from evolved mass losing stars.

Mechanical collimators for EUV spectrometers

M. Melozzi and M. Fibbi

Officine Galileo
via A. Einstein 35, 50013 Campi Bisenzio, Italy

ABSTRACT

The mechanical collimator to limit the field of view of the EUV/FUV Imaging Spectrograph Facility will be realized using a series of thin electroformed plates.

In the present report the plate number and positions are computed and a procedure to test the instrument using visible light is discussed.

INTRODUCTION

High temperature plasmas (10^4 - 10^7 °K) present significant emission in the extreme ultraviolet (EUV) spectral region.

EUV observations are thus particularly useful for solar and star atmosphere investigations and, moreover, they provide significant data on magnetosphere, exchange of matter between stars and interstellar medium and on dynamics of hot interstellar gas in galactic halos.

However, due to the lack of transparent materials and of high reflectivity surfaces at these wavelenghts, system for EUV spectroscopy must employ open structure and a minimum of reflecting surfaces.

An objective grating spectrometer is commonly used for EUV point source observations. However the spectrometer field of view must be limited in the dispersive direction when observing extended sources to provide spectral separation of EUV radiation in the detector plane.

The field of view of the EUV/FUV Imaging Spectrograph Facility (IEH) for astronomical observations during the Hitchhiker program (figure 1), will be limited using a mechanical collimator realized with a series of thin electroformed plates which block the entrance light except for the field angle defined by the end plates.

The plate area is made up of "lands" and "voids" (figure 2).

The off-axis radiation is stopped by identical plates disposed in between the end plates. The collimator transmission can be maximized by making the land dimension, w', as narrow as possible with respect to the void size, w".

A pratical working ratio has been found (w"/w')=2, thus obtaining a nominal point source transmission of 0.66.

For the EUV/FUV grid, w' and w" are 0.125 and 0.250 mm respectivelly.

The plate side dimension is 150 mm thus defining an effective collecting area of 200 cm² when considering the supporting mechanical structure. Every plate contains 400 slits and, since the required field of view is 0.05°, the distance among the end plates is about 286 mm.

In the present paper we present the collimator design and test procedure using visible light.

1. COLLIMATOR DESIGN

As suggested by McGrath and Harwit[1], the criteria for selecting the number and spacing of the grids are:

a. radiation entering the j-th channel must be kept from crossing over the (j+1)-th channel;

b. off-axis radiation entering the collimator is tolerated if the angle of incidence is so large that radiation entering the collimator first channel cannot reach the concave grating (figure 3).

We anticipate that, although we use similar criteria, a different grid minimum number is obtained in the present paper on respect to McGrath and Harwit's work.

1.1 Grid position

According to criterion (a), figure 4 shows that two plates at L_1 and l_1 positions are needed to prevent radiation entering channel j of plate A with field angle θ_1,

$$w'/L \leq tg(\theta_1) \leq (w' + w")/L ,$$

to cross over channel (j+1) of plate B.

Simple geometrical considerations indicate that:

$$l_1 = L \{w'/(w'+ w'')\} = L x$$

$$L_1 = L (1 - x)$$

being L the plate A - plate B distance.

It is worth to point out that l_1 and L_1 plates keep off from crossing over channel (j+1) those rays entering channel j at heights

$$0 \leq y \leq w''/2$$

and

$$w''/2 \leq y \leq w''$$

respectivelly (see figure 4).

In general the number of plates which occur to satisfy criterion (a) for a particular field angle is equal to the void to land grid ratio.

Considering the first and the last previous grid at distance $l_{(n-1)}$ as end plate, successive ripetion of the above argument gives the position of successive grids to form the collimator.

We obtain the following expression for l_n and L_n:

$$l_n = L \{ 1 - (1 - x)^n \}$$

$$L_n = L \{ 1 - x(1 - x)^n \}$$

Every couple of grids at l_n and L_n positions completelly prevent radiation with field angle θ_n ,

$$w'/(L - l_{(n-1)}) \leq tg(\theta_n) \leq (w' + w'')/(L - l_{(n-1)})$$

to cross over the (j+1)th channel of the grid located at distance $l_{(n-1)}$.

1.2 Plate number

The number of grids which must be interposed between the first and last plates is obtained considering criterion (b).

Therefore, referring to figure 3, radiation with field angle greater than θ_f can be allowed to cross over the (j+1)th channel.

The expression for θ_f is:

$$\theta_f = arctg\{[N(w'' + w') -w']/L\}$$

N is given by

$$N = D \cdot L/[(L+d)(w'' + w')]$$

where D is the grating diameter and d the last grid-grating distance.

Therefore criterion (b) is satisfied if

$$arctg[w'/(L - L_t)] = arctg[w''/(L - l_t)] \geq \theta_f$$

Inserting the expression for l_t we obtain:

$$t \geq 1 - log(N-x)/log(1-x)$$

Since every grid at l_n position has a companion at L_n position, the number of grids to realize a mechanical collimator is

$$K = 2(t + 1)$$

where the two end plates are also considered.

However the value of K can be reduced since it is possible to show, with the help of figure 5, that two grids located at distance τ and μ substitute a grid at L_n in stopping the field θ_n (for entrance heights such that $w''/2 \leq y \leq w''$) if

$$\tau - \mu \leq L - L_n$$

For x=1/3 the above expression is always satisfied if $\tau = l_{(n+2)}$ and $\mu = l_{(n+1)}$.

Therefore all grids located at L_n (for n=1 to n= (t-2)) can be removed without compromising the collimator characteristics.
The same arguments indicate that grid $L_{(t-1)}$ can also be removed since it is replaced by the grids at L_t and l_t positions.
Therefore the grid minimum number K' become:

$$K' = t + 3$$

indicating that for the EUV/FUV mechanical collimator at least 15 plates are needed.
Their positions are reported in table 1.

Table 1

plate	l_n (m m)
0	0
1	95.3
2	158.89
3	201.25
4	229.51
5	248.33
6	260.89
7	269.26
8	274.84
9	278.56
10	281.04
11	282.69
12	283.8
13	284.89
14	286

2. TESTING

According to numerical simulations the mechanical plates show negligible diffraction effects when illuminated with EUV radiation; therefore geometrical optical laws can be used to asses collimator properties in the ultraviolet wavelength range.
For visible light, however, diffraction is considerable; the plates show a square wave reticle far field diffraction pattern.
Therefore care must be taken in inferring EUV instrument transparency and collimation properties from visible light measuraments.
However, at least for the collimator construction phase, it is helpful to define a testing procedure to check instrument quality using visible light since it might be difficult to obtain access to EUV collimated sources.

In paragraph 1 we have shown that 15 plates are needed to realize the EUV/FUV mechanical collimator.
In general will be convenient to realize more electroformed plates than needed to successivelly verify which plates maximize the transparency of the collimator mantaining, at the same time, the requested angular characteristic.
The plate selection criteria are:

i) the period and the land to void ratio of the plate reticle structure should be in the tolerance range;

ii) the mechanical reference holes should ensure the allignament of the plates without shadowing effects which would reduce the instrument transparency (figure 6).
In the following we discuss some optical procedures to assess instrument quality according to the above criteria advising, however, that the final quality test will (and must) be made using source of the same wavelength radiation the collimator has been designed for.

2.1 Single plate quality

To verify the single plate quality according to point (i), we have realized an optical system as shown in figure 7.
In the focal plane of an objective L the intensity of the third harmonic (whose amplitude is zero for a square wave reticle with land to void ratio equal to 2) is measured with a detector (PHD), while the zeroth and first diffracted order distance, d, is checked by a lateral effect photodiode (PSD).

Obscuring alternativelly the first and zeroth diffracted order focal spots, the average period of the reticle structure is evaluated according to

$$p = \lambda / \sin(\theta)$$

where λ is the radiation wavelength and $\theta = \text{arctg}(d/f)$ with f the objective focal lenght.

From the average period of the plate reticle structure, the land to void ratio can be evaluated measuring the third diffracted order intensity.

The intensity of the third harmonic is given by:

$$I_3 \approx (\delta w''/p)^2 \cdot I_0 \qquad (1)$$

where $\delta w''$ is the average void deviation from the nominal value and I_0 is the intensity of the incident plane wave.

In table 2 the third harmonic intensity measuraments for 4 plates for which the void value was measured in 20 different points of the structure with a profilometer are reported.

Table 2

plate	$\langle w'' \rangle$ (μm)	I_3 / I_0 [%] measured	I_3 / I_0 [%] computed
1	255.2 ± 3.5	.02	.019
2	256.1 ± 4.5	.03	.026
3	254.8 ± 3	.016	.016
4	254 ± 4.9	.015	.011

The $\langle w'' \rangle$ values were obtained averaging the profilometer measuraments; in the last column the values of (I_3/I_0) as calculated according to (1), with p=.375 mm and $\delta w''$ evaluated from profilometer data, are reported.

As it can be seen a correlation between void deviations and third order intensity exists, indicating that this method can be used for plate quality selection.

For example, according to (1) and considering an acceptation upper limit for the average void deviation of 5 μm, a grid will be discharged if

$$I_3 / I_0 \geq 1.8 \times 10^{-4}$$

2.2 Shadowing effects

The mechanical collimator transparency could be reduced by shadowing effects due, for example, to a difference in the plate mechanical reference holes.

Assuming that the allignement tracks which maintain the plates in their correct positions are without parallelism errors, it would be possible to mount different grid combinations to find the one which maximizes the collimator transparency.

However when considering 15 plates this method seems unpratical and time consuming.

When the plates are alligned all togheter on the tracks, the collimator transparency is determined by the maximum void variation, $\delta w''_{(A,i)}$, between the first collimator plate A and the i-th plate; infact if the void deviations of the other plates in the same direction are lower than $\delta w''_{(A,i)}$, they do not contribute to transparency reduction.

The plate A transparency, T_A, is thus measured with an optical system as shown in figure 7.(Plate A is selected as the plate closest to nominal values after tests such those described in paragraph 2.1).

We define T_A as:

$$T_A = S \cdot \Sigma (A_m / A)^2$$

where A_m and A are the amplitude of the m-th harmonic and of the incident plane wave respectivelly; S is a factor which account for the plate mechanical support.

Positioning grid i on the allignement tracks in direct contact with grid A, any difference in the mechanical reference holes brings to a transparency reduction $\delta T_{(A,i)}$ given by

$$\delta T_{(A,i)} = 2S \cdot \Sigma \{(A_m / A^2) \cdot [d(A_m)/dw''] \cdot \delta w''_{(A,i)}\} = \tau \cdot \delta w''_{(A,i)} \qquad (2)$$

Suppose that the above procedure is repeated to measure $\delta w''_{(A,k)}$ for all grids. If the greatest values are measured for plates j and h, it could be inferred that the final transparency reduction of the mechanical collimator due to shadowing effects will be less or, at least equal to

$$(\delta w''_{A,j} + \delta w''_{A,h}) \cdot \tau$$

In the above expression the sum of the w'' variations has been considered since it is not possible to determine the sign of $\delta w''_{(A,i)}$ when measuring transparency (void variation toward right or left); taking the sum of the deviations in the above expression means, of course, to consider opposite sign for $\delta w''_{(A,k)}$ which corresponds to the worst condition.

The average void variation $\delta w''_{(A,i)}$ due to the i-th plate can be evaluated measuring, for example, the zeroth diffracted order intensity variation δI_0 (m=0 in expression (2)) between the two conditions (only plate A and plate A and i togheter). Infact, from expression (2) we obtain:

$$\delta w''_{(A,i)} = p^2 \cdot (I_{0,A} - I_{0,(A,i)})/(2 \cdot w'' \cdot S) = (p^2/2w'' \cdot S) \cdot \delta I_{(0,i)}$$

Therefore comparing one by one all plates with the first plate A to measure $\delta I_{(0,i)}$, we can select the grids requiring that the transparency reduction of the collimator due to void variations is lower than some prefixed value.

For example, if we assume to tolerate a collimator total transparency reduction of P % respect to first plate transparency, for all grids forming the collimator must be verified that

$$(\delta I_{0,j} + \delta I_{0,h}) \le [2w'' \cdot S/(\tau \cdot p^2)] \cdot P$$

CONCLUSIONS

We have presented an expression to compute a configuration of precision mechanical stops to restrict EUV spectrometer field of view according to some prefixed requirements.

Many other arrangements are possible to obtain mechanical light collimation. As an example we recall that in X-ray astronomy cylindrical tubes with an inside layer of lead are sometimes used as passive collimators[2]. This rapresents the "continuous" solution to the problem of mechanical radiation confinememt as the configuration discussed in our work is a "discrete" one.

Which mechanical configuration to use depends from many considerations such weight, dimensions, radiation wavelenght etc. etc.

The main characteristics of mechanical collimators are field of view and transparency which are checked with respect to nominal values measuring the instrument response to collimated radiation.

However to test mechanical collimators to be used for EUV or X-ray astronomical observations is often problematic since it is not always easy to have access to high energy collimated sources. For this reason in the final part of our paper we have discussed a test procedure which makes use of visible light to help the maufacturer during the fabrication phase in assessing mechanical collimator field of view and transparency.

Acknowledgements

This work was in part supported by the Astronomy Department of the University of Trieste and the C.A.R.S.O. Laboratory (Italy). We are particularly thankful to Professor R. Stalio for his cooperation.

References

1. Mc Grath, J.F. and Harwith, M., " A wide-spacing mechanical collimator", Appl. Opt, 8, 837, (1969)

2. Agnetta, G., Biondo, B., Celi, F., Di Raffaele, R., Giarusso, S., La Rosa, S., Manzo, G., Re, S., Sole, L., "The high gas scintillation proportional counter on board the Italian X-ray astronomy satellite SAX", to be published on Il Nuovo Cimento, (1989)

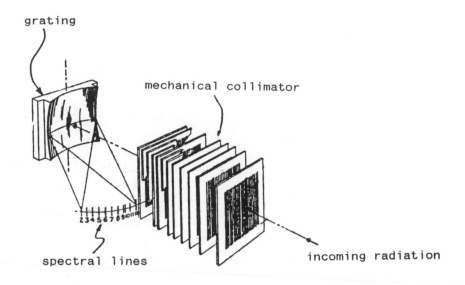

Figure 1. Instrument optical configuration (schematic)

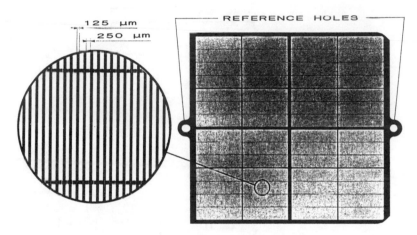

Figure 2. Single collimator plate

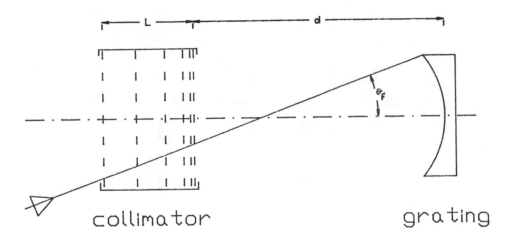

Figure 3. θ_f definition

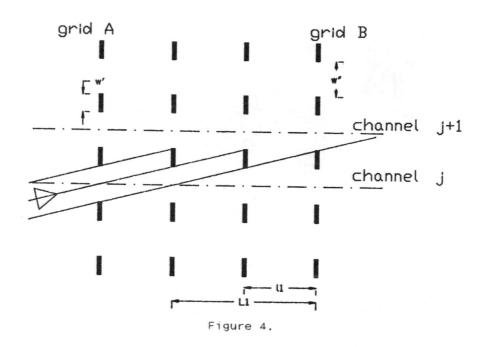

Figure 4.

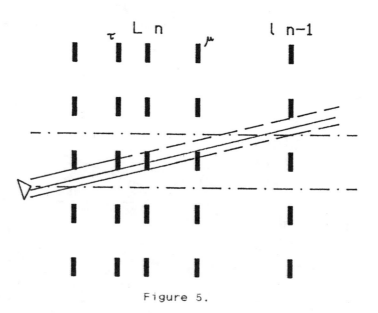

Figure 5.

grid i   grid i+1

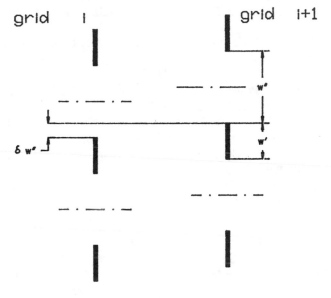

Figure 6.

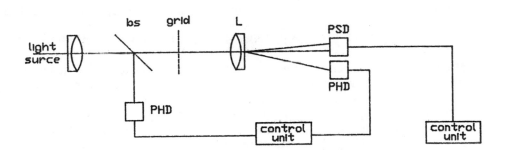

Figure 7. Optical configuration for collimator testing

SOLAR ULTRAVIOLET NETWORK (SUN) :
An Interferometric Investigation of the Fundamental Solar Astrophysical Scales

L. Damé[1], B. Moreau[2], T. Cornwell[3], H. Visser[4], A.M. Title[5] and the SUN Team (L. Acton[5], C. Aime[6], B. Braam[4], M. Bruner[5], P. Connes[7], M. Faucherre[1], B.H. Foing[1], B. Haisch[5], R. Hoekstra[4], J. Heyvaerts[8], R. Jalin[2], P. Lemaire[1], M. Martic[1], R. Muller[9], J.C. Noëns[9], J. Porteneuve[7], E. Schulz-Lüpertz[10] and O. Von der Lühe[11])

[1] Laboratoire de Physique Stellaire et Planétaire (IAS), B.P. n° 10, Verrières-le-Buisson 91371 Cedex, France,

[2] ONERA, BP n° 72, 92322 Châtillon Cedex, France,

[3] National Radio Astronomy Observatory, Socorro, NM 87801, USA,

[4] TNO-TPD Institute of Applied Physics, Postbus 155, 2600 AD Delft, The Netherlands,

[5] Lockheed Palo Alto Research Laboratory, Palo Alto, CA 94304, USA,

[6] Département d'Astrophysique, Université de Nice, Parc Valrose, 06034 Nice Cedex, France,

[7] Service d'Aéronomie, BP n° 3, 91371 Verrières-le-Buisson Cedex, France,

[8] DAEC, Observatoire de Meudon, 92195 Meudon Principal Cedex, France,

[9] Observatoire du Pic-du-Midi, 85200 Bagnères de Bigorre, France,

[10] Kommunikationssysteme und Antriebe, MBB, Postfach 80 11 69, 8000 München 80, FRG,

[11] Institut für Astronomie, ETH-Zentrum, 8092 Zürich, Switzerland.

ABSTRACT

Present Solar telescope projects, on ground or in Space (like the Orbiting Solar Laboratory) are limited in their ambitions to visible wavelengths and to spatial resolutions not better than a tenth of an arcsec. The Solar Ultraviolet Network (SUN) proposal presented in this paper, is an interferometric concept capable of observations with a spatial resolution better than 0.013" (10 km) on the Sun, in the UV range. Based on Stabilized Interferometry principles it consists in 4 telescopes of 20 cm diameter aligned non-redundantly on a 2 m baseline. Despite its size (2.1 x 1.0 x 0.7 m) and its intrinsic complexity, SUN would be perfectly suited for use on the Space Station, when implemented on a pointing platform of performances comparable with the Instrument Pointing System (flown on Spacelab2). The remarkable capabilities of the SUN instrument, resulting from its "compact" non-redundant configuration of telescopes, allow high resolution imaging on a 2 x 2 arcsec^2 field (and with a dynamic on the reconstructed images superior to 100 for phase stabilities $\geq \lambda/10$), on the Solar disk (granulation, flares and micro-flares, prominences and filaments), or at the limb and above, across coronal loops.

1. INTRODUCTION AND SCIENTIFIC RATIONALE FOR HIGH RESOLUTION ON THE SUN

The Space Station offers an unprecedented opportunity to probe the fine structure of a stellar atmosphere with the technique of Interferometry. The Solar Ultraviolet Network is the first proposed interferometric experiment in Space at visible and ultraviolet wavelengths aimed at reconnaissance of solar features at angular scales below 0.1 arcsec, a major scientific objective recommended recently by the Space Science Board of the National Research Council of the American Sciences Academy[1]. With a spatial resolution as high as 10 km on the solar surface, and a spectral resolution of 1 Å in the UV, the SUN investigation presents a unique possibility of observations at the ultimate resolution where the very fine structure of the magnetic field initiate the unstable energy processes responsible for the coronal heating. Though the ultimate temperature gradient scale across a coronal loop might in principle be 25 cm (ion gyroradius), it is smeared out by plasma micro-instabilities (such as drift waves), and the relevant minimum observable scale is more realistically of the order of 1-10 km.

Considerable evidence suggests that all scales of the Sun' structures, as well as other astrophysically interesting objects, are coupled to small-scale processes associated with intermittent magnetic fields and turbulent stresses. Understanding the physics of coronal loops, the creation and decay of these dynamical structures, are essential for a proper description of coronal active regions, flares, or the solar wind. The central objective of the Solar Interferometer is certainly the comprehension of the magnetic fine structures where are developed the energy processes which produce the heating (and presence) of chromospheres and coronae.

In brief, it appears that a breakthrough in high spatial resolution observations should make possible to understand in finer physical details processes like :

* magnetic heating in coronal loops (temperature profiles, time dependance, spatial localization of heating processes);
* coupling between turbulent convective eddies and magnetic fields in the photosphere.

These processes are archetypal of similar ones certainly at work in other stars, accretion disks, or in the magnetosphere of compact objects.

To resume, the scientific objectives of SUN are fourfold : the physics of coronal loops, the plasma heating processes and thermal inputs of flares and microflares, the fine magnetic field structures, and the dynamics of the granulation; they will be addressed through high resolution images, in the UV and in the visible, of coronal loops, flare kernels, internal flux tube structure and granules.

Altogether with high spatial resolution, the SUN investigation is addressing a particularly rich UV spectral domain for scientific diagnostics. SUN will use the spectral information of 1 Å bandwidth images (dispersion free) in several UV lines in the spectral domain from Lyman α (1216 Å) to 2100 Å [like C I (1560 Å), C IV (1550 Å), Si II (1533 and 1527 Å), Si IV (1403 and 1394 Å), and C II (1335 Å), and "hotter" lines in the far UV like N V (1240 Å), Fe XII (1349 Å) and Fe XXI (1354 Å)]. In the visible domain, magnetic field and imaging will also be addressed, with up to 60 mÅ spectral resolution (Fabry Perot), through a selection of photospheric lines and continua. In addition, for the granulation and magnetic structures, SUN will use white light and 8 Å bandwidth isolation filters in and outside the bandhead of CH (4304 Å and 4318 Å).

SUN is a fully stabilized instrument, using the Solar integrated white light to achieve *co-alignment* and *co-phasing* of the telescopes. It has therefore the unique capability of very high sensitivity, since very long integration times can be afforded (several minutes) on weak structures, UV or visible. SUN can integrate as long as the structure itself does not evolve, or as long as the internal instrumental alignment holds. SUN can also follow fast events with instantaneous snap-shot (cuts) across any structure. This is particularly interesting e.g. for coronal loops since the radial profile of a coronal loop will reflects the radial behavior of the length-averaged heating rate : an unvaluable information for the heating process localization and its time dependance[2]. Current observations with limited spatial resolution cannot distinguish between the different heating theories : there is a definite need to access to resolutions below 0.1" (typically 0.01" - 7 km).

During the course of the Space Station Attached Payloads proposal, which was submitted to NASA[3], a comprehensive data processing approach has been worked out to reconstruct the 2 x 2 arcsec^2 solar images obtained with SUN. It clearly indicates, on an example presented hereafter, the remarkably good imaging capabilities of SUN (dynamic of the reconstructed images), when co-phased to a fraction of the wavelength. This working data reduction scheme has been derived and adapted from radio-interferometric techniques since the SUN detection system provides *dispersion free* narrow band interferograms. Further ameliorations could be implemented, but the basic technique of the Data Processing of SUN is already established.

The SUN investigation, with its 4 fixed telescopes, requires a first level pointing platform of the class of the Instrument Pointing System (IPS - flown on Spacelab 2) for pointing *accuracy, stability* requirements and *rotation* around the axis, which is essential for imaging possibilities. A pointing accuracy better than 1 arcsec and a stability of the same order are foreseen and could, according to preliminary studies presently undergoing at MBB/Dornier, be obtained on the Space Station with a second generation of the IPS, developed by ESA[4] : the European Pointing Platform (EPS).

Solar Interferometry implies a more complex data processing (extended object) and stabilization strategy (at low contrast, and with offset pointing also) than Stellar Interferometry, but is more relevant to first implement in Space since the length of the scientifically interesting baseline leads to a reasonable and compact instrument of 2 m instead of 10 or 20 m minimum in the stellar case. Furthermore, Solar Interferometry is a critical test for future larger interferometry projects in Space since the internal complexity of the stabilization and recombination (with offset pointing and co-phasing) will have been mastered, and performances evaluated concretely.

2. INSTRUMENTAL CONCEPT

To achieve high spatial resolutions the SUN instrument is an *interferometer* : a monolithic array of 4 telescopes of 20 cm diameter aligned non-redundantly on a 2 m baseline. It is a fully co-phased array which consequently uses the techniques of active optics for high pointing accuracy, and stabilization of phase delays. Therefore, the instrumental design is intrinsically complex since, beside an already sophisticated fine pointing system with design goal of 5 milliarcsec, an internal optical metering system has to be implemented in order to achieve *permanent cophasing* of the telescopes to a minimum design goal of ± λ/40 (in the visible).

However complex are those techniques, they are now mastered or currently developed up to the performance evaluation stage. The fine pointing done on the solar limb is using the technique developed for the SOUP investigation, which already demonstrated the feasibility of 3 milliarcsec pointing (onboard Spacelab 2). The co-phasing of telescopes, using white light fringe tracking in reference synchrone interferometers, is a currently developed and tested technique that is applied to the 2 telescopes (25 cm diameter) of the I2T/CERGA interferometer[5-7]. These techniques have to be adapted to the solar case (extended object) and to imaging considerations (4 telescopes), but the modifications are straightforward.

In practice, following the aim of the 2-wavelength range Stabilized Stellar Interferometry[5-7], interferometric recordings on very low UV fluxes are possible in clearly separating and optimizing the 3 different functions of an interferometer for flux and S/N ratio considerations. Servo-controlled functions (active pointing and path delay compensations) do not have to be monitored on the "scientific" signal directly. Another source (somewhere on the solar disk and in a much larger bandpass) can be used for much more efficiency (no required dispersion, optimized detector response, and pupil plane interferometry) to control the interferometric metrology. Briefly :

- Fine pointing - tilts correction. The wavefronts are co-aligned in inclinaison to a minimum of $\pm$ 0.025" peak-to-peak (design goal 0.005 arcsec), which represents a $\pm \lambda/10$ (design goal $\pm \lambda/50$) phase match at 1200 Å (reported on the pupil plan of the 20 cm primary of the telescopes); note that this is more constraining that what was first proposed[8,9], but is required since beams recombination (interferences) is now done in the image plane because of the extreme (anticipated) complexity of the images to be reconstructed, which prevent us from using a pupil plane recombination.

- Active fringe tracking of the phase variations and real time compensations. We use a large spectral bandpass (of 3 or 4 thousands Å) in separated Reference Differential Interferometers working simultaneously on two pupil's flat fields. The minimum required and achievable stabilities are $\geq \pm \lambda/40$ (around $\lambda \approx 4800$ Å, i.e. $\pm \lambda/10$ at 1200 Å) since the available flux is large enough, eventhough the contrast of the fringes can be very low (a few %), and the field limited to the diameter of the Airy disk of a single telescope.

- Analysis is performed on dispersion free images of fringes in the image plane. For line profile information, a 1 Å resolution is required. We cannot work in pupil plane since the objects to be reconstrucuted are certainly too complex.

3. INSTRUMENTAL DESIGN

The basic design of the instrument and the observational contraints to be observed were already presented in previous papers[8,9]. In summary, to fulfill the scientific objectives, we need to consider :

- a 10 km spatial resolution (0.013") on the Sun at UV wavelengths, i.e. a 2 m baseline;
- access to the UV spectral range (in between Lyman α and 2100 Å), with a 1 Å spectral resolution on line profiles (and thus access to very low fluxes);
- a 2D field pointing, positioning and stabilization for blind integration of the faint UV fringes;
- co-phasing on a restricted field (Airy disk of a single telescope) of the Solar disk (visible emission), since each point of a structure is resolved and smeared by any of the individual telescopes;
- a high phase stability of $\pm \lambda/10$ at minimum, even on low contrast ($\leq$ 1 %), for image reconstruction purposes;
- a "fast" u,v coverage in order to follow the temporal evolution of the structures (which leads to the concept of the "compact" SUN array rather than a dilute one);
- imaging possibilities which are essential in regards of the complexity and evolution of the structures to be investigated even though, for coronal loops and fast evolving structures, a "cut" across the structures would, in principle, be the prime and sufficient information.

These goals are not easy to achieve due to the very low UV fluxes and high required resolutions; hovewer these contraints can be superseeded and elegant solutions can be proposed using a non-redundant configuration of telescopes and the Stabilized Interferometry know-how that we have acquired in Stellar Interferometry[5].

3.1. Instantaneous u,v coverage

Independently of flux, contrast or wavelength considerations, we need an "instantaneous" coverage of all spatial frequencies for provision against fast evolving structures (e.g. micro-flares), coronal loop temperature profile evolution, and for simplicity of implementation of the telescopes (which are fixed, without mechanisms, on the baseline).

The simpliest solution is a 4-telescope non-redundant array of 2 m baseline which yields a maximum spatial resolution of 0.0125" at Lyman α (cf Fig. 1, baseline configuration). In practice SUN is more than a simple non-redundant array since the low spatial frequencies coverage of any given telescope overlap with the other ones which provides a continuity in between the six spatial frequency ranges defined by the different baselines combinaison of the 4 telescopes. In other words, the 4 telescopes are sufficiently near from each other (d = 30 cm) for their intrinsic frequency coverage to overlap, filling totally the u,v plane in the direction of the baseline, an essential point for the reconstruction of a complex and extended object with high dynamic (there is no hole in the spatial frequencies domain which garanties an excellent reconstruction). In addition to the imaging quality, the advantage of u,v coverage of the SUN interferometer are the "snap shot cuts" possible along any structure with a high resolution in one direction. This is unvaluable for structures like coronal loops or for fast evolving structures.

3.2. Pointing strategy

3.2.1. First pointing level. The access to a first level pointing platform of a precision ≤ 1 arcsec, allows to use fixed telescopes (without pointing mechanisms), and reduce the requirements on the fine pointing system of SUN (obtained by activating telescope secondaries : dynamic of 1000 from a few milliarcsec to a few arcsec). A new version of the Instrument Pointing System (flown on Spacelab2) is currently under study by ESA, for use on the Space Station. This new platform, the EPS (European Pointing System), for which SUN is the driving model payload, would possess the following characteristics :

- absolute pointing, accuracy and stability RMS ≤ 0.7 arcsec;
- possibility of ± 180° rotation around the line-of-sight with a maximum slewing rate of 3° per second (which implies new gyroscopes) with eventually a TBD degradation of performances (no degradation anticipated at 1° per second);
- a resulting control bandpass of 0.7 Hz.

Beside its high pointing performances, what makes the EPS unique for the SUN application, is its possibility of rotating 180°, which allows SUN to synthetize a solar image (in a 2 x 2 arcsec²) with the equivalent resolution of a 2 m telescope. This rotation can either be achieved in successives (discrete) steps (of e.g. 3°), or by continuous rotation (taking 1 to 3 min., or longer for "stable" objects). The EPS, mounted on a pallet, is implemented on a standard interface (APAE) of the truss structure of the Space Station.

3.2.2. Fine pointing level. Solar limb pointing is a prerequisite for the SUN instrument in regards of the final pointing requirement (5 to 25 milliarcsec). The milliarcsec level can in theory be achieved[1], and the Lockheed group, in charge of the pointing in the SUN investigation, has already achieved measured stabilities of 3 milliarcsec with a similar set up for the SOUP experiment on board Spacelab2[10].

However the case of SUN is more complex since SUN needs to point coronal loops above the limb (and in the UV) and thus, the whole instrument, linked to the EPS, is oriented in the pointing direction while the limb sensor requires to be aligned with the Sun center to monitor the solar limb position. The system used to indroduce the required offset in between the on-axis beam and the required field for the stabilization on the limb is a diasparameter, which consists in two ajustable wedges. During imaging, when the EPS is rotating, the wedge system is also rotating to keep the Sun image on the limb sensor. The ajustable and rotating wedges allow to keep the limb sensor fixed, in a more compact realization. The system is also less critic in term of tolerances than the necessary mechanisms for a movable limb-sensor. The telescope and its post-focal assembly are shown on Fig. 2. The finer stabilization stage acts directly on the secondaries of the 4 telescopes (which are mounted on three piezoelectrics actuators).

3.3. Recombination and co-phasing strategy

The general problem of interferometry lies generally in the enlarging needed in fine to observe (and correctly sample) the fringes in the detector plane (in the case of SUN, the Sun diameter would be in the final detector plane of more than 4.8 meters !). This problem was given different solutions, but is finally less severe than could be expected at first (a final equivalent focal length of ~ 500 metres in order to achieve a 6 milliarcsec solar étendue on a detector pixel of 15 μm), if part of the enlarging is reported to the spectrograph. In this case the recombination is easier and possible with a reduced number of optics (9 reflections only before the entrance slit of the spectrograph). A further step is achieved in the SUN investigation in using a combined UV and visible beam recombination thanks to the the UV and visible spectrometer.

At the output of the telescopes the solar images are collimated (beam Ø 20 mm, cf. Fig. 2, mirror 3) and the beams sent through the delay lines (cf. Fig. 1). The collimated beams approach allows to suppress intermediate relay optics that would be

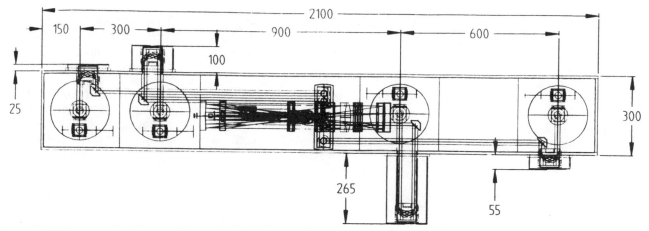

Figure 1. SUN non-redundant configuration (with inter-distances of 1d-3d-2d : 300-900-600 mm) of the 4 telescopes. This "compact" configuration provides us with a coverage of all possible spatial frequencies in a single direction (allowing a high resolution cut across the imaged structure). True imaging can be obtain by a global rotation of the baseline (achievable in practice by the pointing platform).

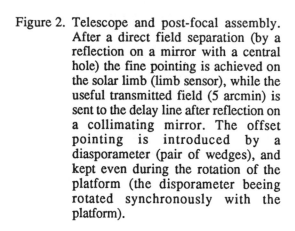

Figure 2. Telescope and post-focal assembly. After a direct field separation (by a reflection on a mirror with a central hole) the fine pointing is achieved on the solar limb (limb sensor), while the useful transmitted field (5 arcmin) is sent to the delay line after reflection on a collimating mirror. The offset pointing is introduced by a diasporameter (pair of wedges), and kept even during the rotation of the platform (the disporameter beeing rotated synchronously with the platform).

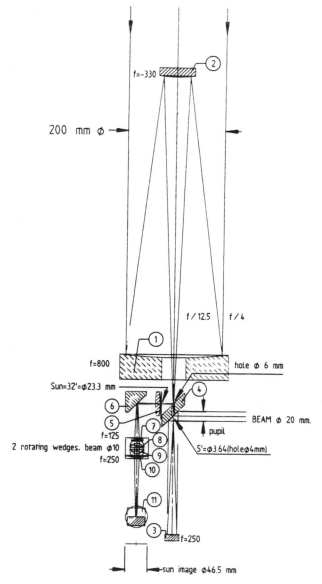

necessary to transfer the pupil, but presents the inconvenient to place the pupil far from the recombination mirror; thus it imposes more contraints on the delay lines since the angle in between the beams needs to be very accuratly kept in order to have access to fringes in an extended field. This imposes to use delay lines with retroreflectors to preserve (homotheticity) the configuration of the entrance and output pupils (pupils' mapping).

SUN is a fully stabilized interferometric concept. The optical path delays (OPD) in between the different telescopes are servo-controlled by using a large visible spectral bandpass, while the observations are carried independently in the UV (or in narrow bandwidths in the visible). There is a full decoupling of the servo-control function and the analysis function (on the contrary from usual stellar interferometry where the displacements of the dispersed fringes are analysed by fast Fourier transform, an unoptimized approach, clearly inconceivable for SUN, which could certainly not develop its full imaging capabilities when stabilized on the weak 1 Å UV line emission of a coronal loop !).

A general view of the interferometric recombination of the SUN instrument is given in Fig. 3. After the delay lines, the collimated beams are reflected up by plane mirrors towards a parabolic one (a slab of 20 cm length), which focalizes the 4 beams down on the entrance slit of the spectrograph. The usefull field for analysis (30") is let through the slit while the remaining (of the 5 arcmin field) is reflected towards the co-phasing system. At this level, the stabilization is necessarily done on an *offset reference field* which will be selected arbitrarily on the solar disk (the 5 arcmin filed allow to point to 2.5 arcmin maximum distance above the limb). Since the reference stabilization field, and the analysis field are not the same, the reference field must not introduce a phase information from an "extended" structure, and thus the field of view of the system has to be limited for the stabilization to less than the Airy disk of a single telescope (in the visible), i.e. ≤ 0.4 arcsec. The phase is then controled and maintained in between the 4 telescopes using the reference field.

Alike in the case of the pointing offset, a diasporameter has to be used to point towards the reference field, but this time it can work simultaneously on the 4 re-imaged pupils. The 4 pupils/beams are then respectivelly splitted in 2 in order to generate combinaison of telescopes 1-2, 2-3, 3-4 and 1-4 (which is redundant and allows to qualify independently the quality of the co-phasing system). The technique used to monitor the optical path delays (OPD), is the same than the one developed by Damé et al.[5] in Active Fringe Tracking Stabilized Stellar Interferometry. A large spectral bandwidth (3000 Å or so) is sent in a Reference Synchrone Interferometer (Fig. 4) where a small delay line introduce a modulation of the OPD on one beam, and where the fringes (in fact the flat field) maximum amplitude is looked for by a synchrone detection approach using a single pixel detector (a Si diode), on which the *pupils* are re-imaged. Since the Solar flux is large, the diodes do not need to be cooled, and the pupil can be of a reasonable size (Ø 2 mm or even 4 mm) since the photon noise will largely dominate the Noise Equivalent Power (NEP) of the diode, and fix the S/N ratio in practice.

Note than when considering the rotation of the EPS, two stabilization strategies could be considered. Either the diasporameter is also rotating synchronously so that the same field is pointed on the Sun during the rotation, and the same (complex) structure is therefore followed and used for stabilization; or (a possibility which does not require to follow properly the same field) the stabilization is achieved on the fringes envelope rather than on the white light fringe. In practice, with a 3000 Å bandpass, only 5 fringes are present in the coherence envelope, which dimensions are reduced to 5 μm in all[6]. If the reference structure changes, the fringes will change in contrast and topology, but the envelope will keep the same extent. A global modulation of the envelope and a fit of its shape, should lead to a minimum precision of 1 % (0.05 μm : λ/10), or better. Laboratory tests should indicate what approach needs to be applied to SUN for the better results.

One should note that the pointing requirements are much less critic in the co-phasing system than in the analysis channel *since the fringes are formed in pupil plane*, which therefore require to achieve precisions on the co-alignment of only about a tenth of the Airy disk, i.e. 0.04 arcsec (but fringes will already manifest themselves for co-alignments of a few tenths of arcsec). This means that, in practice, even a "crude" first step pointing will allow to start the co-phasing process, and that the two servo-loops are then fully compatible in their operational interaction.

The final co-phasing approach is achieved by a coordinated ajustment of the modulation delay lines and the general delay lines in order to optimize the fringe contrast in the spectrograph while still keeping the zero maximum phase contrast in the co-phasing system. Note that such an iterative maximization procedure *is not necessary for the co-alignment*. Effectively, an unperfect co-alignment in the co-phasing system (as long as fringes with reasonable contrast could still be available) does not prevent from looking for the better possible co-phasing; simply the maximum available contrast for the co-phasing will be slightly reduced. This non-access to re-pointing possibility in the co-phasing system implies a reasonably good internal stability of the instrument in between the spectrograph and the co-phasing system (even though not absolutely required since independent lenses could be tilted in the co-phasing system; but this is not essential in view of the anticipated tolerances).

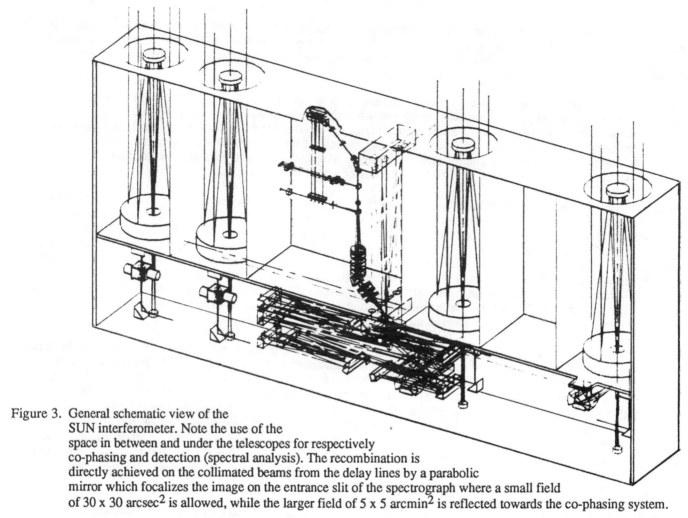

Figure 3. General schematic view of the
SUN interferometer. Note the use of the
space in between and under the telescopes for respectively
co-phasing and detection (spectral analysis). The recombination is
directly achieved on the collimated beams from the delay lines by a parabolic
mirror which focalizes the image on the entrance slit of the spectrograph where a small field
of 30 x 30 arcsec^2 is allowed, while the larger field of 5 x 5 arcmin^2 is reflected towards the co-phasing system.

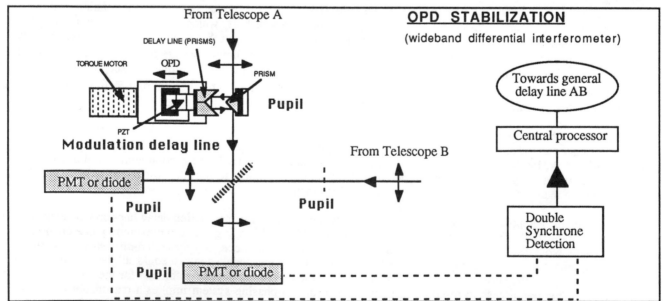

Figure 4. Wideband Differential Interferometers allow, by use of synchrone modulation of the light-path, and synchrone
detection of the intensity variations, to generate the error signals necessary to compensate in real time the OPD in
between pairs of telescopes (monitoring of the fine stage of the delay lines by piezoelectric actuators).

3.4. Detection : the double-grating spectrometer

In the SUN experiment, part of the enlarging is reported to the spectrograph which minimizes the difficulties both on the telescope system and recombination optic (which is reduced in our case to its simpliest expression : a parabolic mirror). This simplicity allows a very high UV throughput since there is only 9 reflections (transmission $\approx$ 0.2) before the spectrograph entrance slit.

It is not our purpose here to describe in details the double-grating spectrometer, UV and visible, suggested for SUN since it represents in itself a complex instrument. It is shown on Fig. 5, and described in more details in a SUN Technote[11]. It presents the advantage of a simultaneous use for the UV and the visible. Resolution of 1 Å are possible both on UV and visible lines. In addition, provision is made to use (with the spectrograph as pre-filter) a narrow band Fabry-Perot (60 milliÅ - for a finesse of 50) for magnetic field investigations. The remarkable quality of the spectrograph is that, in fact, it acts as a filter, since the double-grating set up allows to get in output, in the detector plane, *monochromatic, dispersion free, images*. This point is essential for the following since it allows the use of the image reconstruction techniques developed for radioastronomy. In practice the UV gratings with rotation from 10 to 20° scan the spectral range from 1210 Å to 2133 Å, and the visible gratings, with rotations from 25.2 to 45.2°, the spectral range from 4265 to 7512 Å. The gratings movement is simultaneous (as is the movement of the plane mirror which send the zero order to the large field UV detector, and to the visible spectrograph).

Note that in addition to the small field detectors (2 x 2 arcsec^2) larger field detectors (30 x 30 arcsec^2) are used, both for reconnaissance of the field of view and interest of the structures, and for the pre-calibration procedures of co-alignment and co-phasing at the beginning of an observational run.

3.5. Imaging capabilities and image reconstruction

As was already discussed, when the finite size of the individual telescopes is accounted for, the instrument samples a full range of spatial frequencies ranging from zero up to the maximum of 2 meters. This completeness is unusual in conventional interferometry and has more in common with the Fourier plane coverage of the MMT. It means that the imaging capabilities of the instrument are very good. While these spatial frequencies are potentially accessible, there are a number of different schemes for measuring them since measurement of the fringes is possible in both image or pupil planes. In the image plane, it is necessary to sample the fringes for a given pair of telescopes for all independent positions in the image (every half-Airy disk in practice), while in the pupil plane the equivalent scheme is to measure fringes for a pair of telescopes for a number of different spatial offsets or shears between the pupils. In radio-astronomy, the image plane scheme is used for making images of objects larger than the Airy disk of the elements of an interferometric array, each image plane point being sampled sequentially. However, in this case to image a field of view of 2 arcseconds would require 484 separate fringe measurements for each pair of telescopes. Clearly, then, a superior method is to place all these fringes on one detector at once. We then require to interfere light from all four telescopes on a detector covering a field of view of 2 arcseconds with a spatial sampling of 6 milliarcsec. The image obtained on the detector instantaneously is the true object convolved with the instantaneous point spread function of the instrument (plus photon noise, etc). A sequence of such images obtained for a number of position angles may then be summed to obtain an image with full Fourier plane sampling. Adequate sampling in azimuth requires discrete 3 degree increments in position angle between dumps of the detector, implying a maximum data rate of the full detector every second.

The rotation of the instrument causes one problem for the imaging : the rotation of the detector with respect to the source must be removed before the image for each 3 degree increment are added. Hence all the sub-images must be re-sampled on a stationary grid before co-adding. The full image thus built up must then be corrected for the Fourier-plane sampling using a deconvolution algorithm. For low photon rates, the optimum procedure is to use a Wiener-type algorithm which corrects for the uneven sampling of the Fourier plane. For high-photon rates, a more-sophisticated algorithm such as the Maximum Entropy algorithm can be used to correct for the cutoff in sampling at the maximum baseline of 2 meters. While the computation required in this measurement scheme is not unsignificant, it will not be out of proportion to the rest of the project, given the rapidly falling cost of computers.

The effects of Optical Path Delays (OPD) errors on the final image reconstruction is shown in Fig. 6. We have simulated the imaging properties of the instrument on a complicated object (which could be for example the internal structure of a flux tube), for various level of OPD stability. OPD errors were assumed to be independent every integration time. Photon noise is not included. The image require relatively little deconvolution since the Fourier plane coverage is so good. A Maximum Entropy algorithm was used for the deconvolution. The imaging quality is still quite good to stability of $\lambda/8$ or $\lambda/6$, but degrades noticeably with decreasing stability.

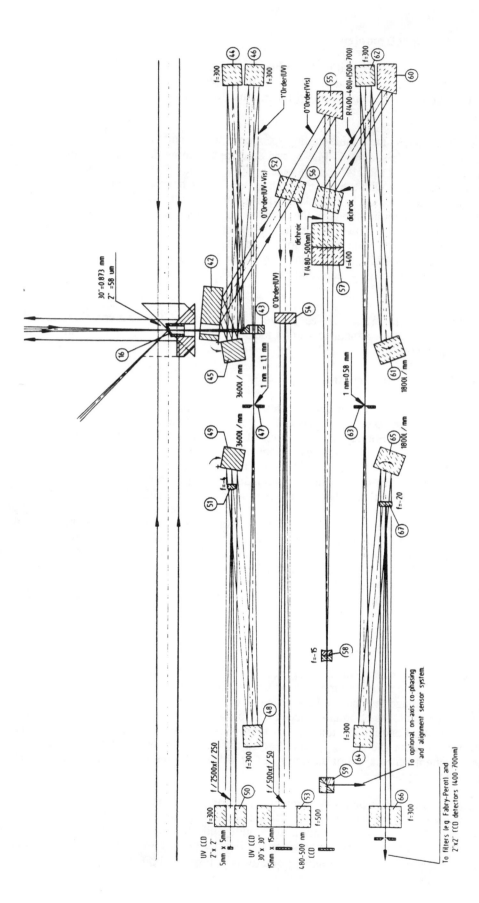

Figure 5. Beams recombination and double-grating spectrometer, UV and visible. From the parabolic mirror (not shown) the solar image is formed on the entrance slit of the spectrograph in which only a limited field of 30 arcsec is let through while the rest of the field is sent to the co-phasing system. Note that the spectrometer itself provides a significant enlarging, and that the use of the double-grating synchronous movement allows to form *dispersion free images* in the detectors plane. The plane mirror (right of the first grating) is moving simultaneously with the gratings, so has to get the zero orders (and thus the visible) accessible all the time.

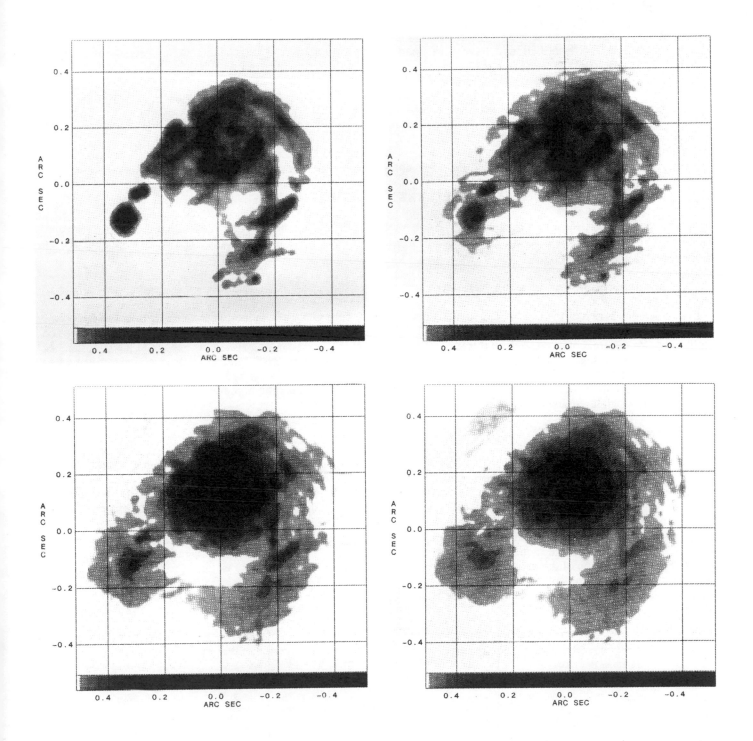

Figure 6. Example of reconstruction of a complicated object in a 1 x 1 arcsec field : (a) original model; (b) Maximum Entropy Method (MEM) deconvolution : stability condition $\pm \lambda/12$, resulting dynamic range (DR) $\approx$ 200; (c) MEM deconvolution : $\lambda/6$, DR $\approx$ 100; (d) MEM deconvolution : $\lambda/4$, DR $\approx$ 70. The deconvolution results from an azimuth sampling in discrete 3 degree increments in position angle.

An important property of these images is that unlike images made with conventional interferometry, *the image quality is determined roughly by the brightest point within an Airy disk diameter,* rather than by the field of view. This means that imaging of weak features is considerably better than that achievable in a pupil-plane interferometer of equivalent stability. Although telescopes as described will have very good imaging properties, we anticipate investigations of possible improvements :

- it may be possible to allow continuous rotation of the telescope if a correction can be made in the deconvolution procedure. We must correct for the smearing of high spatial frequencies caused by instrument rotation.
- Since the instrument offers nearly non-redundant sampling of the Fourier plane, it may be possible to use the closure phases to increase the dynamic range of the images.
- The instrument is unusual in that spatial frequencies near zero are measured with much more weight than the others. This affects the design of the deconvolution algorithm used, especially for images with a significant photon noise.

4. PRE-CALIBRATION AND OPERATION

This review of the SUN instrument would not be complete without some comments on the operation modes in Space and, in particular, the necessary calibration steps to achieve co-alignment and co-phasing after launch and at the beginning of each observational orbit.

4.1. Co-alignment and co-phasing strategy

In practice this is one of the uses of the 30 x 30" field of view of the analysis channel. Direct co-alignment to the beams can be achieved at the 0.04" level (1/10th of the Airy disk), and co-checked with the solar limb information that can thus be recalibrated (for different off-axis angles); this is normally sufficient for the co-phasing system, which could then normally be locked on the fringes. In a second step, for pointing accuracy, the fringes are looked for in the 2 x 2 arcsec field on the edges of the superposed fields (on the disk or in a strong line, at first operation), and an iterative adjustment of the limb sensor reference offset for the better available pointing is done. In a final step, the maximum contrast measured by the co-phasing system could be used, if required.

4.2. Observing modes

All the spatial frequencies (i.e. the characteristic dimensions of the structure) can be obtained, in one dimension, in a single exposure. This provides a "snap-shot" imaging capability, with the high resolution limited to 1 direction accross the object (the other one beeing limited to the resolution of a single telescope, i.e. reduced by a factor 10). This mode is important since it already allows very useful science to be done on the coronal loop temperature profile for example and its (fast) disruptions. It is also essential for micro-flares energy release. The field on the Sun is small (2 x 2 arcsec^2), but the 0.013" resolution already requires a significant number of pixels on the detector (334), in order to sample correctly the interfringe (2 pixels per fringe required at the minimum wavelength). Since we are in the image plane the fringes are in practice formed on the top of the image of the object/structure, which should be relatively isolated (even if extended) since at high resolution most of the solar structures are (or supposed to be) point-like. However, this is really a domain where we cannot do many predictions since most is to be discovered yet.

TABLE 1. Mission Requirements

Orbit		Pointing (EPS)		Instrumental Characteristics	
• Altitude :	150-270 nm (276 - 500 km); nominal: 220 - 250 nm	• Stability :	≥ 1 arcsec	• Mass :	300 kg (incl. 40 kg of electr.)
• Inclinaison :	28.5°	• Precision :	≥ 1 arcsec	• Dimensions :	2.1 m X 1 m X 0.67 m (0.3 m for the central structure; the remaining
• Orientation :	torque equilibrium attitute (LVLH)	• Deviation max. :	≤ 15 arcsec		for the delay lines)
		• Rotation :	180°	• Power :	280 W (average) 320 peak
		• Field of view :	1.2 ° without obstruction (verified)	• Data rate :	400 kbps
				• Data storage :	500 MB (transfered to Space Station)

A discussion on the different latitudes that we have concerning the snap-shot mode or image reconstruction strategy (rotating the EPS) will be addressed in the course of the NASA Detailed Concept Study. For example, to study rapid events, we would like (or will have) to consider "bad" stability (e.g. $\lambda/6$), coupled to low fluxes (and photon noise), resulting in a limited dynamic range. Sampling could also be done on different -larger- degree spacing than the optimum one, to reconstruct an image as fast as the EPS can rotate. A strategy of visible and UV simultaneous observations (e.g. for flares) is also of first importance and will have to be worked in more details. A summary of the mission requirements is given in Table 1.

5. CONCLUSIONS

The main conclusion from these preliminary studies of a Solar Ultraviolet Interferometer, to be implemented on the Space Station, would be that, even though very complex, this compact instrument (2.1 m x 1 m x 0.7 m) is feasible and compatible, through the use of a pointing platform (the EPS, under study by ESA), with the Space Station constraints.

SUN is the ultimate science breakthrough to be expected in Solar Physics since it will give access to the level of spatial resolution where the basic and major physical processes are expected to happen.

The mass budget of the experiment ($\approx$ 300 kg) is compatible with the Attached Payloads programme of the Space Station. Important telemetry (with the Station) will be required during observing runs but the command mode will be limited to the object selection (fringe acquisition, calibration and pointing algorithms are automatic procedures). The SUN programme was proposed in November 1988[3] for a *Detailed Concept Study* to NASA. It will be a unique occasion to understand, through a Research and Development programme, the problems raised by the very low contrast stabilization on an extended source, which are still to be discovered, and mastered. It is also an opening to further larger interferometers than could be proposed, based on the same concept and technology, for stellar observations. Stabilized on a reference star, a 4 x 1 m telescopes stellar interferometer, mounted non-redundantly, like SUN, on the EPS (on a 10 m baseline), and aimed at UV observations, would certainly be the next major step after the Hubble Space Telescope.

6. ACKNOWLEDGMENTS

We are particularly grateful to the European Space Agency which supported several studies that benefited to the improvement of the SUN concept. This work was possible thanks to the direct and efficient support received from ONERA.

7. REFERENCES

1. Report of the Space Science Board of the National Research Council (American Science Academy), *Probing Fundamental Astrophysical Scales with High-Resolution Observations of the Sun : Prospects for the 21st Century*, Report of a meeting held in Tucson in January 1986, (Nov. 1987).
2. J. Heyvaerts, *About the Interest of Solar Interferometric Observations*, in the Proceedings of the ESA Workshop on Optical Interferometry in Space, Ed. N. Longdon and V. Davis, ESA SP **273**, 11 (1987).
3. Luc Damé, Loren Acton, Marilyn E. Bruner, Pierre Connes, Tim Cornwell, Michel Faucherre, Bernard H. Foing, Bernhard Haisch, Jean Heyvaerts, René Jalin, Milena Martic, Bernard Moreau, Richard Muller, Jacques-Clair Noëns, Marc Séchaud, Alan M. Title, Oskar Von der Lühe, *Solar Ultraviolet Network (SUN) : An Interferometric Investigation of the Fundamental Solar Astrophysical Scales*, a proposal submitted to NASA in response to the AO OSSA 3-88 for Space Station Attached Payloads, (Nov. 1988).
4. H. Olthof, *ESA : Space Station Based Interferometry*, ibid. 2., 93 (1987).
5. L. Damé, G. Bourdet, M. Decaudin, M. Faucherre, P. Boutry, M. Martic, N. Coron, B. Moreau, R. Jalin, M. Séchaud, Y. Rabbia, F. Vakili , G. Schumacher and the ASSI Team : M. Bourbon, J.-R. Carteron, G. Dambier, G. Jegoudez, J. Haro, H. Lagardère, J. Leblanc, J.P. Lepeltier, C. Lizambert and M. Dugué, *ASSI : An Optimized Fringe Tracking Stellar Interferometer*, in Active Telescopes Systems, Proc. SPIE **1114**, (to be published, 1989).
6. L. Damé, M. Faucherre, G. Bourdet, M. Decaudin, G. Jegoudez, Y. Rabbia, G. Aubry and G. Passedat, *Active Stabilization in Stellar Interferometry (ASSI) : Progress Report on the Two Bandpass Fringe Tracking Interferometer*, NOAO-ESO Conference on High-Resolution Imaging by Interferometry, 1079 (1988).
7. L. Damé, M. Faucherre, G. Bourdet, Y. Rabbia, F. Vakili, G. Schumacher and the ASSI team (P. Boutry, M. Decaudin, D. Dubé, G. Jegoudez, H. Lagardère, J.P. Maillard, B. Moreau and G. Terrier), *Active Stabilization in Stellar Interferometry (ASSI) : State of the Art at CERGA/I2T*, in the Proceedings of the ESA Workshop on Optical Interferometry in Space, Ed. N. Longdon and V. Davis, ESA SP **273** (addendum), 11 (1988).
8. L. Damé, *Solar Interferometry from the Space Station*, in First IFSUSS meeting on Physics and Astrophysics in the Space Station Era, Venice, October 4-7 1987, (to be published, 1989).
9. L. Damé, C. Aime, M. Faucherre and J. Heyvaerts, *Solar Interferometry with a 4-Aperture Non-Redundant and Stabilized Network*, ibid. 2., 189 (1987).
10. A.M. Title, T.D. Tarbell, G.W. Simon, and the SOUP Team, *White-light movies of the solar photosphere from the SOUP instrument on Spacelab2*, Adv. Space Research 6(8), 253 (1986).
11. H. Visser, R. Hoekstra, B.C. Braam and H.G. Oostrum, *Optical Lay-out of the SUN experiment*, Report TPD-ESA-SUN-TN-002, (Apr. 1989).

Beam Combination in Aperture Synthesis from Space: Field of View Limitations and (u,v) Plane Coverage Optimization

Michel Faucherre

Institut d'Astrophysique Spatiale / CNRS, BP n°10, 91371 Verrières-le-Buisson Cédex, France

Fritz Merkle

European Southern Obs., Karl-Schwarzshild-Str. 2, 8046 Garching-bei-München, F.R.G.

Farrokh Vakili

OCA-Calern, Observatoire de Caussols, 06460 Saint-Vallier de Thiey, France.

ABSTRACT

The limitations of the coherent field of view in Optical Space Interferometry are presented. The size of the field required is inferred from the number of photoevents and from stellar density. Then we examine the limitations of the FOV in both "Michelson" -or planar array- and "Fizeau" -the equivalent of a masked giant telescope- cases in order to assess their maximum size; it is shown that in all cases, the field is too small to include a reference star in the "Michelson" final image field (< a few arcsec) when the input pupil is too diluted; conversely this is not the case for the "Fizeau", but alignment tolerances are extremely severe. The two main limitations in the Michelson type, field curvature effect and pupil geometry conservation, are then derived in terms of tolerances on the optics. The problem of spatial frequency plane coverage is addressed and we finally propose a mission concept that accomodates most of the problems raised in this paper and nevertheless makes use of two off-axis stars for tracking purposes by splitting the fields before recombination: a "Michelson" with flat collectors, making use of fiber optics in the reference channels.

1. INTRODUCTION

The most difficult part in Aperture Synthesis is indubitably Optical Path Difference (OPD in the following) stabilization with enough precision to provide some phase information in the object Fourier spectrum. When there are no longer enough photons during the coherence time -time during which the fringes are not blurred by more than $\approx \lambda/6$- to use the source itself for fringe tracking, then one would like to use fringes from a bright unresolved star in the field, as the object's fringes should move the same way; if the fringes from two guide stars in the same field can be tracked or recorded, the motion of the fringes from the on-axis science object can be entirely predicted or/and compensated in real time for integration.

Unfortunately, this technique cannot be used on the ground as neighbouring stars distant by more than $a_0 \approx 4$ arcsec are affected differently by the turbulent atmosphere. In space however the isoplanatic patch a_0 is quasi infinite and the coherent Field of view (FOV in the following) should be limited by the aberrations of the system itself.

The size of this field is limited by Lagrange's relation n $\overline{AB}$ u= n' $\overline{A'B'}$ u', (where A and B would be the positions of two stars in the field), to apply between the imput and the exit surface of the system, for both individual beams up to the final composite image and the whole array. Within this field, the wavefront emerging from the array appears as if it was coming from a single aperture blocked by a holed mask ; consequently all individual beams in the final image plane arrive :

- in phase (cophasing)
- on top of each other (coalignment)
- with the same magnification (we assume identical subpupils)
- with the same orientation and polarizations.

From this, one can conceive two kinds of arrays in space : the "Michelson" type (Fig.1.a) or planar array, and the "Fizeau" type (Fig.1.b) or the equivalent of a single giant telescope with a mask. For baselines B > 6 meters, only the first type has been used on the ground because the inherent FOV advantage of the second type is useless due to the size of a_0 (in addition to 3D-assembly problems). Both types are considered in this paper to compare their coherent FOV and their upgradability. The expressions found here for each tolerance are calculated for the parameters proposed by the SIST group[1,2] for a first generation space interferometer: Baseline B=30 m, aperture diameter D=30 cm -which means a very diluted mosaic-, 12 to 15 apertures distributed on a ring, wavelenght $\lambda = 0.12$ μm (ultraviolet is a major driver for space).

We first infer in this paper the size of the FOV required from the number of photoevents and from stellar density. Then we examine the limitations of the FOV in both Michelson and Fizeau cases in order to assess what their size should be; it is shown that in all cases, no reference star exists in the restricted Michelson final image field (< a few arcsec) when the input pupil is very diluted; conversely this is not the case for the Fizeau, but alignment tolerances are extremely severe. The two main limitations in the Michelson type, field curvature effect and pupil geometry conservation, are then derived in terms of tolerances on the optics. The problem of spatial frequency plane coverage is addressed and we finally propose a mission concept that accomodates most of the problems raised in this paper and nevertheless makes use of two off-axis stars for tracking purposes by splitting the fields before recombination: a "Michelson" with flat, 45° oriented collectors, using fiber optics for the reference channels.

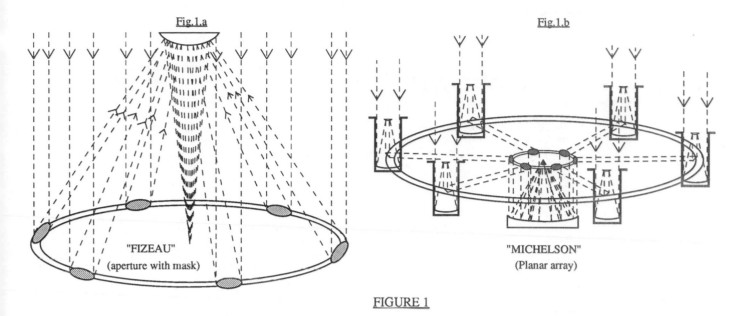

Fig.1.a

Fig.1.b

"FIZEAU"
(aperture with mask)

"MICHELSON"
(Planar array)

FIGURE 1

2. WHAT SHOULD BE THE SIZE OF THE FOV ?

The number of "bright" stars per square degree is very small, as shown by Bahcall et al [3]. Their model, studied for the Space Telescope, gives the number or stars brighter than a given magnitude m_v in each galactic latitude (b) band (Table 1). We can calculate the number of detected photons per aperture[4] in a reasonable coherence time $\tau = 0.1$ sec, which in space will be limited by vibrations and tracking errors affecting coalignment and cophasing of the interferometer :

$$p = q \, \tau(sec) \, \Delta\lambda(nm) \, S(m^2) \times 10^{8-0.4 \, m_v}$$

Let us consider two cases :

- a Fizeau interferometer, characterized by a good optical throughput and a coherent FOV of 10 x 10 arcmin^2 (maximum value to be expected : see chapter 3) ; we therefore assume a total efficiency (detector + optics) q=5%, a 300 nm bandpass (broad band detection) and an aperture diameter of 0.3 m (area S).

- a Michelson interferometer of the type described in Chapter 6, characterized by a maximum efficiency q=1% - due to the large number of reflections expected in such a configuration - and a maximum coherent FOV - limited by the aberrations of the intermediate telescope - of 30 x 30 arcmin^2. Other parameters are the same than for the Fizeau case.

Assuming a Poisson random distribution of the stars inside one square degree, the probability to find a star of magnitude $m_v \leq m_{v_o}$ in a field θ (deg) x θ (deg) is : $P\,(\theta^2) = 1-\exp(-\langle N \rangle \theta^2)$ and the probability to find two is P^2. Table 1 gives both the expected number of photo events and the probability to find two stars in a given field, for visual magnitudes between 10 and 14. More than 5O photoevents per aperture are necessary for non-ambiguous detection[5] in a two-imput Michelson interferometer (cophasing by pairs) used for an off-axis reference star and we can set the probability threshold to 8O % .

m_v	Number N of STARS per (degree)^2			Number p of photoevents per aperture		Probability P^2 (30' x 30')	Probability P^2 (10' x 10')
	min (b=±90°)	mean($\langle N \rangle$) (0°↔90°)	max (b=0°)	q=1% (Michelson)	q=5% (Fizeau)	q = 1%	q = 5%
10	3.5	4	9	210	40%		
11	7.7	10	23	80	430	88%	
12	16	22	58	30	160	100%	20%
13	34	52	138		60		60%
14	70	125	360		25		94%

TABLE 1

We can see from Table 1 that a field larger than 3O arcmin is requested in the second example to get at least two stars of magnitude $m_v \leq 11$, 11 beeing the minimum to get enough photoevents. 10 arcmin is the minimum required in the first example and corresponds to a magnitude between 13 and 14 (nevertheless an aperture diameter of 0.4 m would be more adequate). One assumption made here is arbitrary : we took a coherence time $\tau=0.1$ sec, i.e. ten times better than on the ground; this value is a minimum to justify a mission in space. This time depends on so many parameters -flexures of the structure, vibrations, actuators used for tracking,... - that its estimation is impossible with present knowledge of the behavior of large structures in space at the submicrometer level.

3. LIMITATIONS OF THE FOV IN THE FIZEAU STELLAR INTERFEROMETER

Obtain a reasonably large FOV in a Fizeau interferometer -like a few arcmin- requires extremely tight optical and mechanical tolerances. Nevertheless in that respect, this concept is likely to be the best candidate when tolerance problems will be solved if the goal is to get this large FOV in the final recombined image. Indeed optical and positionning tolerances in the Michelson case with the same FOV are prohibitive. Lets us analyse this situation:

The major difficulty in the Fizeau case comes from the system focal ratio that is required to sample properly the fringes for the largest baseline with an adequate number of detector pixels: The "F number" F# of the system is obtained for the smallest wavelenght (here $\lambda=0.12\mu m$) and the highest resolution (here B=30m). The minimum theoretical sampling required is two pixels per fringe (but by experience a minimum of four is requested). The pixel size in the ultraviolet will not be less than 15 μm. Therefore :

$$\lambda F\# = \lambda(F/B) = 30\mu m \Rightarrow F\# = 250$$

Let us mention that this value is <u>independant of the baseline</u>.With the parameters considered here, this means a system focal lenght of 7500 m...This represents a linear field for a 10 arcmin FOV of: tg(0.167°) x 7500 = 22 m! The tolerances required to align the secondary mirror and for curvature mismatch (or difference between the radii of curvature of the primary mirrors) become extremely severe too, even if the obtention of such a focal lenght is distributed over many optics, which anyway reduces the UV throughput; for example the temperature between the different mirrors has to be maintained to less than 0.05° -considering materials of thermal expansion coefficient of 2.10^{-7} - in order to match the requirement on radius of curvature R ($\Delta R/R<2.10^{-6}$). Conversely positionning tolerances for collectors are large if the primary F number $F_P\#$ is large.

The tolerable axial displacement of the secondary mirror has been computed by R.N. Clark[6]: $\Delta l \approx 128\lambda(F_P\#)^4$, which is equivalent to $\Delta B = (F\# / F_P\#)^2 \Delta l = 128 \lambda (F\# F_P\#)^2 \approx 1 \mu m$ (resp. 0.002 μm) with F# = 250 (resp. F# = 10) and $F_P\#$ = 1 at the Cassegrain focus (if the secondary mirror is segmented to associate one beam to one secondary -in order to minimize the weight-, those expressions become tolerances for relative secondary axial displacements...). The tolerable lateral displacement of the secondary mirror is very small too (less than one micron). We will not present in this paper the complete computation of third-order aberrations; this will be done in another article. The paper by P.Bely et al[7] in these Proceedings presents the results on aberrations obtained for a 6-meter Fizeau interferometer in space; the important result here is that aberrations limit the FOV to less than 10 arcmin, once optics have been polished at the $\lambda/50$ level.

4. FIELD CURVATURE AND PUPIL GEOMETRY CONSERVATION IN THE MICHELSON STELLAR INTERFEROMETER

4.1 Field curvature and distortion

Any Cassegrain telescope will exhibit field curvature (FC in the following, cannot be cancelled with two mirrors only when the back focal distance is ≥ 0). In an array of telescopes -forming the input pupil or used as intermediate relay optics- field aberrations of individual telescopes -like distortion or field curvature-, contribute to degrade the complex degree of coherence, amplitude and phase, in an off-axis composite image (see Ref. 8 for a complete analytical study on FC). An obvious solution would be to use flat-fielded telescopes - requiring correcting lenses or more than three mirrors-, but we want to show here that the tolerance on this flat-fielding is extremely severe for the requested FOV ($\approx 0.5°$).

First we remind a few characteristics of distortion and field curvature FC:

- <u>Distortion</u> is given by $W_{311} \beta^3 r \cos\Phi$ in the Seidel wavefront aberration development, which causes a distortion of the shape of the image since the displacement W is proportional to β^3 (β: image height) and r $\cos\Phi$ (=transverse shift of focus, r is the height of a ray on the pupil).Distortion is like a field-dependant tilt: it causes a displacement of the image point in the Gaussian image plane without loss of quality. W_{311} is proportional to D α^3 (with previous notations) for a 2-mirror parabolic telescope.

- <u>Field curvature</u>, given by $W_{220} \beta^2 r^2$, is a field-dependant defocus, which varies like the square of the position in the field (β^2) and of the aperture (r^2). The wavefront is therefore spherical but focused on a point different from the gaussian image. Image points lie on a spherical surface called the Petzval surface, which is a function of the pupil center position of each telescope if there are several of them. For a 2-mirror parabolic telescope, W_{220} is proportional to $(D^2 / F_P\#) \alpha^2$. Then for an off-axis source (See Fig.2), the wavefront coming from each exit subpupil is spherical and all focal surfaces for all telescopes cannot coincide (because the individual wavefronts are not part of a smooth continuous surface).

Harvey et al[8] calculate the modified complex amplitude in the exit pupil and use a quality image criterium to estimate the off-axis optical performance degradation, while we calculate the degree of coherence of the wave at subpupils[9] to infer amplitude and phase degradation in the object Fourier spectrum: one finds three terms of error for FC (a tilt for each telescope, a piston and a defocus) and two for distortion (a relative piston and a standard distortion). We are more interested here in deriving a tolerance on optics positionning:

Let us consider two beams coming from two separate telescopes 1 and 2 (Fig. 2); without any FC at the output, one expects the beams to arrive in I_{th}. Assuming an identical FC on the exit pupil, the images are now formed in two different points I_1 and I_2 and the beam combiner is looking at two points at finite distance separated by b, distance between the two subpupils. The transverse magnification of this

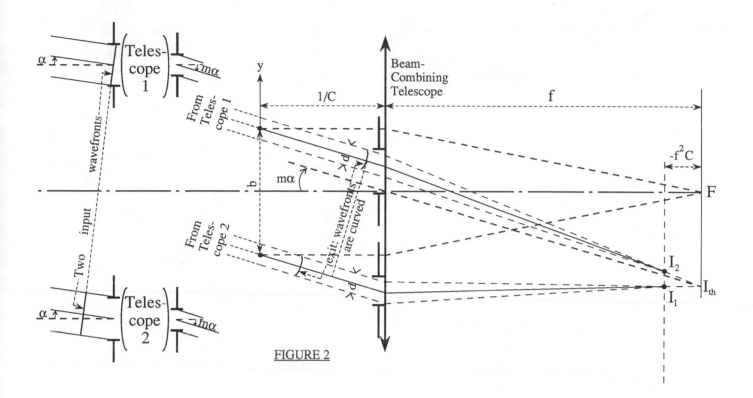

FIGURE 2

"object" of size b is $g_y = - f C$ (see Fig. 2), where C is the inverse of the radius of curvature R or "image proximity" (C = 0 on-axis only where output beams are parallel). In order to get images overlapped (coalignment condition), the two images should not be separated by more than a tenth of the Airy pattern diameter; therefore:

$$|-f C| \times b = \frac{2.44 \, \lambda f}{10d} \quad \Rightarrow \quad C \times b = \frac{0.244 \, \lambda}{d}$$

The maximum sag -or the difference between the curved wavefront in the exit pupil and a plane- is $h = \frac{d^2}{8R} = \frac{d^2 \, C}{8} = \frac{0.244 \, \lambda}{8(b \,/\, d)}$

Taking b / d = 100 (see further: this is to match the entrance pupil geometry) and $\lambda = 0.12 \, \mu m$, we find $h \approx \lambda \,/\, 3000$!

We have with both the distortion -less severe for small field angles[8,9]- and the field curvature a <u>fondamental limitation</u> of the FOV size in a Stellar Michelson Interferometer as those effects result in separating the individual images laterally and longitudinally when going from the combiner focus to the edge of the field; this is aggravated by the great dilution factor of the adopted array . With a tolerance on the wavefront: no more than $\omega = \lambda \,/\, 10$ of wavefront error over the whole FOV, the effect of FC for the 30-m Michelson, if each telescope is a Cassegrain-coudé system, is the following: the FOV cannot exceed two arcseconds.

This result shows that if the geometry of the array has to be conserved in the exit pupil (see Ch. 4.2), then large angular objects cannot be reconstructed as distortion and FC result in tilt and piston errors which depend on the field angle. Nevertheless in Stellar Interferometry one is interested in objects of size < 1 arcsec. The solution is therefore to split the three fields (see Fig.7) before final combination, and use the same technique for stabilization, with the difference that all motions happening after the separation can no longer be compensated; a solution is proposed in Chapter 6 to overcome these difficulties.

4.2 Pupil geometry conservation

In order to obtain a reasonable coherent FOV, one has to keep the same geometry for the exit pupil and the input pupil (as viewed from a point in the focal plane the exit pupil must be superposed to the collecting apertures). A recent overview on this "golden rule", together with its application for the VLT, can be found in ref. 10. In order to guarantee phasing of the desired FOV, on-axis as well as off-axis, the Lagrange invariants of the individual telescopes until the recombiner must be equal, which can be done by correcting the position of the different exit sub-pupils. A reasonable FOV (=a few arcsec) can be reached only if the equality between external OPD and internal OPD is realized at the second order[11]. But the optics adjustment is not so complex in space as one assumes the aperture plane to be always nearly normal to the direction of the science object.

Lets compare the two combination schemes in terms of magnification of the apertures on one side, of magnification of the aperture separations on the other:

Suppose a 2-aperture interferometer - baseline B and aperture diameter = D - and a star at α from the interferometer line of sight (see Fig.3). Assume the exit pupil is made of two pupil images, diameter d, separated by b :

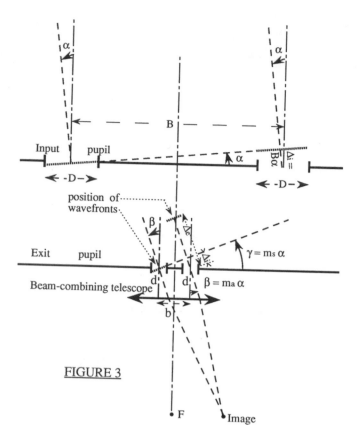

- Direction of composite image : β
- Orientation of the wavefront on exit pupil : γ

We define two factors :

1. Aperture magnification factor : $m_a = \dfrac{\beta}{\alpha} = \dfrac{D}{d}$

2. Separation demagnification factor : $m_s = \dfrac{\gamma}{\alpha} = \dfrac{B}{b}$

Two cases are possible (see Fig.3) :

1) $(m_a \alpha) b = B \alpha \Rightarrow m_a = B/b = m_s \Rightarrow \gamma = \beta = R\alpha$
$\Rightarrow$ whatever the position of the image in the field, the direction of white-light fringe $\equiv$ direction of the composite image center. This situation is what we will call the "Fizeau case".

2) $m_a \neq m_s \Rightarrow \gamma = (m_s/m_a) \beta = m_s \alpha \Rightarrow OPD = 0$ only for a single field angle (see Fig.3). This is the "Michelson case".

FIGURE 3

It is therefore possible to keep the Fizeau concept in a Michelson set up if the rule 1 is respected. Nevertheless the original Fizeau set up (Fig. 1.a) is much simpler in that respects as path equality is naturally realized for all directions within the non-aberrated FOV, like in a large telescope. On the other hand the Michelson concept suffers form the fact that if beams arrive in phase for a given direction α, then beams from another direction $\alpha + \Delta\alpha$ cannot be cophased because the two exit wavefronts ar no longer part of the same surface, as illustrated in Fig. 3. In other words, the OPD depends on $\Delta\alpha$ and therefore fringes for the second object can be contrasted only if the coherence lenght of the light is large enough. Finally, we now determine the tolerance on the optics in the Michelson configuration in order to fulfill the condition 1).

If we name Δ_i and Δ_e the relative piston errors between imput and exit beams respectively, we can infer from Fig. 3 the net piston error due to an incorrect mapping of the entrance pupil laterally :

$$| \Delta_i - \Delta_e | = | B \sin \alpha - b \sin \beta | = | B \sin \alpha - \frac{B}{m_s} \sin (m_a\alpha) | \approx B \alpha \left| 1 - \frac{m_a}{m_s} \right| = B \alpha \varepsilon = \alpha b m_s \varepsilon$$

where the error ε has been studied by Harvey et al[8] to match an image quality criterium, and by Traub[12] ; Harvey et al consider several examples : e.g. for the MMT, ε must be kept within $\varepsilon_o = 8.10^{-5}$ in oder to limit the rms wavefront error to $\lambda / 13$ within a FOV of only 1 arcmin. We assume here that beams should be cophased within $\lambda/10$:

$$\alpha b \varepsilon m_a = \frac{\lambda}{10}$$

Assuming e.g. that the input pupil comprises strictly afocal telescopes and therefore that there is no error on the magnification m_a (see chapter 6), we have :

$$\Delta b = \frac{\lambda}{10 \alpha} \Delta \left[\frac{1}{\varepsilon m_a} \right] = \frac{\lambda}{10 \alpha} \frac{1}{m_a}$$

This expression gives the requirement on the position of the mirrors which fold the beams into the beam combiner. Consider the example given in this paper : suppose we can afford $b_{max} = 1$ m, then $m_s = 30 = m_a$; $\alpha = 0.25°$ and $\lambda = 0.12 \mu m$, one finds $\Delta b \approx 0.1 \mu m$. Even with an active control of the distance between folding mirrors -using wavefront sensors for the reference stars- it will be very hard to reach such a precision. Obviously both large semi-field angles and high dilution ratios contribute to degrade the performance. Conversely one can choose to limit the size of the FOV to the maximum size of the science object, say 1 arcsec ; the tolerance on the folding mirrors is then relaxed to $\Delta b \approx 80 \mu m$: this is now feasible.

5. DISTRIBUTION OF THE SUBAPERTURES: TOWARDS AN OPTIMIZED SET UP

This chapter is not directly linked to the discussion on the coherent FOV presented in this paper. It has been included to illustrate additional problems raised by using many telescopes and to prepare Chapter 6. A ring-shaped array has probably the most suitable geometry for a space interferometer: the optical paths are "naturally" equal for the converging beams from the ring to the central correlation point. Therefore there is no need for cumbersome and light consuming delay lines, besides the uniform (u,v) coverage which can be obtained with such a geometry. If mechanically possible, it is much desirable to rearange the input-pupil distribution, by displacing for example a few telescopes[13]. Therefore, during an observational run the resulting spatial filter obtained from the (u,v) points in the MTF, may adaptively sample the fourier spectrum of the science object observed with the interferometer.

These geometries can be optimized, depending on the target (u,v) coverage defined by the observer, using iterative techniques borrowed from the well-known Fienup error-reduction algorithm. Figure 4 represents the flow-chart of a personnal computer-based programme that we have used to compute the (u,v) coverage for a 12 telescope array. Depending on the desired MTF, the algorithm might stagnate in local and spurious solutions. An additional relaxation loop, which rotates the telescopes between them by a predefined angle, has successfully overcomed this difficulty, and we were able to obtain the corresponding MTF in a few tens of minutes.

An alternative to fill uniformly the (u,v) plane (with a small number of telescopes), is to rotate the whole array around the optical axis of this array. To illustrate this point, we give an example. Fig. 5.a shows an array of 12 telescopes with a non-redundant pupil distribution. Fig. 5.b is the corresponding MTF, optimized for better rotation synthesis coverage ; this is shown in Fig. 5.c, which represents the pupil coverage after 60° rotational syntheses by 5° steps about the array optical axis and in Fig. 5.d (corresponding MTF). Fig. 6.a, b and c, represent the transmission in amplitude of the 12 telescopes, the corresponding diffraction pattern and MTF respectively. The final number of measured Fourier points after rotation is 792 which means, if correctly processed[14], that the minimum redundancy is produced between successive rotations to reduce the final number of unknown visibilities exactly to the available closure phase equations. When increasing the number of subaperture to ≈ 27, we obtain a quasi-uniform (u,v) coverage up to the cut-off frequency, which would allow to do direct imaging without having to use deconvolution techniques.

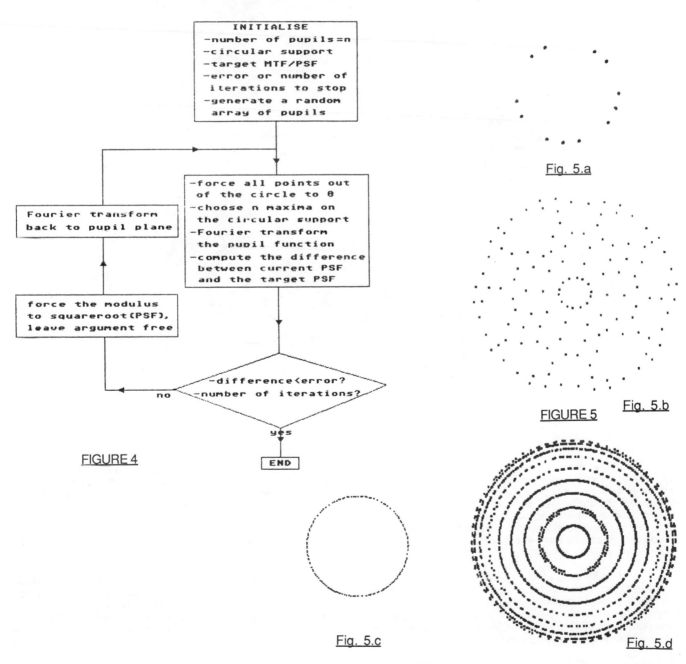

FIGURE 4

FIGURE 5

Fig. 5.a

Fig. 5.b

Fig. 5.c

Fig. 5.d

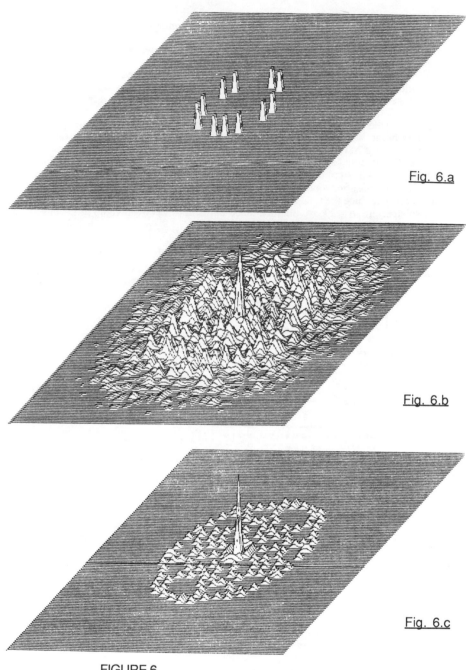

Fig. 6.a

Fig. 6.b

Fig. 6.c

FIGURE 6

6. A STRAWMAN DESIGN

The Fizeau recombination was finally rejected by us because optical and mechanical tolerances for baselines larger than 10 meters become too tight with state of the art technology. The Michelson recombination is very demanding too only if one wants to match the exit pupil geometry to the input pupil. Otherwise and if the science object is less than a few arcsec in size, than there is a possibility to split the fields before the final image plane and nevertheless recombine the beams from an off-axis star in a coherent way. At this point we considered that stabilization of the structure using one or two reference sources was essential -if possible- to guide the overwhole structure and as well as to compensate relative OPD before combination, as laser metrology and accelerometers would make any instrument of this type too complex when there would be no other element to provide error signals. Their use should be minimized to get some '"optical rigidity".

On the other hand set the individual telescopes far from the center of the structure was a major concern for us in terms of spacecraft mass distribution. We then choosed to use flat collectors on the ring, 45 ° oriented, overdimentioned to let two reference stars, 30 arcmin apart (Fig. 7 shows a simplified view of how it works), to be acquired by aplanatic Cassegrain telescopes located inside the central station. Telescopes are unavoidable to get the necessary system focal ratio, even for poor pupil geometry mapping - i.e. for a FOV of a few arcseconds -. A detailed study of one 30cm Ritchey-Chretien telescope was started at the "Institut d'Optique d'Orsay" in order to evaluate residual distortion and FC / astigmatism in a two-mirror telescope. Now the "originality" of the proposed instrument lies in the off-axis star acquisition system: A telescope with a ≈ 30 arcmin non-aberrated FOV is "looking at" a flat mirror. In the image plane two stars are simultaneously acquired by feeding two optical fibers of which the head is movable in the ≈ 12cm linear field by means of 2D stages (each beam is intercepted by a diverging lens which directs it on a semi-boule aplanatic lens ending on the fiber head). At this point there is a need for identical telescopes: the relative magnification errors have to be matched to within 1/1000 in order to overlap correctly the diffraction patterns. Once at least 50% of the flux is captured into the core, then it feeds a double-input interferometer in the central station , of which the other input comes from the corresponding image in the adjacent telescope The lenghts of the fibers can be as small as 1 meter and are passively set to the right value, because the active fringe-tracking systems can be set upstream in the beam. Indeed starting at the telescope level, up to the final composite focus, everything can be cast in rigid blocks, which relaxes the need for an active control of the central station optical elements.

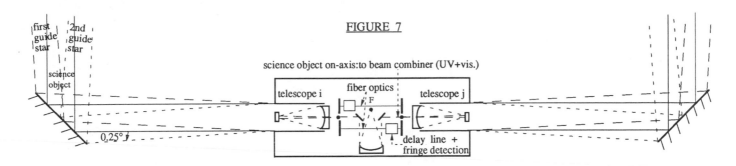

FIGURE 7

7. CONCLUSION

This paper analyses the differences between Fizeau and Michelson types of space interferometers in the image plane. It is shown that phasing of a wide field of view, which is desirable in space, can be achieved only if the pupil geometry is preserved, both in position and in relative orientation within tight tolerances. The problem of relative pupil rotation has been shown up recently by Beckers[15] and leads to very tight tolerances too in the Michelson type. We describe here the positionning tolerances and the constraints due to field aberrations, showing that "pupil mapping errors" and field curvature in the individual beams may limit the phased FOV to less than a few arcsec. It is then proposed to split the reference stars and science object fields before combination and combine them separately. A scheme is proposed in that sense; we are now going to study the different parts in this proposition and make numerical simulations in order to know the effect of these different sources of error on the contrast and phase in the reference star fringes. Up to now, analyses were assuming that the measurement was done in the image plane; we started to study the described perturbations in the pupil plane of the interferometer, for which Fourier technics (FTS) seem to be very promising. The SIST group is now planning to concentrate on pupil plane measurements in different areas.

8. ACKNOWLEDGEMENTS

This work was partly supported by a ESA contract (ESTEC Contract 7978 / 88 / NL / PB (SC). We want to thank Michel Cagnet from "Ecole Supérieure d'Optique" for several appropriate suggestions and James Harvey from the Perkin-Elmer Corporation for profitable exchanges we had on Michelson versus Fizeau concepts.

9. REFERENCES

1. M. Faucherre, A.H. Greenaway, F. Merkle, J.E. Noordam, M.A.C. Perryman, F. Vakili, S. Volonté and G.P. Weigelt , "Aperture Synthesis in Space : An overview and results from the ESA Study Group", in Diffraction-limited imaging with very large telescopes, D. Alloin & J.M. Mariotti ed., published by Kluwer Academic Publishers (1989).
2. M. Faucherre, A. Greenaway, F. Merkle, J.E. Noordam, M.A.C. Perryman, F. Vakili, S. Volonté and G.P. Weigelt , "Aperture Synthesis in Space: Review of the field and trends", these Proceedings (1989).
3. J.N. Bahcall and R.M. Soneira, "The distribution of stars to V=16th magnitude near the north galactic pole : Normalization, clustering properties, and counts in various bands" , Astroph. J. 246, 122 (1981).
4. F. Roddier, "How to achieve diffraction limited resolution with large space telescopes", Adv. Space Res., 2, 3 (1983).
5. M. Shao, M. Colavita, D.H. Staelin, K.J. Johnston, R.S. Simon, J.A. Hughes, J.L. Hershey, "The Mark III Stellar Interferometer", The Astronomical Journal, 93, 1280-1286 (1987).
6. R.N. Clark,"Cassegrain telescopes: limits of secondary movement in secondary focusing", App. Opt. 15, No.5, 1266 (1976).
7. P. Bely, C. Burrows, F. Roddier, G.P. Weigelt, "6-meter optical interferometer for space", these Proceedings (1989).
8. J.E. Harvey, P.R. Silverglate and A.B. Wissinger, "Optical performance of synthetic aperture telescope configurations", SPIE Vol. 540, 110 (1985).
9. M. Faucherre, "Comparative study of Michelson and Fizeau concepts", Annex: Field Curvature and Distortion, ESA/TRP Report No 1 (IAS Report G-03), June 1989.
10. F. Merkle, "Synthetic-aperture imaging with the European Very Large Telescope", J.O.S.A., 5, 904 (1988)
11. J. Beckers, "Field of view considerations for telescope arrays", SPIE Proceedings, 628, 255 (1986).
12. W. Traub, "Combining beams from separated telescopes", App. Opt., 25, No 4, 528 (1986).
13. F. Vakili and L. Koechlin, "Aperture Synthesis in Space: Computer Fringe Blocking", these Proceedings (1989).
14. N.R. Arnot, P.D. Atherton, A.H. Greenaway and J.E. Noordam, "Phase closure in optical astronomy", Traitement du Signal, vol. 2, No 2, 129(1985).
15. J. Beckers, "The VLT Exit Pupil Configuration, Requirements and Tolerances", VLT-IFP R&D Note 89-3 (internal report), May 25, (1989).

SESSION 4

Imaging and Spectroscopy in Astrophysics

Chair
Patrick Wayman
Dunsink Observatory (Ireland)

Speckle Imaging and Speckle Spectroscopy *

Gerd Weigelt

Max-Planck-Institut für Radioastronomie
Auf dem Hügel 69, 5300 Bonn 1, Fed. Rep. of Germany

ABSTRACT

The atmosphere of the earth restricts the resolution of conventional astronomical imaging to about 1 arcsec. Much higher resolution can be obtained by speckle methods. The Knox-Thompson method and the speckle masking method (bispectrum or triple correlation processing) yield diffraction-limited images in spite of image degradation by the atmosphere and by telescope aberrations. For example, with a 3.6-m telescope a resolution of 0.03" can be obtained at a wavelength of 400 nm. The limiting magnitude is about 18. We will discuss the theory and applications of speckle masking. High-resolution images and simultaneously the spectrum of each resolution element can be obtained by objective prism speckle spectroscopy and projection speckle spectroscopy methods. Finally, we will discuss the application of speckle masking to coherent arrays of telescopes. For example, observations with the 4x8-m ESO VLT can yield the fantastic angular resolution of about 2 milli-arcsec.

1. INTRODUCTION

The Knox-Thompson method [1] and the speckle masking method [2-5] can reconstruct diffraction-limited images from speckle interferograms. One of the additional advantages of speckle masking is that it can reconstruct all closure phases. Therefore, it can be applied to all types of coherent arrays.

We will discuss the Knox-Thompson method, speckle masking, speckle spectroscopy, and optical long-baseline interferometry. A discussion of other speckle methods can be found in various review papers [6,7]. Image reconstruction by shearing interferometry techniques is discussed in Refs. 8-10.

2. KNOX-THOMPSON METHOD

In the Knox-Thompson method and in speckle masking the same speckle raw data (speckle interferograms) are reduced as in Labeyrie's speckle interferometry [11]. The intensity distribution $I(r)$ of speckle interferograms can be described by the incoherent, space-invariant imaging equation

$$I(r) = O(r) * S(r), \tag{1}$$

where $O(r)$ denotes the object intensity distribution and $S(r)$ the instantaneous p.s.f. of atmosphere/telescope. $r = (x,y)$ is a 2-dimensional space vector and $*$ denotes the convolution operator.

---

* Based on data collected at the European Southern Observatory, La Silla, Chile.

The first processing step of the Knox-Thompson method is the calculation of the cross-spectrum

$$\langle \hat{I}(f)\hat{I}^*(f+\Delta f)\rangle = \hat{O}(f)\hat{O}^*(f+\Delta f)\langle \hat{S}(f)\hat{S}^*(f+\Delta f)\rangle, \tag{2}$$

where Δf is a small shift vector with $|\Delta f| \sim 0.2\, r_o/\lambda$ (see Ref. 6). r_o is the Fried parameter (~ 10 to $30\,cm$ at optical wavelengths) and λ is the wavelength of light. If we divide Equation (2) by the Knox-Thompson transfer function (KTTF), we obtain the Knox-Thompson spectrum of the object:

$$\hat{O}(f)\hat{O}^*(f+\Delta f) = \langle \hat{I}(f)\hat{I}^*(f+\Delta f)\rangle \,/\, \langle \hat{S}(f)\hat{S}^*(f+\Delta f)\rangle. \tag{3}$$

The KTTF is derived from the speckle interferograms of an unresolvable object, which is observed before or after the object. For the Knox-Thompson spectrum of the object we can write

$$\hat{O}(f)\hat{O}^*(f+\Delta f) = |\hat{O}(f)|\exp[i\varphi(f)]\,|\hat{O}(f+\Delta f)|\exp[-i\varphi(f+\Delta f)], \tag{4}$$

where $\varphi(f)$ denotes the desired phase of the object Fourier transform $\hat{O}(f)$. If we take the phase terms of Equation (4), we see that we have

$$\exp[i\varphi(f)]\exp[-i\varphi(f+\Delta f)] = \exp\{i[\varphi(f)-\varphi(f+\Delta f)]\} \quad \text{or the}$$

$$\text{phase difference } \Delta\varphi(f) \equiv \varphi(f+\Delta f) - \varphi(f) \tag{5}$$

between coordinate $f+\Delta f$ and f. In other words, we have a recursive equation for calculating the desired phase of the object Fourier transform:

$$\varphi(f+\Delta f) = \varphi(f) + \Delta\varphi(f). \tag{6}$$

From the object Fourier phase measured by the Knox-Thompson method and the Fourier modulus a diffraction-limited image of the object can be reconstructed. Applications of the Knox-Thompson method are, for example, described in Refs. 12 (μ CAS), 13 (α ORI), and 14 (IR objects).

3. SPECKLE MASKING

Speckle masking consists of the following processing steps:

STEP 1: *calculation of the ensemble average triple correlation*

$$C(r_1,r_2) = \langle \int I(r)\,I(r+r_1)\,I(r+r_2)\,dr\rangle \tag{7}$$

or the ensemble average bispectrum

$$\hat{C}(f_1,f_2) = \langle \hat{I}(f_1)\hat{I}(f_2)\hat{I}^*(f_1+f_2)\rangle, \tag{8}$$

where $\hat{I}(\mathbf{f}_1)$, $\hat{I}(\mathbf{f}_2)$, and $\hat{I}^*(\mathbf{f}_1+\mathbf{f}_2)$ denote the Fourier transforms of $I(\mathbf{r})$. $\langle...\rangle$ denotes ensemble average over many speckle interferograms and the hat $\char`\^$ denotes Fourier transforms. $\mathbf{f}_1$ and $\mathbf{f}_2$ are 2-dimensional vectors in Fourier space.

In most applications it is advantageous to use the bispectrum processing. The advantage of the triple correlation is that it can be easily visualized and that it can be used for photon-counting triple correlation techniques [15]. In the text below we will discuss the theory of bispectrum processing.

STEP 2: compensation of the photon bias in the ensemble average bispectrum [16,17].

STEP 3: compensation of the speckle masking transfer function: From $I = O * S$ follows $\hat{I} = \hat{O}\hat{S}$. If we insert $\hat{I} = \hat{O}\hat{S}$ into equation (8), we obtain

$$\hat{C}(\mathbf{f}_1,\mathbf{f}_2) = \langle \hat{O}(\mathbf{f}_1)\hat{S}(\mathbf{f}_1)\hat{O}(\mathbf{f}_2)\hat{S}(\mathbf{f}_2)\hat{O}^*(\mathbf{f}_1+\mathbf{f}_2)\hat{S}^*(\mathbf{f}_1+\mathbf{f}_2)\rangle$$

$$= \hat{O}(\mathbf{f}_1)\hat{O}(\mathbf{f}_2)\hat{O}^*(\mathbf{f}_1+\mathbf{f}_2)\langle \hat{S}(\mathbf{f}_1)\hat{S}(\mathbf{f}_2)\hat{S}^*(\mathbf{f}_1+\mathbf{f}_2)\rangle \quad (9)$$

or object bispectrum $\hat{C}_0(\mathbf{f}_1,\mathbf{f}_2) =$

$$\hat{O}(\mathbf{f}_1)\hat{O}(\mathbf{f}_2)\hat{O}^*(\mathbf{f}_1+\mathbf{f}_2) =$$

$$\langle \hat{I}(\mathbf{f}_1)\hat{I}(\mathbf{f}_2)\hat{I}^*(\mathbf{f}_1+\mathbf{f}_2)\rangle / \langle \hat{S}(\mathbf{f}_1)\hat{S}(\mathbf{f}_2)\hat{S}^*(\mathbf{f}_1+\mathbf{f}_2)\rangle. \quad (10)$$

STEP 4: derivation of modulus $|\hat{O}(\mathbf{f})|$ and phase $\varphi(\mathbf{f})$ of the object Fourier transform $\hat{O}(\mathbf{f})$ from the object bispectrum $\hat{C}_0(\mathbf{f}_1,\mathbf{f}_2)$: We denote the phase of the object Fourier transform by φ and the phase of the object bispectrum by β, i.e.,

$$\hat{O}(\mathbf{f}) = |\hat{O}(\mathbf{f})|\exp[i\varphi(\mathbf{f})] \text{ and} \quad (11)$$

$$\hat{C}_0(\mathbf{f}_1,\mathbf{f}_2) = |\hat{C}_0(\mathbf{f}_1,\mathbf{f}_2)|\exp[i\beta(\mathbf{f}_1,\mathbf{f}_2)]. \quad (12)$$

Inserting equations (11) and (12) into equation (10) yields

$$\hat{C}_0(\mathbf{f}_1,\mathbf{f}_2) = |\hat{C}_0(\mathbf{f}_1,\mathbf{f}_2)|\exp[i\beta(\mathbf{f}_1,\mathbf{f}_2)]$$

$$= |\hat{O}(\mathbf{f}_1)|\exp[i\varphi(\mathbf{f}_1)]\,|\hat{O}(\mathbf{f}_2)|\exp[i\varphi(\mathbf{f}_2)]\,|\hat{O}(\mathbf{f}_1+\mathbf{f}_2)|\exp[-i\varphi(\mathbf{f}_1+\mathbf{f}_2)]$$

$$\longrightarrow \exp[i\beta(\mathbf{f}_1,\mathbf{f}_2)] = \exp[i\varphi(\mathbf{f}_1)]\exp[i\varphi(\mathbf{f}_2)]\exp[-i\varphi(\mathbf{f}_1+\mathbf{f}_2)]$$

$$\longrightarrow \beta(\mathbf{f}_1,\mathbf{f}_2) = \varphi(\mathbf{f}_1) + \varphi(\mathbf{f}_2) - \varphi(\mathbf{f}_1+\mathbf{f}_2)$$

$$\longrightarrow \varphi(\mathbf{f}_1+\mathbf{f}_2) \equiv \varphi(\mathbf{f}) = \varphi(\mathbf{f}_1) + \varphi(\mathbf{f}_2) - \beta(\mathbf{f}_1,\mathbf{f}_2). \quad (13)$$

This equation is a recursive equation for calculating the phase of the object Fourier transform at coordinate $\mathbf{f} = \mathbf{f}_1+\mathbf{f}_2$. For the recursive calculation of the object Fourier transform $\varphi(\mathbf{f}) \equiv \varphi(\mathbf{f}_1+\mathbf{f}_2)$ we need in addition to the bispectrum phase $\beta(\mathbf{f}_1,\mathbf{f}_2)$ the starting values $\varphi(0,0)$, $\varphi(0,1)$, and $\varphi(1,0)$.

Since $O(\mathbf{r})$ is real, $\hat{O}$ is hermitian. Therefore, $\hat{O}(\mathbf{f}) = \hat{O}^*(-\mathbf{f})$, $\hat{O}(0) = \hat{O}^*(0)$, and $\varphi(0) = 0$. $\varphi(0,1)$ and $\varphi(1,0)$ can be set to zero since we are not interested in the absolute position of the reconstructed image.

The advantage of this recursive phase calculation is the fact that for each element of the object Fourier phase $\varphi(\mathbf{f})$ there are many different recursion paths and that it is possible to average over all $\varphi(\mathbf{f})$-values to improve the SNR.

$$\exp[i\varphi(\mathbf{f})] = const. \sum \exp[i\varphi(\mathbf{f}_1)]\exp[i\varphi(\mathbf{f}-\mathbf{f}_1)]\exp[-i\beta(\mathbf{f}_1,\mathbf{f}-\mathbf{f}_1)].$$
$$0 < \mathbf{f}_1\cdot\mathbf{f}/f \leq f/2 \quad (14)$$

Since not all recursion paths for the same $\varphi(\mathbf{f})$-value lead to the same SNR, different weighting factors have to be chosen for different paths. The modulus $|\hat{O}(\mathbf{f})|$ can be derived from the object bispectrum in various ways (see, for example, Ref. 18).

Modifications of speckle masking are photon-counting triple correlation processing [15], cross-triple correlation processing [17], and tomographic speckle masking [15].

Speckle masking has been applied to various types of objects, for example to double stars [3], star clusters [5, 19, 20], Seyfert galaxies [19] and other objects. Figure 1 shows a speckle masking observation of the central object in the H II region NGC 3603 [5,19].

4. OBJECTIVE PRISM SPECKLE SPECTROSCOPY

Objective prism speckle spectroscopy [21-24] yields objective prism spectra with diffraction-limited angular resolution. The raw data for this technique are objective prism speckle spectrograms, which are obtained by inserting a prism or grating into a pupil plane (in the speckle camera). In this case each speckle is dispersed in a linear spectrum. From the objective prism speckle spectrograms a diffraction-limited objective prism spectrum can be reconstructed.

5. WIDEBAND PROJECTION SPECKLE SPECTROSCOPY

A disadvantage of objective prism speckle spectroscopy is that it cannot be applied to general objects since in many cases the spectra of different object parts will overlap, as in the case of ordinary objective prism spectroscopy. This disadvantage can be overcome by the projection speckle spectroscopy technique [24]. This method yields $O(x,\lambda)$-reconstructions. $O(x,\lambda)$ is a spectrally dispersed version of a 1-dimensional projection of the 2-dimensional object. A laboratory simulation of this method is described in Ref. 24.

6. OPTICAL LONG-BASELINE INTERFEROMETRY

The great advantage of optical long-baseline interferometry is the fact that it can yield images and spectra with fantastic angular resolution. For example, at $\lambda \sim 600$ nm and with 75 m baseline a resolution of 0.002" can be obtained. Possible image reconstruction methods are the phase closure method [25-27] and the speckle masking method [2-5, 28, 29]. Various computer simulations of speckle masking with optical arrays are described in Refs. 28-30. The experiments show that speckle masking can easily be applied to arrays of large telescopes ("multi-speckle mode"). Figure 2 shows a computer simulation of the application of speckle masking to a 10 telescope array [29].

7. REFERENCES

1. K.T. Knox, B.J. Thompson, Astrophys. J. Lett. 193, L45 (1974).

2. G. Weigelt, Opt. Commun. 21, 55 (1977).

3. G. Weigelt, B. Wirnitzer, Optics Lett. 8, 389 (1983).

4. A.W. Lohmann, G. Weigelt, B. Wirnitzer, Appl. Opt. 22, 4028 (1983).

5. K.-H. Hofmann, G. Weigelt, Astron. Astrophys. 167, L15 (1986).

6. J.C. Dainty, "Stellar Speckle Interferometry", in Laser Speckle and Related Phenomena, ed. J.C. Dainty, Springer-Verlag, 2nd edition 1984, chapter 7, 1975.

7. F. Roddier, Physics Reports (North Holland) 170 (2), 97 (1988).

8. K.-H. Hofmann and G. Weigelt, Appl. Opt. 25, 4280 (1986).

9. F. Roddier and C. Roddier, Opt. Commun. 66, 350 (1986).

10. E. Ribak, Appl. Opt. 26, 197 (1987).

11. A. Labeyrie, Astron. Astrophys. 6, 85 (1979).

12. M. Karovska, P. Nisenson, and R.V. Stachnik, Astron. J. 92, 898 (1986).

13. M. Karovska, P. Nisenson, and R.W. Noyes, Astrophys. J. 308, 260 (1986).

14. J.D. Freeman, J.C. Christou, D.W. McCarthy, Jr., and M.L. Cobb, Soc. Photo-Opt. Instr. Eng. 828, 40 (1987).

15. D. Schertl, F. Fleischmann, K.-H. Hofmann, and G. Weigelt, Soc. Photo-Opt. Instr. Eng. 808, 38 (1987).

16. B. Wirnitzer, J. Opt. Soc. Am. A 2, 14 (1985).

17. K.-H. Hofmann and G. Weigelt, Appl. Opt. 26, 2011 (1987).

18. G. Weigelt, "Interferometric Imaging in Optical Astronomy," in Evolution of Galaxies. Astrophysical Observations (EADN School I), eds. I. Appenzeller, H.J. Habing, and P. Lena, Lecture Notes in Physics (Springer-Verlag, 1989).

19. G. Baier, J. Eckert, K.-H. Hofmann, W. Mauder, D. Schertl, H. Weghorn, and G. Weigelt, The Messenger (ESO) 52, 11 (1988).

20. K.-H. Hofmann and G. Weigelt, Astron. Astrophys. 203, L 21 (1988).

21. G. Weigelt, "Speckle Interferometry, Speckle Holography, Speckle Spectroscopy, and the Reconstruction of High-Resolution Images from Space Telescope Data," in Proc. Scientific Importance of High-angular Resolution at Infrared and Optical Wavelengths, M.H. Ulrich, K. Kjär, eds., ESO Conf., Garching p. 95 (1981).

22. W. Stork and G. Weigelt, "Speckle Spectroscopy," in Conf. Proc. of the 13th Congress of the International Commission for Optics, ICO-13, H. Ohzu, ed., Sapporo, Japan, 20-24 Aug. 1984. p. 624.

23. G. Weigelt, G. Baier, J. Ebersberger, F. Fleischmann, K.-H. Hofmann, and R. Ladebeck, Opt. Eng. 25, 706 (1986).

24. F. Grieger, F. Fleischmann, and G. Weigelt, "Objective Prism Speckle Spectroscopy and Wideband Projection Speckle Spectroscopy," in Proc. High-Resolution Imaging by Interferometry, F. Merkle, ed., ESO Conf., Garching, FRG, 15-18 March 1988, p. 225.

25. R.C. Jennison, Mon. Not. Roy. Astr. Soc. 118, 276 (1958).

26. W.T. Rhodes and J.W. Goodman, J. Opt. Soc. Am. 63, 647 (1973).

27. J.E. Baldwin, C.A. Haniff, C.D. Mackay, and P.J. Warner, Nature 320, 595 (1986).

28. K.-H. Hofmann and G. Weigelt, J. Opt. Soc. Am. A 3, 1908 (1986).

29. T. Reinheimer and G. Weigelt, Astron. Astrophys. 176, L 17 (1987).

30. T. Reinheimer, F. Fleischmann, F. Grieger, and G. Weigelt, "Speckle Masking with Coherent Arrays," in Proc. High-

resolution Imaging by interferometry, F. Merkle, ed., ESO Conf., 15-18 March 1988, Garching, FRG, p. 581.

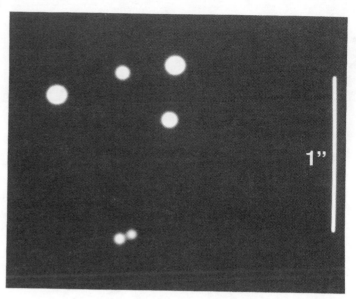

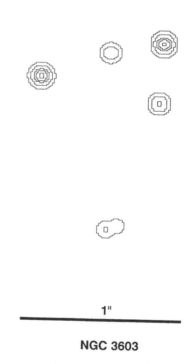

NGC 3603

Figure 1. Speckle masking observations of the central object in the giant H II region NGC 3603. The diffraction-limited image shows 6 stars. The separation of the close double star at the bottom is about 0.08". The astronomical magnitudes of the stars are in the range of 12 to 15. The image was reconstructed from 300 speckle interferograms recorded with the 2.2-m ESO/MPG telescope.

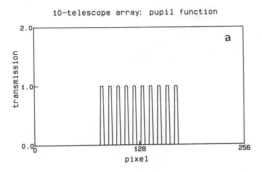

10-telescope array: pupil function

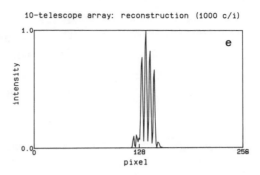

10-telescope array: reconstruction (1000 c/i)

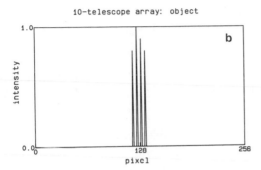

10-telescope array: object

Figure 2. Computer simulation of speckle masking with a 10 telescope array. The figures show:
a: pupil function
b: object
c: one of 2000 simulated speckle interferograms of the object
d: diffraction-limited image reconstructed from 2000 speckle interferograms with photon noise corresponding to 10 000 photon events per speckle interferogram
e: same as d, but photon noise of 1000 photon events per speckle interferogram

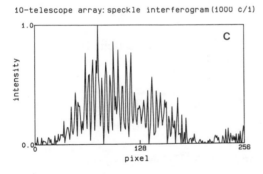

10-telescope array: speckle interferogram (1000 c/i)

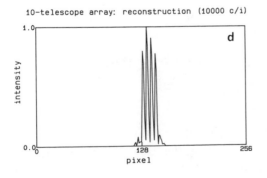

10-telescope array: reconstruction (10000 c/i)

Buttable Optical CCD Mosaics: Concept and first Results at the European Southern Observatory

Roland Reiss, Harry Bauer, Sebastian Deiries,
Sandro D'Odorico, Antonio Longinotti.
European Southern Observatory
Karl-Schwarzschild-Str. 2, 8046 Garching, FRG

ABSTRACT

New techniques to build and operate CCD mosaics consisting of Thomson THX31157 buttable CCD image sensors have been developed under the convention between ESO-INSU for the development of CCD detectors for astronomy.

A split-field microscope is used to align the CCDs with respect to a precision sapphire template thus avoiding cumulative positioning errors in large mosaics. A 2 by 2 prototype CCD mosaic has been aligned with errors of less than 3 μm.

A new generation CCD controller, based on commercially available VMEbus boards and newly developed CCD interface boards has been designed, built and successfully tested. The controller is able to read out up to 16 CCDs in parallel. The CCD camera is controlled by a 68020 microcomputer running under the UNIX-like real-time operating system OS-9/V2.2. Rudimentary image pre-processing software has been included in the controller to assemble the single CCD images into one image compatible with IHAP or FITS format.

A newly designed cryostat with very high mechanical stability (1 μm) has four built-in preamplifiers to guarantee low noise operation even in noisy environments. Noise levels of less than 5 electrons RMS for the complete mosaic have been measured using A-grade THX31157 CCDs.

The results of extensive laboratory testing of the mosaic are presented in this paper.

1.INTRODUCTION

At the beginning of 1987, the European Southern Observatory and the INSU/CNRS of France have agreed to work in collaboration on a project centered on the production of mosaics of small CCDs with minimal inter-CCD gaps. The Optical Instrumentation Group in the ESO Project Division and the Groupe d'Imagerie at the Observatoire de Toulouse are the two counterparts in the development, which is aimed at providing an alternative route to the procurement of large size detectors for astronomical observations.

In this paper we briefly outline the characteristics of the project and give its status as of March 1989. An earlier report was published in [6].

2.THE BUTTABLE CCD

For many instrumental applications CCD detectors of a size exceeding the present standard size of about 15x10 mm² are desired. Many manufacturers (Tektronix and Ford in the USA, EEV in England and Thomson in France among others) are working on the production of devices with 1000 or even 2000 pixels square with pixel sizes between 15 and 27 μm. The prospects are encouraging, but so far the development phase of these devices is not yet completed and the exact time of appearance on the commercial market is uncertain.

An alternative way to built up a large size CCD is by butting together standard, small size ones. This approach is hampered by the present layout of the single CCDs, where the ceramic baseplate and the electrical connectors extend beyond the photon sensitive surface. A mosaic built up by today CCDs would then have relatively large "dead" spacings between the single components, making the use in spectroscopy ackward and requiring unnecessarily large fields for the optics and dewar windows.

To our knowledge there is no mosaic of small size CCD in regular operation at any observatory. The 4-Shooter instrument operating at the 5 m Palomar telescope is based on 4 CCDs physically separate, with an optical system splitting the field between the four detectors [5]. An alternative and more versatile field-splitting approach is described in [12]. Other instruments operate more than one CCD but at different foci.

In 1987 ESO and INSU/CNRS decided to support jointly the industrial development of buttable CCDs, that is CCDs derived from standard ones but with the bondings of the connectors on one side only with a ceramic base narrower than the sensitive area. This configuration permits the butting of CCDs on three sides with minimal non-sensitive inter-chip gaps (Figure 2). The development was carried out at Thomson CSF. The buttable CCD (THX 31157) is derived from the standard CCD TH7882 of which it reproduces most of the characteristics. It is a front-illuminated device, with 579 rows and 400 columns and pixels 23 μm square. The quantum efficiency peaks at about 40Some charge transfer inefficiency at very low charge levels has been reported in the literature [10]. The buttable CCD version includes, apart from the repositioning of the connectors, a modification of the horizontal readout register, which has two phases instead of four. Four fiducial crosses are also added to the mask at the corners of the sensitive surface, to facilitate the alignment process. A photograph of the THX 31157 chip is shown in Figure 1.

3.THE MOSAIC MOUNTING AND ALIGNMENT MACHINE

The mounting and alignment of the individual buttable CCDs on a common substrate was an important step of the project. It was decided at the outset that the pixels of the different CCDs of the mosaic should be aligned so that they form a common (phased) pixel raster, i.e. the gaps between the CCDs correspond to an integral number of pixels and the columns and rows are aligned. This was to simplify the data reduction procedure and to minimize the loss of resolution that would occur if the pixels were rebinned. The specification for the inter-chip pixel alignment precision was 0.1 pixel, or about 2.5 microns over the whole area of the mosaic. This is comparable to the optical distortion that would be introduced by a focal reducer, for example, and also comparable, as it turns out, to the position accuracy of the fiducial marks on the CCDs. This is sufficient for essentially all foreseen applications. For some, such as spectroscopy, a lower precision could be tolerated without adversely affecting the quality of the data.

The target co-planarity of the different CCDs was specified so that the maximum deviation from the mean image plane of the mosaic should be not larger than 15 microns. This is considered acceptable for an F/3 camera.

An alignment and mounting machine (MAM) was conceived by the Optical Instrumentation Group at ESO and the Groupe d'Imagerie of Toulouse and designed and built at Toulouse between March 87 and January 1988. Figure 3 is a photograph of the machine which identifies the main components. On the table of a split field microscope the support for the mosaic (a sapphire baseplate) and a reference template, both specially made, are mounted. The single CCDs are positioned one by one on the support with a drop of UV-curing glue in between. The alignment between the fiducial marks on the CCD and on the reference template is effected by manually controlled motion of the chip via a vacuum finger in the x and y directions and rotation around the z axis. Co-planarity is achieved by the z motion and by rotation around the x and y axes. When the optimal configuration is achieved, a UV discharge lamp is used to polymerize the glue and fix the CCD at its position. Figure 4 shows a photograph of an assembled mosaic of prototype CCDs.

In the present configuration the MAM can be used to build mosaics of up to 2x4 CCDs. After initial testing in Toulouse, the machine was transferred to a temperature controlled room at ESO in Garching, where it is now available for mosaic preparation.

4.THE MOSAIC CRYOSTAT

The design and construction of a new large cryostat was necessary because the old design didn't offer enough space to accommodate a 2x2 mosaic and its front end electronics. The new cryostat not only allows mounting of very large detectors like the TK2048 (if it ever becomes available) but has some additional new features. The mechanical stability has been optimized to guarantee worst case deviations of about 1 μm. The detector can very easily be accessed by removing the top flange making electrical and mechanical adjustments extremely simple. To improve noise immunity and detector safety we have decided to integrate the first preamplifier stage and some filter circuits into the cryostat. Space problems at some instruments did not allow to put the front end electronics in an external box fixed to the dewar. The circular shaped PC board is connected to the "warm" part of the dewar and thermally shielded from the cold detector mounting plate. The connection to the CCDs is done with flexible PC boards offering reasonably good thermal insulation. Each CCD has its own preamplifier with differential inputs and outputs.

At present the number of chips in a mosaic is limited to four, assuming that classical printed circuit board technology is used. Also the individual clock wiring of each single chip requires a significant number of hermetic connectors to the outside world. The number of connectors can be reduced if the clock and bias signals of several or all chips are tied together. Experience during the first evaluation of the mosaic chips has shown that the same clock and bias voltage settings can be used for almost all CCDs in a mosaic. A compromise could be to connect the CCDs to two groups with a different setup. That would allow a mosaic of 8 chips with the same number of connectors. Spare video lines are already foreseen in the present wiring scheme. The space problem of implementing more than four preamplifiers and clock filter circuits can be circumvented using SMD (Surface Mount Device) technology and/or flexible printed circuit boards.

It is worth mentioning that the same cryostat and electronics are used to operate the THX31156 (1024x1024) CCD from Thomson. This detector is mounted on a 21x14 ZIF PGA socket (Zero Insertion Force Pin Grid Array). This socket allows rapid exchange of the detector. The same socket (with modified pin layout) can be used for a wide range of CCDs, from the small TH7882 to the big P88300 from EEV.

The four preampliers can be used to read out the THX31156 in four quadrants simultaneously to shorten readout time.

5.THE MOSAIC CCD CONTROLLER

Starting in 1986 ESO has developed the hardware and the software of a CCD control system which makes use of both commercially available VMEbus boards and custom-made boards interfacing CCDs to the VMEbus. The minimum VME configuration consists of:

- An ELTEC E5 CPU board (68020, 16MHz, 4 MByte RAM, SCSI interface, bootstrap loader for OS-9, optional MMU and FPU).

- A RAM Disk module with two exchangeable battery-backed-up RAM cartridges (512 kByte each) containing operating system and CCD control software.

- An ESO Sequencer board with 2kx64bit high speed RAM, Bus Interrupter.

- An ESO DMA controller with CCDbus interface board.

The first (single CCD) version of the camera has been tested successfully at the 1.5m telescope in La Silla in February 1988. The hardware of a multiple CCD version to be used to operate 4 CCDs in parallel has been completed during 1988 and is currently used in the laboratory. Figure 5 shows the block diagram of this multiple CCD camera. Parts of the control software, including that needed for re-arranging of the 4 CCD frames into a single, coherent frame, has been written at ESO . Additional control software and a smart 4-channel DMA controller performing the image assembly in real time during readout is currently under development at the Toulouse Observatory.

5.1.CPU The CPU is a very powerful 32-bit single-board computer fast enough to perform all control tasks of the CCD system (communication with host, shutter and bias light control, CCD readout, image pre-processing) in virtually real-time. The exposure time is controlled by the system real-time clock with a resolution of 10 msec. Communication is done via an RS-232C fibre-optic link, the CCD image data is dumped through a special 16-bit port with strobe and some select lines (ESOPORT) located on the CCDbus interface board. In our current version this is transferred to the host computer via a CAMAC parallel input port. Because all signals of the ESOPORT are differentially driven and opto-isolated at the receiver side, cable lengths of more than 30m are possible. We have investigated the usage of a Local Area Network (LAN) running under a standard protocol like TCP-IP or OS9NET but the achieved transmission rates (40..100 kByte/sec) are much to slow for large amounts of image data. In the future we plan to use OS9NET together with Virtual Terminal software to replace the RS-232C connections.

During software development the CPU is complemented by a 40 MByte hard disk with an SCSI controller board. This is a local extension to the CPU and does not affect load on the VMEbus. After software modifications have been made all executable files are then copied to the RAM Disk, from where they are executed during 'normal' operation. The ELTEC bootstrap loader allows booting from either RAM disk, hard disk or floppy. The user's choice is stored in a non-volatile RAM on the CPU board.

5.2.RAM Disk We have little experience with the long term reliability of hard disks mounted to a telescope so we decided to use a solid state mass storage unit ('RAM Disk') with 1 MByte or eventually 4 MByte capacity. Currently all the software needed for the CCD controller (including OS-9) occupies about 400 kByte and fits easily into the present RAM Disk.

5.3.Sequencer The heart of the system is a microcoded programmable sequencer (clock pattern generator) supplying all the digital signals necessary to run one or more CCDs. It is built around the ADSP-1401 Word-Slice Program Sequencer from Analog Devices. This device has four built-in decrementing counters, absolute, relative and indirect addressing capability and a configurable 64-word internal RAM. The ADSP-1401 supports programming requirements like looping, jumping, branching, subroutines, condition testing and interrupts. An on-board highspeed RAM contains the microcode with instructions and the clock bits which control the Correlated Double Sampling (CDS) timing, the CCD video multiplexer, the ADC and the CCD clocks. Table 1 shows how the microcode RAM of 2Kx64 bit is organized.

Function	Instruction	Misc.	Data/Delay	Spare	MUX	ADC/CDS	H-Clocks	V-Clocks
No.of bits	8	8	16	8	4	4	8	8

Table 1: Organization of microcode RAM.

The delay field in the microcode allows suspension of the 10MHz sequencer clock for n clock cycles to stretch a single command to up to 6.5 msec ($2^{16} * 100$ nsec). Thus the microcode stays compact even if rather long delays e.g. for CDS timing are needed. If such a delayed instruction would be embedded into a nested loop controlled by one or more of the built-in 16-bit counters of the ADSP-1401 virtually any desired time interval could be generated.

The four counters are normally preloaded with the number of horizontal pixels, the number of vertical lines and the horizontal and vertical binning factors. The counter contents can be pushed to and popped from the internal stack making multiple usage of one counter possible. The nesting level of loops is therefore limited by the size of the internal stack (max. 64 words).

5.4.DMA Controller and Interface This module consists actually of two boards: ESO's single-euro DMA board with an expansion connector on the bottom side, and the slightly larger interface board containing the CCDbus interface, shutter and bias light control, the ESOPORT and some additional circuitry.

During CCD readout one of the four DMA channels is connected to the ADC output. The $\overline{XFER}$-line from the ADC serves as a DMA request signal. The DMA controller then writes a single CCD data word to the CPU memory or an external memory board. The DMA controller tries to keep the bus for a certain time before relinquishing it. Thus, for a burst of four CCD words arriving within about 10..20 μsec only one bus arbitration cycle is needed. Between to bursts (ca. 100 μsec) the bus is released and can be used by the CPU or another master. The 68450 DMA chip only can transfer blocks of max. 64k words. The 'address chaining' capability of the 68450 allows automatic re-programming after each block without any CPU intervention. The block size is freely selectable and chosen in multiples of 4 CCD lines. This avoids that re-programming happens during a burst of the 4 CCD words. At the end of a line, during the vertical shift, there's plenty of time to fetch the new parameters.

5.5.CCDbus A synchronous bus carrying the CCD clock signals, 16 data/address lines and some control and handshake lines has been designed to inter-connect the CCD boards in a simple fashion. The boards are single extended euro boards (220x100 mm^2) with a 96-pole DIN connector plugged into a backplane. The backplane interconnects 64 of the 96 pins. The center row of 32 pins is used for individual module wiring (DC bias and clocks to CCDs, video from CCDs etc). The following boards are required to run four THX 31157 CCDs.

- A 16-bit fast Analog-to-Digital Converter board ,

- Two two-channel Correlated Double Sampler boards with output multiplexer.

- Two Bias boards each with 8 independent DC voltages.

- Two Clock Driver boards each with 16 phases organized in 6 groups.

- A Reference board with 16-bit DAC to monitor digitized video.

This configuration allows independent control of the clock voltages of all four CCDs. By simply adding more boards (one set of CDS, Bias and Clock Driver boards per pair of buttable CCDs) the system can easily be expanded. The wiring from the chassis rear panel to the backplane is done with cable assemblies containing the Bendix cable connectors on a piece of rear panel on one side and crimped single-row Berg connectors on the other end. To adapt the system to the desired number of CCDs takes less then 30 minutes as long there are free slots available on the CCDbus. The maximum number of slots is currently limited to 22 (19 inch chassis with 84TE).

The system architecture allows concurrent operation of up to 16 CCDs of the same type in any configuration. That means it is possible to leave a certain number of chips integrating while some other chips are simultaneously read out.

It is also possible to connect up to 16 CCDs of different type and size to the system. But this requires the use of different micro-programs (clock patterns) for each CCD type. The sequencer memory is able to store the micro programs for about 4 different CCD types. If more CCD types have to be read out then the sequencer has to be re-programmed prior to readout. Re-programming of the whole microcode memory takes a few milliseconds and is therefore negligible for most applications.

5.6.16-bit ADC This board is designed around the ADAM-826 sampling A/D converter from Analogic. In addition to its very high speed ($t_c = 2.5$ μsec) it offers true 16-bit accuracy. Because this ADC occupies a lot of board space, consumes about 5 watts and is rather expensive (comparable to the price of a single

CCD) we have decided to use only one ADC in connection with a video multiplexer. The differential video MUX is built with high speed analog switches in double-T configuration located on each CDS board and has a cross-talk attenuation of more than 100dB. The switched outputs of all CDS boards are connected to the differential input of the ADC board.

The ADC is also used for telemetry readout of all important voltages within the system. Each Bias and Clock Driver board has 16 telemetry channels which are subsequently switched to a telemetry line on the CCDbus. By means of a relay the ADC input can be toggled to either this line or the video input. Because it makes little sense to read the telemetry during CCD readout, the system performance is not degraded by this double use of the ADC. On the other hand the 16-bit resolution offers a telemetry range of +/- 32V with 1mV resolution! Some of the telemetry multiplexer inputs are connected to GND and a 10V reference voltage. By reading these inputs it is possible to automatically calibrate the gain and offset of the telemetry circuitry. This calibration is performed prior to each telemetry readout.

6.SOFTWARE

Most parts of the control software are written in the 'C' programming language under the OS-9 operating system. Only a few functions like interrupt and exception handling of the 68020 CPU are written in assembler.

6.1.Microcode Progamming

A rudimentary assembler for the ADSP1401 allows easy generation of microcode programs. The sequencer assembler written at ESO basically converts ASCII source files into binary data which is then downloaded to the sequencer memory. The ASCII code is devided into several fields reflecting the organization of the microcode RAM.

By using the 'C' preprocessor prior to the assembly phase it is possible to make symbolic definitions in the source file. All the mnemonics of the ADSP1401 command set are available in this way. Further, each CCD clock state can be defined as a symbol which is subsequently used in the microcode program. Most of the CCDs are read out in basically the same way, only the physical clock patterns differ from type to type. Symbolic definition of these clock patterns at the beginning of a source file allows the usage of the same program body for many CCDs. Thus the time to write new microcode programs for new CCD types is drastically reduced. Figure 6 shows a typical microcode program for the horizontal readout of four THX31157 devices.

6.2.Control Programs

The complete software to program the sequencer, to prepare the DMA controller, to read out the CCD and telemetry data is split into numerous small programs (OS-9 modules). These modules can be executed from the OS-9 shell by typing the name and optional parameters on a terminal.

The exchange of information between the executable OS-9 modules is realized via so-called data modules, a kind of named global variables. All relevant parameters like hardware addresses, CCD chip size, exposure type and time etc. are stored in these data modules and are available to all programs.

To simplify communication between CCD CPU and host computer a command interpreter has been written, which receives an incoming high level command through an RS-232C interface, executes then all necessary OS-9 modules and returns status and error information to the host. With a similar program it is possible to translate simple FORTH commands used to normally operate Princeton Scientific Instruments CCD controllers into corresponding OS-9 calls. Due to this special command interpreter the ESO VME CCD controller is software compatible to the PSI GEN5 camera.

7.FIRST RESULTS WITH THE MOSAIC

7.1.Voltage Setup

Most of the chips tested have been operated with the voltages listed in Table 2. To simplify wiring drastically it would seem possible to operate all mosaic CCD chips in parallel. Of course it would be necessary to pre-select matching chips prior to the assembly of the mosaic.

Vertical clocks high	11.00 V	VDD (output drain)	21.00 V
Vertical clocks low	0.00 V	VRD (reset drain)	12.50 V
Horizontal clocks high	13.00 V	VGS (output gate)	2..3V
Horizontal clocks low	0.00 V	VSS (substrate)	-2.00 V
Reset clock high	10.00 V		
Reset clock low	0.50 V		

The video outputs are loaded with 40 kOhms to analog ground.

Table 2: Typical operating voltages

7.2.Gain and Noise have been tested using the photon transfer technique described in detail in [1]. The variation of the total gain includes tolerances of the preamplifier gain, the gain of the dual slope integrator as well as the gain of the CCD. Table 3 shows the close matching of the four CCD channels without any external adjustment of overall gain. The variations of the RQE values are not much higher than the variation within a single chip! The correlated double sampling time was $2 * 40$ μsec as recommended by Thomson. Shorter integration times gave significantly more noise (about 7 e^-RMS at 20 μsecs). Longer times did not yield significant better performance.

Chip No.	Gain $[e^-/DN]$	Noise $[e^-RMS]$	RQE (@ 700 nm) [%]
1	1.65	4.1	39.0
2	1.73	4.1	41.5
3	1.75	4.3	41.5
4	1.70	4.3	41.0

Table 3: Gain, noise and sensitivity of the 4 single chips of the mosaic

7.3.Quantum Efficiency The RQE has been measured by calibrating the CCDs against NBS traceable Si-photodiodes. The light source used is a highly stable tungsten halogen lamp filtered with narrow-band interference filters. Several chips have been measured. The results shown in Table 4 have been obtained with a setup grade and four A-Grade CCDs and are very similar to the results obtained with other front illuminated Thomson, EEV and TEK CCDs. The matching of the RQE of the A-grade devices was better than +/-5% (see also Table 3).

The setup chip was coated for test purposes using ESO's fluorescent acrylic coating technique [7]. This coating has been modified for Thomson CCDs to increase adhesion because of the very smooth surface of these chips. Unfortunately, the quantum efficiency is somewhat lower than that of the original formula used for i.e. EEV or TEK CCDs and gives an RQE of roughly 13% at 340 nm. We are currently investigating the feasibility of coating a complete mosaic. Assembling a mosaic from pre-coated CCDs is difficult because the inter-CCD gaps disturb the flow of the acrylic film during deposition. On the other hand, it seems difficult to glue already coated chips together because the coating accumulates on the chip edges making perfect alignment impossible.

7.4.Charge Transfer Efficiency The CTE has been measured using the EPER (Extended Pixel Edge Response) technique [2] at different signal levels. The values in Table 5 clearly show that the chips are able to handle even very low charge levels, making them suitable for high resolution spectroscopy at low light levels. The vertical CTE of the THX31157 has been greatly improved over the CTE of the TH7882.

7.5.Dark Current The dark current has been measured by taking the charge difference between active and

Wavelength [nm]	RQE (uncoated Setup) [%]	RQE (UV-coated Setup) [%]	RQE (uncoated A-Grade) [%]
320		13.8	
340		13.4	
360		12.6	
380		14.6	0.2
400		14.0	1.5
450	12.5	14.9	12.6
500			25.9
550	34.1	35.7	33.3
600			39.5
650	40.4	40.3	37.4
700			41.1
750	39.2	38.6	35.6
800			23.4
850	21.9	19.9	18.5
900			11.0
950	7.3	5.7	5.0
1000			1.4

Table 4: Quantum Efficiency for uncoated and UV-coated chip

overscan pixels at various integration times. The results are tabulated in Table 6.

7.6.Cosmic Ray Events The cosmic ray event rate was measured using our new standard method of counting *events* independently of the number of affected pixels per event. The rate was about 1.3 events/min/cm^2; a typical value for front illuminated CCDs.

7.7.Remanence The chips were exposed through a special test pattern (white grid on dark background) to peak signal levels ranging from 100.000 e^- to 500.000 e^- with immediately following dark integrations of ten minutes. Above about 200.000 e^- the CCDs show significant remanence, a ghost image of the grid is still visible even after several hours of integration. Signal levels above about 100.000 e^- should therefor be avoided. This corresponds well with the upper limit of 110.000 e^- fixed by the ADC assuming a gain of about 1.7e^-/DN.

7.8.Mechanical Alignment Images taken with high resolution test targets indicate an alignment accuracy of about a tenth of a pixel. Optical measurements show a peak positional error of the fiducial marks relative to the template reference of 3 μm, with an RMS error of typically 1 μm or better. Although the alignment has still to be checked more carefully, there seems to be no significant alignment problem.

8.CONCLUSION

The results obtained with a fairly large number of chips (in total we have evaluated 10 A-grade CCDs) have demonstrated the excellent quality of the THX31157 CCDs. Several mosaics have been assembled with the desired precision. During the extensive tests in the laboratory the new ESO CCD controller has proven to be very stable, reliable and to have a high degree of flexibility allowing a fast optimization of clock patterns and operating voltages.

The cost of a 2x2 CCD mosaic is about 50% less than the price for a single 1024x1024 chip. The price for the additional electronics is less than 5 kDM. Buttable CCDs are now commercially available in reasonable

Signal Level	Chip No.	Horizontal CTE	Vertical CTE
70.000 e^-	5	0.999996	0.999999
	6	0.999997	0.999999
	7	0.99999	0.999998
	8	0.99999	0.999999
8.500 e^-	5	0.99996	0.999993
	6	0.99996	0.999996
	7	0.99992	0.999987
	8	0.99991	0.999998
1.300 e^-	5	0.9998	0.999989
	6	0.9998	0.999985
	7	0.9997	0.999922
	8	0.9997	0.999993
220 e^-	5	0.9994	0.99991
	6	0.9995	0.99993
	7	0.9993	0.99962
	8	0.9991	0.99994

Table 5: Charge transfer efficiency of the mosaic

Chip No.	Dark Current [$e^-/pix/hour$]
5	29
6	24
7	22
8	22

Table 6: Dark Current

quantities, which is not (yet) the case for 1k-by-1k CCDs. The same multiplexing technique necessary to operate several CCDs in parallel can also be used to read out the two or four amplifiers of large CCDs like the EEV P88000 and the Thomson THX31156.

9.FUTURE PLANS

ESO plans to use the 2x2 mosaic CCD detector at the telescope in La Silla in late 1989, most likely in direct imaging mode.It is further planned to build a mosaic of 2 CCDs arranged in long direction dedicated to spectroscopy. A 2x3 mosaic is also considered, but this would require some modifications to the current dewar electronics and connectors.

In the preliminary studies of VLT spectroscopic instruments CCD detector sizes of 150 mm in one dimension are being considered. The experience currently being gathered with the mosaics of small chips could become very useful for the future development of such instruments.

ACKNOWLEDGEMENTS

We wish to thank M. Cullum, H. Dekker and G. Huster at ESO and J.P. Dupin at the Toulouse Observatory for their contributions to the project.

FIGURE CAPTIONS

Fig. 1 An enlarged view of the buttable CCD THX 31157.

Fig. 2 The mosaic geometry. The gaps corresponds to 9 and 17 pixels in the vertical and horizontal dimensions respectively.

Fig. 3 The Mounting and Alignment Machine (MAM) built at the Observatoire de Toulouse.

Fig. 4 2x2 mosaic built with mechanical prototype CCDs mounted and aligned on a sapphire baseplate.

Fig. 5 Block diagram of the ESO Mosaic CCD camera system.

Fig. 6 Example of a microcode source file showing horizontal readout and correlated double sampling.

REFERENCES

[1] Janesick J. et al., Recent Developments in Large Area Scientific CCD Image Sensors. SPIE Vol 1071-11. 1989

[2] Janesick J. et al., Fano-noise limited CCDs. SPIE, San Diego, 1988.

[3] Janesick J. et al., Present and Future CCDs for UV and X-Ray Scientific Measurements. SPIE Proc.

[4] Gunn J.E. et al., The Palomar Observatory CCD Camera. PASP June 1987.

[5] Gunn J.E. et al., Four Shooter: A Large CCD Camera for the Hale Telescope. Optical Engineering, 26 779 (1987).

[6] D'Odorico S. et.al., The CCD Mosaic Project by ESO and CNRS/Observatoire de Toulouse, ESO Conference on Very Large Telescopes and their Instrumentation, Garching 1988, Vol.II p.1075.

[7] Cullum M., D'Odorico S., Deiries S., Reiss R., Spectroscopy to the Atmospheric Transmission Limit with a Coated GEC CCD. Astron. Astrophys. 153, L1-L3, 1985.

[8] Bauer H., Programmable Sequencer Hardware Manual. ESO 1989.

[9] Reiss R., VME CCD System Hardware Manual. ESO 1989.

[10] Jorden P., Thorne D. et. al. Laboratory and Astronomical Comparison of RCA, GEC and Thomson CCDs. SPIE Vol. 627 1986.

[11] Thomson CSF, THX31157 data sheet. 1988.

[12] Cullum M., Proceedings, Second Workshop on ESO's VLT, Venice 1986, p.331.

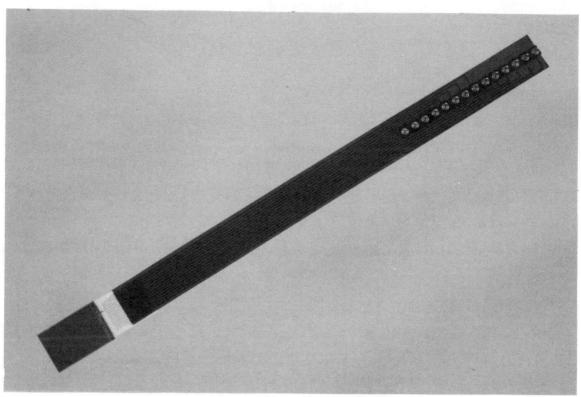

Figure 1: The THX31157 CCD.

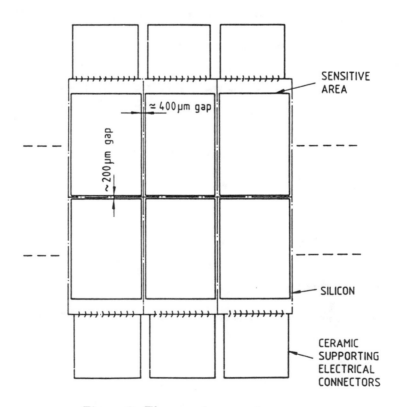

Figure 2: The mosaic geometry.

Figure 3: The Mosaic Alignment Machine (MAM).

Figure 4: 2x2 mosaic built with prototype CCDs mounted and aligned on a sapphire baseplate.

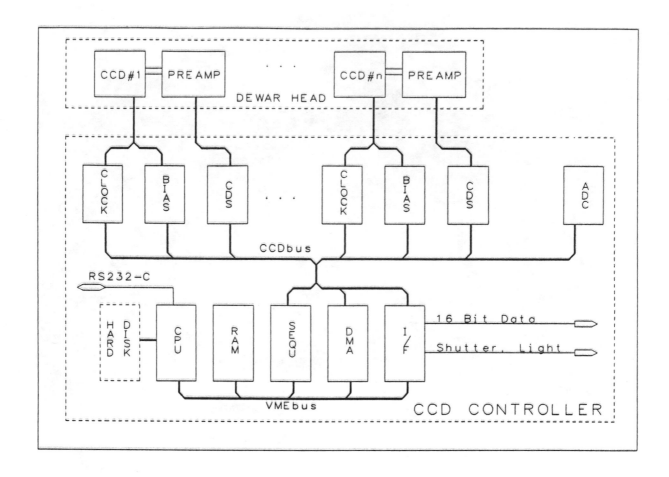

Figure 5: Block diagram of the ESO Mosaic CCD camera system.

```
#include "adsp1401defs.h"

#define                        VREST      11101110
  ⋮                              ⋮          ⋮
#define                        HREST      10001100
#define                        H1         HREST
#define                        H2         10000011
#define                        H3         H1
#define                        RESET      11111100
#define                        RSTINT     00000000
#define                        REFINT     00000001
#define                        SIGINT     00000010
#define                        CLAMP      00000100
#define                        HOLD       00000011
#define                        CONVRT0    00001011
#define                        HOLD0      00000011
                                 ⋮          ⋮
#define                        CONVRT3    00111011
#define                        HOLD3      00110011
```

Page	Instruction	Address	Delay	CDS	Horizontal	Vertical
page9	dccntr2	00	00	HOLD	H1	VREST
	rtns	00	00	HOLD	H1	VREST
	cont	00	04	HOLD	H2	VREST
	jda	09	00	HOLD	H3	VREST
page14	dccntr0	00	01	RSTINT	HREST	VREST
	dccntr0	00	01	RSTINT	HREST	VREST
	rtns	00	01	RSTINT	HREST	VREST
	cont	00	0a	RSTINT	HREST	VREST
	cont	00	0a	CLAMP	HREST	VREST
	cont	00	04	HOLD	HREST	VREST
	cont	00	64	REFINT	HREST	VREST
	pscntr2	00	05	HOLD	HREST	VREST
	jsa	09	00	HOLD	HREST	VREST
	ppcntr2	00	00	HOLD	H3	VREST
	cont	00	20	HOLD	H3	VREST
	cont	00	64	SIGINT	H3	VREST
	cont	00	24	HOLD0	H3	VREST
	cont	00	14	CONVRT0	H3	VREST
	cont	00	24	HOLD2	H3	VREST
	cont	00	14	CONVRT2	H3	VREST
	cont	00	24	HOLD1	H3	VREST
	cont	00	14	CONVRT1	H3	VREST
	cont	00	24	HOLD3	H3	VREST
	cont	00	14	CONVRT3	H3	VREST
	jda	0e	00	RSTINT	HREST	VREST

Figure 6: Example of a microcode source file showing horizontal readout and correlated double sampling.

A review of availability of IR detectors

R Wade and I S McLean

Royal Observatory Edinburgh & J.A.C. Hawaii
Blackford Hill, EH9 EHJ.   665 Komohana St. Hilo, HI 96720

ABSTRACT

The last two to three years have seen a revolution take place in Infrared Astronomy. Prior to this time virtually all observations at wavelengths longer than about 1 micron had to be made by either scanning a single detector or by using small arrays of individually wired detectors. This has been as true for spectroscopic instruments as it has for photometric and mapping instruments. The revolution which has taken place has been the availability to astronomers of true imaging detector arrays for use at infrared wavelengths.

The main impact of these devices so far has been at the shorter wavelengths using ground based telescopes. In future years this impact will be extended to longer wavelengths and to space based observations.

A review of currently available devices and technologies will be presented. Prospects for the near- and mid-term future will be outlined and some desired characteristics for devices will be given.

1. INTRODUCTION

Historically visible astronomy has enjoyed a number of advantages over the new astronomies of infrared, radio, x-ray etc. Principal among these is the ability of the human eye to form images at visible wavelengths which has triggered a deep seated interest in the nature of the heavens and given us an opportunity to study the morphology of a range of objects using just simple telescopes. The invention of photographic emulsions allowed the further development and blossoming of the subject. More recently the ability of the most well developed semi-conductor material, silicon to detect visible light, has allowed very sensitive, low light level imaging devices to be developed for both imaging and spectroscopic applications.

Infrared is typical among the new astronomies in that it has enjoyed none of these advantages. Thus our view of the infrared sky has had to be painstakingly built up by raster scanning either single elements or small numbers of detectors. In spectroscopy the rich stellar spectra, so important in visible astronomy have not been available. Infrared spectroscopists have had to content themselves with individual line measurements or FTS spectra of the brightest objects. Not only have we lacked the ability to 'see' in the infrared or indeed to take true infrared photographs but as a final irony the semi-conductors which respond to infrared radiation have been relatively underdeveloped compared with silicon.

Despite these disadvantages the wealth of astrophysical information available at infrared wavelengths has led astronomers to persevere with time-consuming single detector observations and to push for the technical advances necessary to provide infrared imaging devices. Much of this technical development in the end has its roots in military technology. However, the success of infrared astronomy in recent years is now leading to the development of devices specifically tailored for ground-based as well as low-background space applications.

Examples of a number of recent developments along with some astronomical results are described elsewhere in these proceedings.

In this paper we review the range of currently available detector arrays and look forward to some of the devices predicted to be available in the next couple of years. Finally we look at some of the desired characteristics for future arrays.

2. CURRENTLY AVAILABLE ARRAYS

In a field which is developing so rapidly any review such as this is likely to be somewhat dated even by the time these proceedings appear. Evidence of this rapid development was apparent at the recent Infrared Detector Workshop held at NASA Ames Research Centre[1] in February 1989. Comparison with the presentations at the Hilo Conference on Infrared Astronomy with Arrays[2] held just two years earlier demonstrated the significant progress over this relatively short time. In order to give as up-to-date as possible a view of the current status of infrared detector arrays, most of the information presented in this section is derived from the Ames Workshop, with some supplementary information from the proceedings of the Hilo Conference.

A summary of the characteristics of a range of currently available arrays as well as some in an advanced stage of development is given in Table 1. A number of developments based on some of the devices in this table are worth highlighting.

As part of the NICMOS II detector development at Rockwell, 256x256 HgCdTe SWIR arrays of comparable performance to the 128x128 devices are likely to be developed over the next couple of years.

SBRC are likely to build on the success of the 58x62 InSb ground based arrays and the Pt:Si Schottky Barrier 256x256 multiplexer by developing a 256x256 InSb array for ground based astronomy. The development of the HgCdTe MWIR detector for 1-4.8μm at Rockwell should produce real competition for the InSb devices.

TABLE 1

Manufacturer	Rockwell	Honeywell	SBRC	SBRC	SAT France	Hughes	Rockwell	SBRC	LETI-LIR France	SBRC	Rockwell
Material	HgCdTe	HgCdTe	InSb	InSb	InSb CID	Pt:Si Schottky Barrier	HgCdTe	Si:Ga	Si:Ga	Si:Sb	Si:As Si-BIBIB
Developed for	HST NICMOS	HST HIMS	Ground Based	SIRTF IRAC	ISO ISOGAM	-	-	SIRTF IRAC ****	ISO ISOCAM	SIRTF IRAC	
Wavelength range	1-2.5μm	1-2.5μm	1-5μm	1-5μm	2.5-5μm	1-2.5μm	1-4.8μm	5-14μm	5-17μm	15-30μm	5-24%
Number of elements	128x128	128x128	58x62	58x62	32x32	256x256	256x256	58x62	32x32	58x62	10-50
Pixel size	50μm		75μm	75μm	100μm	30μm		75μm	100μm	75μm	135μm
Full well capacity	3×10^5e		10^6e	10^6e	$2-4\times10^6$e	4×10^5e	2.5×10^7e	7×10^5e	1.2×10^6e	$>10^5$e	2×10^6e
Read noise	<50e	100e	200-400e	168e	≤1300e	40e	490e	~50e	<500e	100e	80e
Dark current	4-12e/s, 1.6e/s	*	50-100e/s	2.4e/s		<10e/s		78e/s		10e/s	80e/s
Operating temperature	77K, 60K		35K	8K	4K	60K		6K	4K	8K	4.2K
Quantum efficiency	~50%	**		45%	33% ***	a few %	mean 60%	30%		1?%	20%

Notes for Table 1

*Currently this is limited by self luminessence to >200e/s the predicted figure is more like 10e/s.

**The relative quantum efficiency at 1μm falls to 20% of its value at 2μm.

***This figure includes read efficiency as well as quantum efficiency.

****A device of this type has also been used in a ground based camera by Dan Gezari of Goddard.

The figures quoted are mainly those reported by SBRC however.

Finally the development in France of the arrays for the ISOCAM hold out the hope of a future European source of arrays for ground based astronomers. Indeed French astronomers are already gaining experience with cameras based on the arrays developed for the ISO project.

3. DESIRED CHARACTERISTICS FOR FUTURE ARRAYS

3.1 General considerations

A clear aim for anyone designing an infrared instrument for a telescope, be it ground-based, airborne or space-based must be to fill the available unvignetted field of the instrument with as many seeing or diffraction limited pixels as possible. (Wherever possible each of these pixels should be background limited. This will be discussed further in section 3). The significance of the above statement is that it will determine the wavelength range over which true solid state imaging devices as opposed to small arrays of individual elements will be required. The reasoning behind this is as follows. In the near IR (1-5μm) observations will generally be made using ground-based optical/IR telescopes. The available unvignetted field for these instruments will be measured in degrees so that even assuming moderate seeing of an arcsecond or so, it is clear that the largest possible format of solid state array will be required. The same statement will generally be true in the mid-IR region (5-30μm) although for space-based missions in this region (e.g. ISO, SIRTF) arrays of 32 or 64 elements square will be sufficient to cover the available focal plane with diffraction limited pixels. As we move into the Far IR (30-200μm) observations will be limited for the near-term future at least to small balloon, airplane or space telescopes. The diffraction effects in these instruments will mean that small arrays of the order of 10x10 pixels at most will be sufficient. This region will be catered for by current developments in helium cooled photoconductors of both stressed and unstressed, suitably doped silicon.

Finally in the sub-mm region although ground-based dishes of 10-30m diameter will be employed it is again likely that due to diffraction small arrays of 10x10 pixels will be sufficient. This region will be covered by very low temperature (~100mK) bolometers.

In summary then it will be a design goal for arrays for ground based facilities working in the 1-30μm range to have as large as possible formats, while wavelengths longer than this will be covered by small arrays of individual photoconductors or bolometers.

For space applications it is likely that the current developments for ISO and SIRTF will yield devices of sufficient size and sensitivity that their performance will be dominated by the effects of cosmic background, source confusion and energetic particle impacts. A significant development in the case of particle impacts is the development of radiation hard devices (e.g. Blocked Impurity Band or BIB detectors). These detectors may have a major impact on the SIRTF mission. They come too late to be of benefit to ISO however. As far as ground based application is concerned it is likely that their availability, particularly for non-US groups, will be restricted at least for the immediate future.

The requirements for the second generation HST instrument will be similar to those for ground based spectroscopy and will be dealt with below.

It is in the application of arrays to ground based observations that major advances could be made in the next few years. For the purpose of looking at the desired characteristics for these future arrays it is possible to divide the $1-30\mu m$ region into two sections each with a completely different design requirement. In the SWIR region ($1-2.5\mu m$) the requirement will be for quieter arrays with very low dark currents. For the longer wavelengths ($2.5-30\mu m$) where thermal background dominates the requirement will be for arrays with larger well capacities, faster readout and/or multiple outputs. The requirements for these two regions will be considered separately below.

3.2 Requirements for SWIR arrays

The design goal for arrays in the SWIR region will be to be able to achieve background limited operation over the wavelength range in both imaging and moderate to high resolution spectroscopic applications ($\lambda/\Delta\lambda \sim 10^3$). In order to achieve this goal we require two things. First, that the read noise is low enough that after a reasonably practical on-chip integration time the noise on the accumulated background signal is greater than the read noise. For this to be the case the well capacity needs to be large enough to allow these long integrations but this is generally not a problem. The second requirement is that the dark current of the device is much less than the background flux. At the short wavelength end of the region this flux can be very small, particularly for spectroscopic application.

The design goals in terms of read noise and dark current are summarised in Table 2 for both imaging ($\lambda/\Delta\lambda \sim 5$) and spectroscopy ($\lambda/\Delta\lambda \sim 10^3$) at both 1 and 2 microns.

TABLE 2

Desired Characteristics for Background Limited operation of SWIR detector arrays

	Imaging		Spectroscopy	
	$1\mu m$	$2\mu m$	$1\mu m$	$2\mu m$
Read Noise (electrons)	<500		50	100
Dark current (electrons/sec)	800	5000	4	25

Comparison of Tables 1 and 2 indicates that present devices should be capable of background limited operation over the whole of the SWIR region for imaging application, but that while they are close for spectroscopy they still have some way to go particularly for the highest resolutions at short wavelengths.

3.3 Requirements for high background arrays

In contrast to the SWIR region, the design constraints for systems operating in the range $2.5-30\mu m$ are dominated by the very high photon fluxes at these wavelengths. To illustrate the problem consider the example of a typical imaging application at $10\mu m$. For a pixel field of view of 0.5 arc seconds a resolution $\lambda/\Delta\lambda$ of 5 and emissivity of 10% the detection rate of photons will be of the order of 10^9ph/sec. Assuming a well depth of 10^6 electrons this implies a saturation time for these wells of just a millisecond. This is just too fast for the current generation of devices which are therefore generally used in a spectroscopic mode of some kind to reduce the background.

In principle there are three possible solutions to this problem:

- larger well capacity
- faster drive and readout electronics
- multiple output channels

One or more of these will have to be developed if arrays working at the longer wavelengths particularly in the $8-14\mu m$ region are to have a major impact in a broad band imaging mode.

Although a possible solution comes in the form of the blocked impurity devices under development at both Rockwell and Hughes, as stated earlier, their availability is likely to be limited particularly to the non-US community.

4. CONCLUSIONS

Array detectors for infrared astronomy have come a long way in the last few years and offer the real prospect of scientific progress in a number of areas of astrophysics. We would of course like to have larger format arrays and this must be a design goal at all wavelengths between 1 and $30\mu m$. Perhaps more important is the goal of producing arrays which can be used in a broad band imaging mode in high background ground based applications.

Finally there is a requirement for both space based imaging and ground based spectroscopy in the SWIR region to have devices with lower read noise and dark current than are presently available.

5. REFERENCES

1. Proc. 3rd Ames Detector Workshop (February 1989)
2. Infrared Astronomy with Arrays (Proc. of the Hilo Detector Workshop, University of Hawaii) 1987.

Si:Ga DVR arrays optimized for 10 μm astronomical observations from ground

Pierre-Olivier Lagage(1), François Sibille(2), Luc Audaire(3),
René Jouan(1), Christian Lucas(3), André Tarrius(1)

(1) Service d'Astrophysique, CEN Saclay, F-91191 Gif-sur-Yvette;
(2) Observatoire de Lyon, F-69230 Saint-Genis Laval;
(3) LETI/LIR, CEN Grenoble, F-38041 Grenoble

ABSTRACT

Si:Ga DVR detector arrays specially designed for broad-band observations in the 10 μm atmospheric window, are currently developed by the LETI/LIR. The originality of these detectors is a large capacitance able to store the huge number of electrons generated by the 10 μm background photons. A prototype array with 32*32 pixels has already been delivered to the Service d'Astrophysique, at Saclay. A 64*64 array with a full well capacity of more than 2.10^7 electrons will be delivered in the middle of this year. This paper brings up the results of the first set of tests on the 32*32 prototype.

1. INTRODUCTION

1.1. General Context

An increasing part of Astrophysics deals with the infrared radiation of the Universe. The reasons for such an interest are numerous, but one can mention:
i) the large data-base left by the satellite IRAS, which has made, in 1983, an all sky survey in 4 bands centered at 12, 25, 60 and 100 μm[1];
ii) the development of new instruments for ground-based telescopes, such as cameras[2];
iii) the perspectives of new satellites dedicated to infrared observations: ISO, to be launched in 1993[3], and latter on SIRTF.

The observations from satellites have the advantage of covering the whole spectral range, while ground-based observations are limited to a few atmospheric windows. Even in the filters corresponding to these atmospheric windows and particularly for the L, M, N, Q bands (respectively centered at 3.6, 4.8, 10 and 20 μm), a higher sensitivity can be achieved from space. Nevertheless, for the sake of efficiency, all the observations that can be done from ground, has to be done from ground. Furthermore, as the telescopes to be embarked on satellites are much smaller than those existing on ground, the high angular resolution obtained from ground cannot be achieved in space.

These last years, ground-based observations have undergone a real revolution, thanks to the possibility of making images of the sky. Technological developments in the field of detector arrays have been the driving force of this revolution. To some extend, these developments can be compared to those which have led to the CCD's for the visible. But, one can still foresee more profound consequences in the infrared where, prior to the detector arrays, it was very difficult and lengthy to make sky images, while the photographic plate was already available for the visible.

Up to now, most of the detector developments dedicated to Astronomy have been oriented towards the use of these detectors in space environment. By chance, at short wavelength (2-5 μm), the detectors developed for space can be used in ground-based cameras; for instance, both the short wavelength channel of the ISO camera (ISOCAM) and the ground-based camera CIRCUS are equipped with quite similar InSb CID arrays[4]. Unfortunately, at 10 μm, the situation is much less favorable.

1.2. Why do we need optimized detectors for ground-based observations?

We are surrounded by objects at a temperature of 300 K. The emission of a black-body at such a temperature peaks around 10 μm. That is why one can expect a high photon background at this wavelength. One could imagine cooling the telescopes, but it would not help much, because we would still be left with the background photons from the atmosphere itself. Even in the case of such a good site as Mauna Kea at about 4.2 km elevation, the atmospheric background still represents about 1/4 of the telescope background[5]. To be more quantitative, let us consider a telescope of diameter D, with warm optics of emissivity ε; the number of electrons generated per pixel, during a time t_i, is:

$$n_b(\lambda,T) = \varepsilon \; \frac{B(\lambda,T)}{(hc/\lambda)} \; \frac{\lambda}{R} \; \frac{\pi}{4} \; D^2 \; \Theta_{fov}^2 \; T_{opt} \; f_f \; \eta \; G \; t_i, \qquad (1)$$

where $B(\lambda,T)/(hc/\lambda)$ is the number of photons emitted per steradian, per cubic centimeter and per second by a black-body of temperature T; Θ_{fov} is the pixel field of view, R the filter spectral resolution and T_{opt} the transmission of the optics; the detector parameters which enter in the calculation are the filling factor f_f, the quantum efficiency η, and the photoconductive gain G.

We have seen that the specificity of ground observations was their large spatial resolution. Then, we will operate most of time with Θ_{fov} close to λ/D, the diameter of the diffraction figure of the telescope, which we may express by $\Theta_{fov} = Coef.\lambda/D$, with Coef of the order of unity. This is also the best sensitivity versus spatial resolution trade off, since it satisfies the adapted filtering condition. Formula (1) can now be written:

$$n_b(10\ \mu m) = 2\ 10^9 \; Coef^2 \; \frac{\varepsilon}{0.2} \; \frac{2}{R} \; \frac{f_f}{0.8} \; \frac{G\eta}{0.3} \; \frac{T_{opt}}{0.5} \; t_i. \qquad (2)$$

In satellites, it is worthwhile to cool the telescope because of the absence of atmosphere. Just the photon background due to the zodiacal light remains, but, its intensity is very low. A maximum of 10^4 electrons per second will reach the pixels of ISOCAM. Because of the particle radiation, the integration time will be limited to a few tens of seconds; then, during a typical integration time, the total number of electrons due to the background is less than about 10^5 electrons. The associated photon noise is very low, so that the noise requirements on these detectors are quite severe. In order to reach this goal, the trend is to reduce at the limit the integration capacitance so that only a stray capacitance less than 0.1 pF is left. This minimizes some sources of noise, like the KTC noise, but also the available electron storage capacity, which is typically of the order of 10^6 electrons.

With background conditions typical of ground-based environment, such a capacitance would be saturated in 0.5 ms. In order to read an array of 64*64 pixels at this rate, the speed of the electronics (including sampling, analog-digital conversion, coaddition of images in order to reduce the flow of data) should be 0.1 μs per pixel. This is much too high. Of course, it is possible to observe only with narrow band filters and to spread the diffraction beam on several pixels (for example[6,7]), but the price to pay is an important lost in sensitivity. A more attractive solution consists in having detectors with a larger full well capacity[8].

2. DEVICE GENERAL PRESENTATION

The project ISOCAM[9] has prompted the development in France of infrared arrays. Making of the detector arrays for the long wavelength channel (5-17 μm) has been committed to the LETI/LIR. We have profited from this development so that the detectors optimized for ground-based observations are quite similar to those for ISOCAM[10], except their full well capacity (10 times larger) and, in a second step, their complexity (64*64 instead of 32*32).

2.1. Device description

The device is constituted of an array of 32*32 gallium doped silicon photoconductors hybridized by indium bumps to a Direct Voltage Readout (DVR), achieved on silicon (see Figure 1). The pixel size is 100*100 μm^2. The gallium doped silicon photoconductors, with a cutoff at 17 μm, are well suited for the wavelength range involved here (8-14 μm). These photoconductors have to work at a temperature lower than 20 K in order to limit the dark current. The DVR silicon circuit permits to operate at such a temperature. The detector has 32 outputs in order to avoid possible noise introduced by column multiplexing.

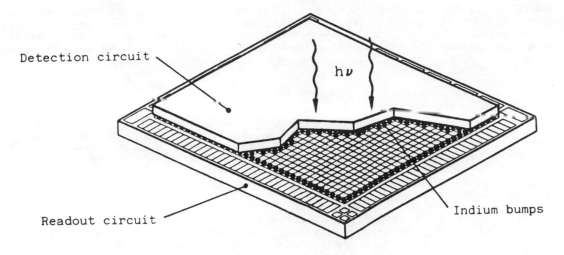

Figure 1: Device structure

2.2. Elementary point description

The electrical equivalent diagram of the elementary point is sketched on Figure 2 as well as the phase sequence. The photoconductor is connected to the input of a follower MOS transistor by an indium bump. After a reset to V_r by means of transistor T_r, the input voltage $V_e(t)$ is increasing towards V_{pc} because of the finite resistance R_{pc} generated by the photon flux. The output signal $V_s(t)$ is sampled at the beginning and at the end of the integration period by addressing transistor T_a. $\Delta V_s = V_s(t_1) - V_s(t_2)$ is representation of of the incident photon flux.

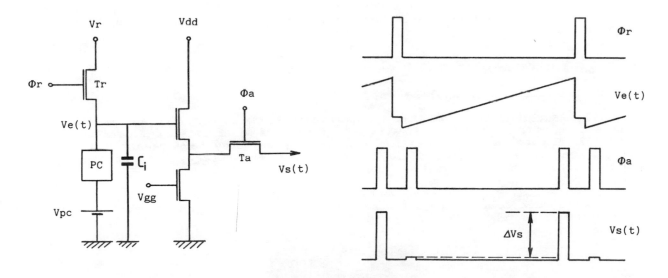

Figure 2: elementary point electrical diagram and operation

3. TESTING FACILITY

The tests on these detectors are important to several extent. First, one must well optimize the operating parameters of the detectors before using them on a telescope. This necessity is particularly true in our case, as the detectors have not been tested in ground conditions (high photon flux, high speed...). Furthermore, the tests of the 32*32 arrays have been undertaken with the possibility of feedback on the design of the 64*64 arrays. At last, we have figured out that the tests on the stability of the detectors were important for optimizing the observation techniques. Taking into account these various reasons, an important effort has been devoted into setting up a testing facility.

3.1. Cryostat

The initial tests have been done in an Infrared Laboratory cryostat with very simple mechanics: a diaphragm, a filter and the detector. By now, we have duplicated the long wavelength channel of the INSU camera, named C10μ and destined to the CFHT (Canadian France Hawaii Telescope). This camera has two wheels one with 10 filters and 2 CVF, the other one with 2 lenses in order to change the pixel field of view (from 0.5 to 0.8 arcsecond).

3.2. Electronics

The main characteristics of the electronics is its relatively high speed: 1.3 μs per pixel (for the whole chain). The difference ΔV_s is performed analogically in order to gain in rapidity. For the same reason, we use a 12 bits ADC. This may seem a bit too short for the full well capacity we have. But, an electronic offset can be used to remove up to 75% of the background. In these conditions, we can gain 1 or 2 bits for the useful signal, which is enough. Note also that the noise of this electronics is sufficiently low for our purpose.

3.3. Data acquisition system

The data are stored in CAMAC fast memories (type EC599), controlled by an EC601 controller. This controller and another home made CAMAC module permit to coadd or cosubstact images. Then the data are, at least for the moment, treated by an HP1000 to be replaced soon by a more up to date computer.

4. PERFORMANCES

The first task was to search for the optimized applied biases to put on the device. The following biases were found to be the best in our working conditions:

V_{dd} = 5.5 Volts; V_r = 2.5 Volts; V_{gg} = 1.5 Volts;
V_{pc} = 25 Volts; Φ_r = 0 to 8 Volts; Φ_a = 0 to 8 Volts.

4.1. Behaviour at high speed

4.1.1. Requirements. We have to operate these detectors with an image frame rate time of 1 ms for a 32*32 array; that means a pixel rate of 1 μs. Although the 32 outputs were designed for another purpose, they have been found to be very useful, as the time scale for addressing the detector is not the time scale for one pixel but 32 times longer.

4.1.2 Results. On Fig. 3, we can see the analog signal of one pixel. The detectors work well at the speed required; we can address and reset it in less than the 32 μs required.

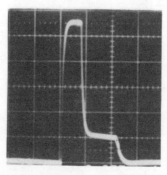

Figure 3: time scale for addressing and resetting a pixel (10 μs per division).

4.2. Storage capacity.

4.2.1. Requirements.
Given the flux of photons received by a detector located at the focus of a 3.6 m telescope with a field of view at the diffraction limit and a pixel readout time of 2 μs, we need a storage capacity of 6 10^6 electrons for a 32*32 array and 4 times more for a 64*64 arrays. Note that if we consider larger telescopes, still used at the diffraction limit, the capacity required remains the same but, of course, the total field of view decreases.

4.2.2. Results.
For the 32*32 array, the manufacturer has put a capacitance of about 0.5 pF on 30*32 pixels and 1 pF on the remaining 2*32 pixels, in order to make tests for the follow up 64*64 arrays. The detector has also been optimized in order to have the maximum output signal, which we have measured to be of 3 Volts. Given the gain of the source follower stage (about 0.6), we have an input storage capacity of respectively 1.5 10^7 and 3 10^7 for the 0.5 pF and the 1 pF; exactly what we wished.

4.3. Quantum efficiency

4.3.1. Requirements.
Obviously, we would like the highest quantum efficiency possible, as the signal to photon noise ratio is proportional to $\eta^{1/2}$.

4.3.2. Results.
Actually, we have direct access only to the quantum efficiency times photoconductive gain product. The measured value of $G\eta$ is around 0.3 for a photoconductor bias of 20 Volts. However, measurements carried on by the LETI/LIR give a value of η of the order of 25%, which means G around 1. This value is expected to be improved a bit by laying down optical coatings on the illuminated face of the photoconductor and by using photoconductors with higher doping level. But, here, a trade off has to be found between the increase of η and the parallel increase in breakdown phenomena.

The variation of the responsivity with wavelength is shown on Figure 4. As can be seen, the detector can still be used at 3 μm without too much lost in quantum efficiency.

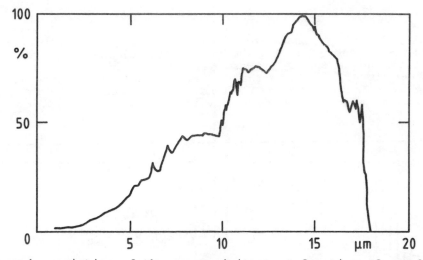

Figure 4: variation of the responsivity as a function of wavelength

4.4. Homogeneity.

4.4.1. Requirements.
As most of the signal is due to the background, we have an electronic offset which is able to remove 75% of the signal, in order to code the useful signal on several additional bits. But to do this operation the homogeneity of the array must be good. If it is 50% peak to peak, we gain 1 bit; for 25%, we can gain 2 bits.

4.4.2. Results.
Responsivity chart of the detector is shown on Figure 5; we have just eliminated the edges of the array. As can be seen the homogeneity is better than 50 %; most of the pixel responsivities differ from less than 25%. The pixels outside this range originate essentially from one column which responds much less than the others.

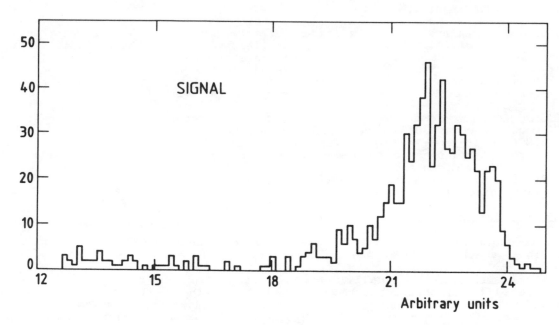

Figure 5: Histogram of responsivity

4.5. Noise

4.5.1. Requirements. This is very simple, we want to be limited by the photon noise. By changing the integration time we can always operate near the saturation of the well capacity. That means that for a storage capacity of 2 10^7, we want a detector with a noise lower than:

$$(4 \ G \ 10^7)^{1/2} = 6000 \ G^{1/2} \text{ electrons} \tag{3}$$

4.5.2. Results. At low signal level, the noise is quite reasonable (less than the photon noise expected at high level of signal) and we have not tried to reach the lowest noise possible. Unfortunately, an unexpected increase of the noise with the level of the signal makes the detector noise exceeding the photon noise by a factor evaluated around 2-3 at high signal. This increase is not due to some pixels which become noisy as can be seen on Fig. 6.

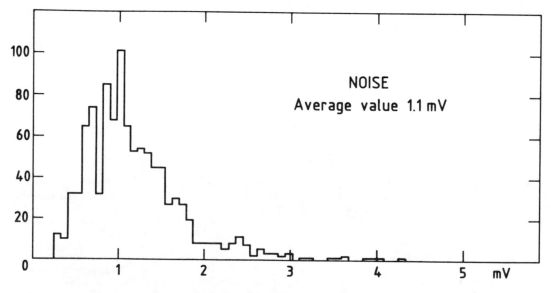

Figure 6: noise histogram

4.6. Temporal stability

4.6.1. Requirements.
The stability of the detector is important for determining the way of observing. The minimum that we impose is that the detector has to be stable during two chopping periods (typically 100 ms). But if the stability appears to be excellent over longer periods, it can be envisaged to avoid chopping.

4.6.2. Results.
For the moment, we have just tested that the detector was stable on the time scale of chopping. We are now investigating the stability over longer periods.

5. CONCLUSIONS AND PERSPECTIVES

The results on the 32*32 prototype give satisfaction in many respects (speed, storage capacity, homogeneity...). One point is not yet completely satisfactory: the noise at high signal. But, still some ways of operating the detector have to be explored. We also hope that the 64*64 array, to be delivered in the middle of this year, will be better than the prototype, as the new conception has taken into account the results of the tests on the first one.

The 32*32 array has now been integrated in a camera built for INSU by Observatoire de LYON and Service d'Astrophysique at SACLAY. Technological tests of this camera at Observatoire de Haute Provence (OHP) have been successful; we have been able to observe in the N band without being saturated. The next step is to test the performances of the camera in a very good site like Mauna Kea in Hawaii.

This camera will enrich the number of 10 μm cameras, which for the moment are not numerous, in contrast with the abundance of short wavelength cameras. Of course, the observations at 10 μm are difficult, but the performances that can theoretically be achieved are quite good (for point sources, better than IRAS) and it will be a good way to prepare the future observations with ISO.

5. ACKNOWLEDGEMENTS

It is a real pleasure to thanks Pierre Mestreau who has developed the electronics of the camera, Yvon Rio who has developed the acquisition system of the testing facility and Françoise Gaulier who has made part of the soft to treat the data.

6. REFERENCES

1. Neugebauer G. et al., Astrophys. J., 278, L1-L6 (1984).
2. Proceedings of the Workshop "Ground-based Astronomical Observations with Infrared Array Detectors", University of Hawaii at Hilo, 24-26 March 1987, C.G. Wynn-Williams and E.E. Becklin editors (1987)
3. M. Kessler, Salamanca workshop, in press (1989)
4. D. Tiphene at al., Ref. (2), p. 237 (1987)
5. W.A. Traub and M.T. Stier Applied Optics, Vol. 15, N° 2, p.364 (1976)
6. D. Gesari, Proc. 3rd Ames Detector Workshop, in press (1989)
7. J.F. Arens et al., Aplied Optics, Vol 26, N° 18, p. 3846 (1987)
8. P.O. Lagage et al., Ref. (2), p.87 (1987)
9. C. Cesarsky et al., these proceedings
10. P. Agnese et al., SPIE/SPES Symposium on Electronic Imaging, 15-20 Jan. 1989, Los Angeles, in press (1989)

Recent results from the UKIRT infrared camera, IRCAM

Ian S. McLean and Richard Wade

Joint Astronomy Centre, Hawaii and Royal Observatory, Edinburgh

ABSTRACT

The cryogenic infrared camera, IRCAM, has been operating routinely on the 3.8m UK Infrared Telescope on Mauna Kea, Hawaii for over two years. The camera, which uses a 62 x 58 element Indium Antimonide array from Santa Barbara Research Center, was designed and built at the Royal Observatory, Edinburgh which operates UKIRT on behalf of the UK Science and Engineering Research Council.

The system is capable of read noises of about 450 electrons rms and dark currents of about 100 electrons per second. IRCAM achieves background-limited performance throughout the 1 - 5 micron region for all broad-band imaging applications and even for narrow passbands (1% of the wavelength) for wavelengths longer than 2 microns. Performance characteristics including linearity and spatially non-uniform response are discussed.

Over the past two years at least 60% of the available time on UKIRT has been allocated for IRCAM observations. Examples are given of recent results which illustrate the power of IR imaging in astrophysics.

1. INTRODUCTION

A near infrared imaging system called IRCAM has been in use at the 3.8m United Kingdom Infrared Telescope since September 1986, and a second camera was introduced toward the end of 1988. Both of these cryogenic imaging systems are "facility" or "common-user" instruments. In competitive scientific proposals, IRCAM has been requested as the instrument of choice for 60 - 70% of the available telescope time, and is virtually always available as a backup for other instruments. Both cameras use the 62 x 58 pixel Indium Antimonide (InSb) Direct Readout (DRO) array manufactured by Santa Barbara Research Center (SBRC). Several different detectors have been evaluated over the past two years in a wide range of ground-based astronomical applications, and a considerable amount of observational experience has been gained.

Naturally, the advent of near infrared imaging systems has led to what might be termed an explosion in "infrared picture-taking"! The ease with which seeing-limited images of a wide range of objects - often invisible at optical wavelengths - could be obtained has led to a huge increase in morphological studies, surveys and studies in which much new insight is gained even if the photometric accuracy is limited to 10-15%. Gradually, that situation is changing to include precise astronomical photometry as more experience is gained on how to calibrate infrared array data.

In this paper we describe some of the properties of the 62 x 58 InSb detector which influence astronomical performance, describe some of the observational techniques and illustrate the progress in ground-based IR astronomy with recent results.

2. THE CAMERA SYSTEM

IRCAM is described in detail elsewhere[1,2,3] so only a brief summary of its major characteristics are given here.

Optically, IRCAM employs un-cooled gold-coated mirrors to collimate the f/36 beam (at 1.53 arcsecs/mm) from the telescope before it passes through the calcium fluoride window of a vacuum chamber within which is housed the cryogenic camera assembly; the low temperatures are achieved by attaching the vacuum chamber to a large LHe/LN2 dewar. Re-imaging is achieved by one of three cold (77 K) lenses of AR-coated zinc selenide, selected prior to cool-down, which transfer the telescope focal plane image onto the detector array. Filters are placed in the collimated beam near the position of the Lyot-stop (an image of the entrance pupil). A piezoelectrically scanned Fabry-Perot etalon, manufactured by Queensgate Instruments, can be placed in the collimated beam immediately outside the dewar window to give an imaging mode with spectral resolving powers in excess of 3500. There is also an infrared polarimeter option, a "grism" mode providing about 1% spectral resolution across the K-band, and a coronagraph mode - developed by Ben Zuckerman at UCLA - has also been used. The instrument is a side-looking construction fed by a 45-degree inclined dichroic mirror near the UKIRT f/36 focus, and is one of a cluster of four semi-permanently mounted instruments.

At present, three image scales are available with IRCAM namely, 0.63, 1.25 and 2.5"/pixel, and a good choice of broad and narrow band filters are contained in IRCAM's two 10-position filter wheels. In addition to the standard JHKL filters there are 1% bandwidth filters for the Brackett alpha and Brackett gamma lines of hydrogen, the S(1) v=1-0 vibrational transition of molecular hydrogen, CO bands at 2.30 microns, ice band at 3.08 microns and the emission feature at 3.28 microns associated with very small grains.

IRCAM is controlled from a console with a simple set of command procedures which prompt the user for required input. All high-level software is written in FORTRAN, and a full suite of image processing software is available on-line. Instrument status is shown on a monitor at all items and images can be displayed immediately on a high resolution color image display screen with hardcopy facilities. Complex data reduction, such as median filtering of sky flat-fields, can be carried out while integrations are in progress, there is an on-line "magnitude" program using mean zeropoints, and there are many "procedures" which can be called to execute a repetitive or tedious sequence. Sky conditions (mean level and noise) can be monitored with selectable pixels on the array and displayed on the status monitor.

3. DETECTOR CHARACTERISTICS AND PERFORMANCE

The detector itself has been described in detail elsewhere[4][5]. Briefly, the detector is a "hybrid" formed from an array of reverse-biased InSb photodiodes bonded by indium "bump" interconnects to an array of silicon MOSFET devices thereby associating a Source Follower amplifier to each detector. The silicon Read Out Integrated Circuit (ROIC) is called the CRC-228 Direct Read Out or "DRO" and was developed by the Hughes Micro-Electronics Center in Carlsbad, California. Each source follower MOSFET - or "unit cell" - can be (randomly) accessed using an on-chip multiplexing scheme. Hence the term Direct Read Out. Photocharge is accumulated on the combined capacitance (C) of the junction of the reverse-biased diode (0.65 picofarads in the latest devices), the gate of the source follower FET and the indium bump contact (about 0.1 pF together). The potential on this storage capacitance can be reset through an FET switch to a certain "reset" level although in practice the actual level or "pedestal" after reset is uncertain - the so-called "kTC noise". Odd and even numbered pixels are read out separately via two output amplifiers. Saturation (or full-well condition) of the device corresponds to a fully de-biased detector; the detector is still light sensitive and does not bleed or bloom but integration ceases.

In IRCAM, the 62 x 58 InSb detector is typically operated at a temperature of about 35 Kelvin to minimise any loss of quantum efficiency or DRO performance, while achieving acceptably low dark currents over most of the array. Operating parameters are given in Table 1.

Table 1. Operating Conditions for SBRC 62 x 58 Arrays in IRCAM

Parameter	Value
Detector Bias	-250 mV
Detector Temperature	35 K
Gate Voltage (typical)	-1.5 V
System Gain	30 e/ADU
kTC noise	~120 e
Readout Rate (normal)	130 ms/frame

A summary of the characteristics of four of our detectors is given in Table 2.

Table 2. Performance figures for SBRC 62 x 58 InSb Arrays

Parameter	FPA061	FPA118	FPA175	FPA180
QE	all in range 50-70% over 1-5 microns			
Readout Noise	450 e	500 e	480 e	400 e
Dark Current	150 e/s	120 e/s	105 e/s	60 e/s
Full Well	all about 1 x 10E6 e			
Bad pixels	112(3%)	25(0.7%)	15(0.4%)	75(2%)

For FPA118 and earlier devices, an anti-reflection coating with a peak near 3 microns was used on the InSb; later devices have a coating which peaks between 1.6 and 2.0 microns.

Detectors are normally baked in a vacuum oven before installation into the camera and every effort is made to avoid subsequent contamination with water vapour. If this is not done then an unstable, "ring-like" region of high "dark" current will be observed spreading inwards from the edge of the array. A gate voltage is derived which minimises "dark" current over most of the array; we have generally found that in our cryostats this voltage settles out about (2.0 +/- 0.5) Volts more negative than that recommended in the SBRC data sheet. The reset drain voltage (Vrd) must be reduced to a minimum (about 1.5 V) to eliminate light emission effects and extreme care must be taken to protect the device from static build-up.

4.   CAMERA PERFORMANCE

The camera, or more precisely, the system performance - including the telescope - is generally background-limited. The system efficiency, that is the product of QE and total transmission of all optics, is about 20% and extraneous background entering the dewar is controlled and constrained as much as possible by a series of baffles and cold-stops, and by careful mechanical design. Observed backgrounds are reasonably consistent with detailed models[6] and yield typically 10,000 e/s/pixel in the 0.6 "/pixel mode in the K band. However, in the Fabry-Perot imaging spectroscopy mode the etalons are external to the cryostat, i.e. at dome temperature, and consequently the background is markedly greater than expected for the very narrow passband.

For a readout noise of 500 electrons rms the accumulated photocharge must exceed 250,000 electrons before the system begins to become background-limited. This is equivalent to about 25% of full well capacity. Exposure times "on-chip" are optimised to avoid detector saturation yet give background-limited operation by filling the wells to about 75% full; values range from 50 ms at the longest wavelengths to ten minutes or more with narrow bands at the shorter wavelengths.

4.1.   Calibrations

Several corrections to "raw" images are required including dark current (+ bias level) subtraction, flat-fielding and non-linearity. The success of these will depend on the stability of the detector system and on the observing strategy used. It is important to realise that the observing strategy can vary considerably from one case to the next depending on the scientific goal, but it is nevertheless true that it is rare to find anyone spending TOO MUCH time on calibrations.

4.1.1.   Non-linearity. The SBRC InSb DRO array is inherently non-linear in its response to photon illumination due to the dependence of the capacitance (C) on the value of the reverse bias voltage which itself is a decaying function of time due to photocharge and/or dark current[6]. In other words, high photon fluxes give smaller output signals (in A/D units) than would be expected from a linear extrapolation from signal outputs associated with much lower illumination levels. The magnitude of the effect in all practical circumstances is less than 10% (typically around 8% at 70% of

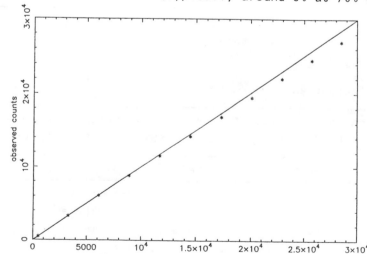

Figure 1. A plot of the output signal counts versus the true input signal counts for the SBRC 62 x 58 array. The departure from linearity is easily calibrated.

full well) and easily calibrated as shown in Figure 1. A correction is usually applied
to "bias-subtracted" images as a first step in data-processing to linearise the signals
to an accuracy of about 0.1%.

4.1.2. Dark current and bias. The "bias" level is the electronic offset or signal
obtained for an extremely short exposure with no incident illumination whatsoever. The
latter condition is achieved with a "dark slide" at 77 K. A "dark current" frame is
obtained with the same conditions but using a much longer exposure. Dark current is
spatially non-uniform and therefore must be carefully determined when it is an
appreciable fraction of the background signal.

4.1.3. Flat-fielding. Spatial variations in the response of the detector to light are
calibrated by dividing by a uniformly illuminated scene - a "flat-field" - after dark
subtraction. That is the basic algorithmn is

$$\frac{\text{Object frame} - \text{dark frame}}{\text{Flatfield frame} - \text{dark frame}}$$

We have found that flat-fields are best derived from multiple observations of relatively
"blank" sky. Since at some level there will always be sources in the blank sky area,
the best technique is to take many images (>5) with the telescope pointing to a slightly
different place (by ~5 arcsecs say), normalise these and calculate the median value for
every pixel. This procedure produces a very clean "master" flat-field. With this
technique the spatial non-uniformities, of order 20%, can be readily reduced to better
than 0.1% and in an extended survey to very faint levels at 2.2 microns IRCAM has
achieved a flat-field precision of 0.007%.

4.2. Astronomical performance

In Table 3 we summarise the sensitivity or "limiting-magnitude" performance of IRCAM
in its high-resolution mode of 0.63 arcseconds per pixel which is well-matched to
typical seeing conditions.

Table 3. Sensitivity of IRCAM

Scale	J	H	K	nbL
0.6 "/pix	21.9	20.9	20.9	14.7

The values are 3 sigma detections in 30 minutes expressed in equivalent magnitudes per
square arcsecond. The centre wavelengths of the JHKnbL set are respectively 1.26, 1.65,
2.2 and 3.6 microns; passbands are about 20% of the wavelength except for nbL which is
2%.

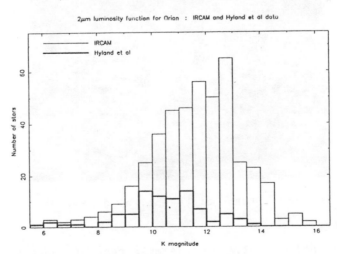

Figure 2. The frequency distribution of K magnitudes in the Orion Trapezium star
cluster. If the sun were located at the distance of this cluster its K magnitude would
be about 13. (Adapted from McCaughrean 1988.)

5. RECENT RESULTS

Infrared imaging systems like IRCAM are now being used fairly widely, in both hemispheres, and in diverse applications. Popular reviews have been given by McLean[6] and by Gatley et al.[9]. Progress has been very rapid since the pivotal workshop on "Infrared Astronomy with Arrays" held in Hilo, Hawaii in March 1987[10]. A personal selection of some of the most interesting results from UKIRT over the past two years is given below.

5.1. Star forming regions

A complete, high resolution (seeing-limited) image of the high-mass star forming cluster in the Orion Nebula was obtained with the array camera leading to a Luminosity Function at 2.2 microns - a plot of the number of stars per unit magnitude interval - (see Figure 2) and then to a multi-color study of over five hundred embedded stars[2 6].

Many other star forming regions have also been observed, and in several cases the polarization of scattered light from deeply embedded sources has been used to locate the source and distinguish it from a bright knot of nebulosity.

Images have been obtained in the light of molecular hydrogen emission of regions such as HH7-11 and DR21 which show clear evidence of "bow" shocks[11].

5.2. Galaxies

The first infrared images of several peculiar IRAS galaxies and known interacting-galaxies have been obtained. One example is NGC4038/9 (Arp244) - the Antennae - which has been observed with sufficient resolution to reveal the detailed morphology, such as bright embedded knots in the connecting "arm" and a bar-like feature in one nucleus of the pair, and at a sufficiently long wavelength to eliminate the strong reddening variations across the object[12].

Wright, Casali, Walther and McLean obtained the first high resolution, completely sampled infrared image of the giant spiral galaxy M51 at 2.2 microns (see Figure 3). The infrared image traces the older stellar population and very clearly delineates the spiral structure unimpaired by dust.

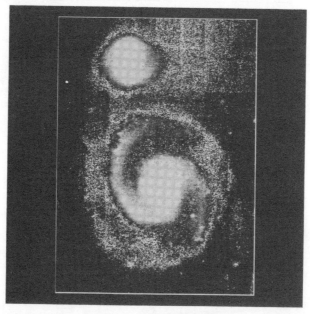

Figure 3. A 2.2 micron (K band) image of the spiral galaxy M51 and its companion.

5.3. The Galactic Centre

Continuous infrared imaging at 2.2 microns at a rate of about 4 frames per second was obtained of the Galactic Centre during a unique opportunity when the Moon occulted the source on three occasions visible from Mauna Kea[13 14]. The imaging data have made it possible to re-interpret aperture photometry data and have enabled the components of IRS16 to be distinguished.

In another unique study, the first "velocity-resolved" images of the Galactic Centre were obtained using a near-infrared imaging Fabry-Perot interferometer tuned to the Brackett gamma line of hydrogen at 2.167 microns and with a velocity resolution of about 90 km/s; the spatial resolution was seeing-limited at about one arcsecond[15][16]. The FP was scanned over a velocity range of 1045 km/s yielding ~3,600 spectra in only 30 minutes of integration time.

5.4. Planetary nebulae

Images of a shock-heated toroidal ring of molecular hydrogen have been obtained[17] of the planetary nebula NGC7027 which contrasts dramatically with the optical and radio appearance of this object. The radio maps show a shell structure and the optical image is peculiar and irregular due to extinction by dust. McLean et al. re-classify NGC7027 as a "butterfly" or "bow-tie" planetary probably in a fairly early stage of formation. A multicolour study of an even younger or "proto-planetary nebula" called M2-9 reveals very clearly a hugh circumstellar disk[18].

5.5. Supernova remnants

Using narrow band filters and the wide-field mode of IRCAM (2.5 arcsec/pixel) spectacular molecular hydrogen emission in supernova remnants, such as the Cygnus Loop and the Crab Nebula, has been observed with unexpected results which may indicate, for the first time, the occurrence of non-radiative precursor shocks[19].

5.6. Deep Cosmological surveys

Using a cumulative observation time of almost 12 hours and very careful median-filtering techniques for flat-fielding, the deepest ever infrared images of faint, distant galaxies have been obtained. The limiting magnitude (noise) in these studies is around K = 23, whereas the brightness of the infrared background at 2.2 microns is approximately equivalent to K = 13 per square arcsecond - a factor of 10,000! Combined with deep optical CCD images, a population of galaxies at high redshift (z ~3.0) has been discovered with extremely flat spectral energy distributions characteristic of vigorous star formation suggesting that these objects may be "protogalaxies" or galaxies formed earlier but now undergoing a rejuvenation phase[20]. One example is shown in Figure 4.

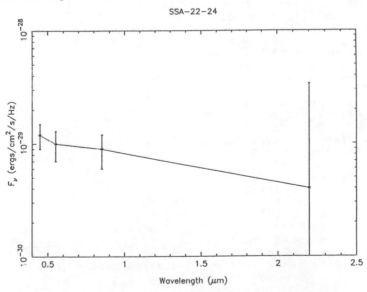

Figure 4. The BVIK flux levels of a faint galaxy (V=23.8) showing an exceptionally "flat" spectrum characteristic of vigorous star formation. The object is at z ~3.4. (From Cowie et al. 1988.)

6. CONCLUSIONS AND PROSPECTS

These and many other studies barely scratch the surface of what is possible with photometrically calibrated infrared imaging systems. Despite certain limitations, we have been successful in demonstrating flat-fielding accuracies to better than 1 part in 10,000 and relative photometry to better than about 0.01 mag or 1%.

There is no doubt that the 62 x 58 InSb array from SBRC has been an astounding success and that this device has catapaulted infrared astronomy forward at an incredible pace. Even so, the need for larger format detector arrays with lower readout noise and the highest possible quantum efficiency are already urgent. We discuss the availability of IR array detectors in a separate paper in these proceedings.

7.   ACKNOWLEDGEMENTS

It is pleasure to acknowledge our many colleagues at the Joint Astronomy Centre, Hawaii and at the Royal Observatory, Edinburgh whose efforts have made IRCAM a success.

8.   REFERENCES

1. I.S. McLean, T.C. Chuter, M.J. McCaughrean and J.T. Rayner, "System Design of a 1-5 micron Infrared Camera", Proc. SPIE 627, 430-437 (1986).
2. I.S. McLean, "Results with the UKIRT Camera", in Infrared Astronomy with Arrays, C.G. Wynn-Williams and E.E. Becklin, eds., Institute for Astronomy, University of Hawaii, 180-192 (1987).
3. I.S. McLean, "Optical or Infrared - the Elusive Boundary", in Instrumentation for Ground-based Optical Astronomy; present and future, Proc. Santa Cruz Summer Workshop, Lloyd Robinson, ed., Springer-Verlag, (1988).
4. G. Orias, A.W. Hoffman and M. Casselman, "58 x 62 InSb focal plane array for infrared astronomy", in Instrumentation for Astronomy VI, Proc. SPIE, 627, 408-417, 1986.
5. A.M. Fowler, R.G. Probst, J.P. Britt, R.R. Joyce and F.C. Gillett, "Evaluation of an indium antimonide hybrid focal plane array for ground-based astronomy", Optical Eng., 26, 232-240, (1987).
6. M.J. McCaughrean, "The astronomical applications of infrared array detectors", Ph.D. Thesis, University of Edinburgh, Scotland (1988).
7. I.S. McLean, "Infrared Astronomy's New Image", in SKY and TELESCOPE, Vol. 75, No. 3, 254-258, March (1988).
8. I.S. McLean, "Infrared Astronomy: A New Beginning", in ASTRONOMY NOW, August (1988).
9. I. Gatley, D.L. Depoy, A.M. Fowler, "Astronomical Imaging with Infrared Array Detectors", in SCIENCE, Vol. 242, 1217-1348, (1988).
10. C.G. Wynn-Williams and E.E. Becklin, Infrared Astronomy with Arrays, Institute for Astronomy, University of Hawaii, Honolulu (1987).
11. R. Garden and A. Russell, in prep. (1989).
12. G.S. Wright and I.S. McLean, "Near Infrared imaging of interacting galaxies", in Infrared Astronomy with Arrays, C.G. Wynn-Williams and E.E. Becklin eds., Institute for Astronomy, University of Hawaii, 355-359 (1987).
13. I.S. McLean, C. Aspin, A.J. Longmore and R.I. Dixon, "The January 1987 Galactic Centre occultation observed with the UKIRT IR camera, IRCAM", in Infrared Astronomy with Arrays, 321-325, (1987).
14. Longmore et al. in prep (1989).
15. D.L. Depoy, I. Gatley and I.S. McLean, in The Galactic Center, proc. of UCLA conference (1989).
16. G.S. Wright, J. Bland and I.S. McLean, "An infrared imaging Fabry-Perot study of the Galactic Centre", in 22nd ESLAB Symposium on Infrared Spectroscopy, Salamanca, (1989).
17. I.S. McLean, I. Gatley, P. Brand, T. Hasegawa, S. Hayashi, "The molecular toroid in NGC7027", submitted to Ap.J. (1989).
18. C. Aspin, I.S. McLean and M.G. Smith, "The IR morphology of the protoplanetary nebular M2-9", Astron. Astrophys., 196, 227-232 (1988).
19. J.R. Graham, G.S. Wright, A.J. Longmore, "Infrared spectroscopy and imaging of supernova remnants", in 22nd ESLAB Symposium on Infrared Spectroscopy, (1989).
20. L. Cowie, S.J. Lilly, J. Gardner, and I.S. McLean, "A cosmologically significant population of galaxies dominated by very young star formation", Ap.J Letters, 332, L29 (1988).

Results in Extragalactic Astronomy using a 32 × 32 IR Camera

P. Gallais, D. Rouan, F. Lacombe, D. Tiphène

DESPA, Observatoire de Paris-Meudon, 92195 Meudon, France

ABSTRACT

This paper presents the CIRCUS infrared camera and recent results in extragalactic astronomy obtained using this 32 × 32 array camera. Observations were carried on starburst galaxies, $3.3\mu m$ PAH emission line at large scale in NGC 891 and the twin quasar Q0957+561.

INTRODUCTION

The recent technological progress of 2-dimensional infrared arrays, has drastically improved direct infrared imaging in ground-based astronomy and is now available to astronomers on several large telescopes.

The new devices allow an observational methodology easier than monodetector raster scanning with a more accurate positionning of observations ones with respect to the others, a better study of the spatial extend of an object, up to now made with multiaperture procedures, and of course we benefit from the huge saving of time in proportion to the number of pixels.

The camera presented below features the same type of array detector, a 32 × 32 InSb Charge Injection Device, than the short-wave channel of the ISOCAM camera aboard ISO (Infrared Space Observatory). It is devoted to the $1 - 5\ \mu m$ atmospheric windows and is now available to the astronomical community on the 3m60 Canada-France-Hawaii telescope at Mauna Kea, Hawaii.

In the first section, we present briefly the instrument and the observational procedures.

We present, in a second section, several results on the nuclear region of nearby spiral galaxies and interacting galaxies, were an intense star formation (starburst) is responsible of the infrared emission. In the third section, we report on a succesful observation on the extended emission of PAHs feature at 3.3 μm in the edge-on galaxy NGC 891. Finally, further away of our Galaxy, we obtained a direct image of the famous "double quasar" Q 0957+561, and the lens galaxy responsible for the gravitational mirage. The rather high magnitude of this object is a good indicator of the surface photometry limits on faint extended objects.

I. THE INSTRUMENT, THE DETECTOR AND THE OBSERVATIONAL PROCEDURES

1.1. The detector and the instrument

The CIRCUS camera is built around a 32 × 32 InSb Charge Injection Device (CID) cooled at liquid helium temperature to reduce dark current, and indeed the integration time is bakground limited in any cases, even at short wavelength, and the noise performances are within a factor two from BLIP conditions. The camera is equiped with the standard filters J($1.25\mu m$), H($1.65\mu m$), K($2.2\mu m$), L($3.6\mu m$) and M($4.8\mu m$), and also with two circular variable filters for low resolution spectro-imaging ($\lambda/\Delta\lambda = 60$) in the $2.4 - 5.5\ \mu m$ range. The instrument can be mounted on the 3m60 CFH telescope, at the f/36 cassegrain focus, where the pixel size is 0.5×0.5 $arcsec^2$ on the sky and the field of view is 16×16 $arcsec^2$. The main features of the detector and camera are displayed in table 1, and for more informations, the reader will refer to Tiphène et al.[1] and Lacombe et al.[2]

• Detector material	: InSb (Indium-Antimonide)
• Manufacturer	: S.A.T. (Société Anonyme des Télécommunications)
• Read-out	: Charge Injection (CID)
• Number of pixels	: 32×32
• Pixel size	: 70×70 μm^2
• Geometrical filling factor	: 73 %
• Charge storage capacity	: 2×10^6 e^-
• Operating temperature	: 4 K
• Integration time	: Background limited
• Number of dead pixels	: 5
• Electronic read-out noise	: $\sim$ 600 e^-
• Overall system read-out noise	: $\sim$ 1800 e^-
• Crosstalk	: 17 %, corrected at reduction $\Longrightarrow$ < 1%
• Response uniformity	: $\sigma = 10\%$

Table 1: Caracteristics of the detector

1.2. Observationnal procedures.

At infrared wavelength, the detectivity is mainly limited by two sources of noise: the read-out noise and the fluctuations (statistical and time dependant) of the atmopheric and telescope emissions, which are drastically increasing at largest wavelengths (L and M). In order to compensate for the background and the dark current, we can hardly use a portion of the frame as estimator of the contribution as it is done in optical range with CCD, because of the small field of view of the camera (especially when the observed object is extended) , also because of the moderate homogeneity of the response across the array and the scatter of dark currents. The method used consists in substracting to the image of the object, an image of the sky, assumed uniform, obtained with the same integration time and same conditions. We use for that purpose the wobbling secondary mirror or depoint the telescope (*starring*). Despite the overhead due to depointing, the latter method is prefered because the detector sees always the same fixed emission from the telescope.

The integration time is chosen as close as possible to the saturation limit and thus imposed by the background level (thermal emission or air-glow at shortest wavelengths). Several elementary integrations are co-added in real-time and/or when reducing the data. Note that the link of the data acquisition system to the local network allows a fairly good efficiency of observation, even at long wavelengths where the data rate is very high: e.g. the time devoted to photon detection is typically 86 % of the total time at 3.6 μm.

1.3. Data reduction.

The data reduction is done using a software available on a μVAX II . It usually consists of: *i)* substraction of the offset due to background and dark charge using the sky image, *ii)* substraction of the background variations and of a common mode pick-up signal by selecting several *background* pixels and substracting their average, *iii)* correction by matrix inversion of a pure electrical coupling (15 % typically) between neighbouring pixels of same parity on a given line, *iv)* substraction of the residual offset, postulating that the estimated histogram of the background must be centered on zero.

Flat field are obtained on the blank sky at sunrise and sunset, or using the sky emission measured on the reference field. In the former case, the slope of the response is used as the estimator of the relative sensitivity of the pixels, while in the latter case, dark current must be measured to give the offset of each pixel.

The photometric calibration is made by observing standard calibration stars during the night. Air mass correction is applied with the corresponding atmospheric extinction averaged over the entire run of observations. The table 2 displays the limiting magnitude derived from these observations extrapolated to one hour equivalent integration time at S/N=1. Because of overhead and time loss, experience teachs than results of one magnitude lower may be expected.

Band	Limiting magnitude	N	$T_{max}(s)$
J	22.6	60	60
H	21.1	60	60
K	20.6	60	60
L	17.3	18000	0.2
M	15.7	36000	0.1

Table 2. Limiting magnitudes for 1 hour integration with $S/N = 1$. The noise is taken equal to the spatial noise $\sigma_s = 3300 e^-$. N represents the number of co-added frames necessary to obtain an equivalent integration time of 1 hr, since integration per frame (T_{max}) is always limited by background emission.

II. STARBURST GALAXIES

It is commonly accepted that the strong excess of far-infrared emission compared to visible light in a galaxy is due to intense, and necessarily short, event of star formation. The origin of these events is not yet totally clear, but is certainly related to the existence of non-axisymmetric potential due to either a strong stellar bar or to the interaction with another galaxy. The near infrared emission may originate in different components: the population of red super giants created in the burst, hot dust, free-free emission from HII regions, gaseous emission from exited gas, non-thermal nucleus if any. The color indices are sensitive to the origin of the emission of these various components. The central part of a galaxy, where dust, gas and stars are mixed, cannot be seen in the visible because of the large opacity and the wavelength dependence of the absorption allows a much deeper probing in the infrared.

Here, we focus our attention on a few objects where starburst activity has been put in evidence and where the spatial resolution and sensitivity of near infrared arrays provide a good tool for their study. Two types of objects are considered : i) barred spiral galaxies and ii) interacting or merging galaxies.

2.1 The spiral barred galaxy M83.

Messier 83 (NGC 5236) is a bright southern spiral galaxy. Located at 3.75 Mpc (assuming $H_0 = 75 kms^{-1} Mpc^{-1}$), it is the nearest barred spiral from our galaxy. Its central region was studied at X-ray[3], UV[4], optical[5], infrared[6,7] and radio[8] wavelengths. These studies have shown a complex extended structure of the nuclear region. The emission at 10 μm is extended and the important far-infrared luminosity suggest starburst activity in the nuclear region. The central region has been mapped with the CIRCUS camera in the three colors J, H and K, and the corresponding images are displayed on figure 1.

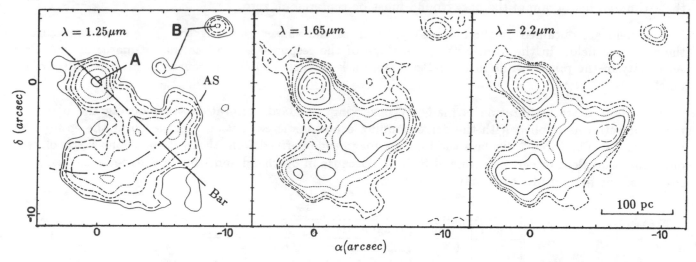

Figure 1. Isophotes maps of NGC 5236 at J, H and K. Regions A (nucleus), B (6cm/10μm peaks) and AS (arc-like structure) referred in the text are quoted on the J map; direction of the bar is also drawn. Contours are separated by 0.5 $mag/arcsec^2$, lowest contours are 16.5 $mag/arcsec^2$.

2.1.1. Complex structure, identification of the nucleus.

As in the visible (Pastoriza[5] classified it as an "amorphous" nucleus), this galaxy presents at near-infrared, a patchy structure in the central 16 $arcsec$. The complex nature of the nuclear region is also indicated by the large variations of the color indices as seen from comparison of images in the different colors (see also Fig. 2). The main features are a point-like source which is proheminent, an arc extending from the south to the west of the point source, and a fainter point source at NE.

The main point source is clearly identified as the stellar nucleus, because of its small angular size, its brightness and the color indices which are well within the region of the (J-H)-(H-K) color-color diagram occupied by nuclei of spiral galaxies[9], provided that some reddening (Av = 2) and nebular emission is also present.

2.1.2. Identification of visible 10 μm and radio sources.

There is an excellent correspondance between the IR map and the visible plate[10] at all scales, including the fainter N-E source and details on the lowest contour. Note that in visible the nucleus is not so proheminent as in IR. There is also a good correspondance of the two emission maxima at 10 μm with two point sources of the J image, specially the N-E one. On the other hand it was established that those two 10 μm sources have direct counterpart on the 6 cm map[8]. These two sources and the associated extended emission around them clearly dealinate the region of maximum star formation in M83, and we can draw the following conclusion from the found correspondance:

i) The star forming region cannot be very compact and completely embedded since it still has a counterpart at visible and near-IR wavelength: it must extend to the edge of the concentration of matter.

ii) The active ridge of star formation (10 μm "bar") does not appear to be directly connected to the nucleus itself since its extension does not cross the nucleus.

iii) The general shape of the near-IR extended emission combined with the radio/10 μm region describes an arc, elongated in a direction perpendicular to the bar. This suggests that the gas is confined into elliptic orbits between the inner Linblad resonances which we have localised at about 100 and 400 pc respectively, using CO measurements[11]. Such a configuration is indeed predicted by the theory.

iv) The southmost region has indices typical of giants and/or super giants, while going towards the north gives indices more and more characteristic of emission from ionised gas. This distribution of color indices along the arc strongly suggests a time evolution, with the oldest phase of the burst at south being now in the phase of producing super-giants, but no longer ionising photons, while youngest ionising stars are more and more predominant when approaching the presently active star-forming region, delineated by radio/10 μm. This picture suggests a chain reaction mechanism of star formation triggered by SN explosions, as proposed by Condon et al.[12]

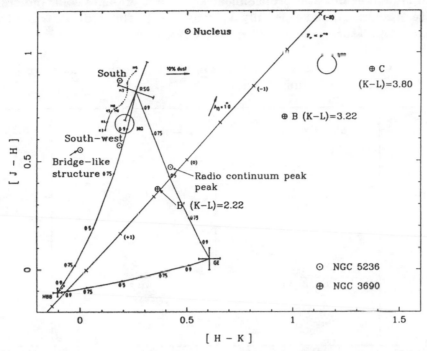

Figure 2. Two-colours diagram (J-H)-(H-K). ⊙ and ⊕ refer respectively to NGC 5236 and NGC 3690. The colours of three possible infrared contributors, red super giants (RG), gaseous emission (GE) and a 42500K blackbody (HBB) are plotted joined by mixed lines (from Campbell and Terlevich[9]). Straight line represents colours of a power-law with various spectral indexes and filled circles represent the area populated by "normal" galaxies (NG) and quasars (QSO).

2.1.3. A link between the nucleus and the tore of star formation.

The most striking feature on our images is the thin bridge of emission, appearing at all wavelengths but especially at J, and which connects the nucleus to the arc. This structure is in a direction close to the bar. The color indices of this region are also peculiar (see Fig. 2), with no satisfactory fit with any of the classical sources of near-IR emission: stars, nebular emission or hot dust. We do not know what is the exact nature of this structure and suggest that it may be linked to the very high speed component detected in UV[4] and which was tentatively attributed to a jet[13] and/or to the gaseous bar that may be the final channel along which a nucleus can be fuelled with fresh matter as recently proposed[14].

2.2. The starburst galaxy NGC 3690 in the interacting system Arp 299

This object is a typical case of a starburst induced by a strong interaction between two galaxies. We have observed one of the galaxy of system, NGC 3690 in four colors (J, H, K, L). As previously demonstrated by Fowler et al.[15], three point sources are seen (B, B' and C), the two southmost being very close one to the other with a separation of 2 arcsec. The new point here is the L image and the multi-color photometry at good resolution which allows to put severe constraints on the nature of the three sources.

The source B' appears only on the J, H and K images and has color indices which are well representative of star forming region, with an important contribution of gaseous emission. Its position at ~ 500 pc from B suggest that it is the dominant region of nuclear stellar formation associated to the nucleus of NGC 3690, while B is the nucleus itself. The color indices of B can be understood as those of a "standard" nuclei (see Fig. 2), only if very hot dust contribute significantly to push the (H-K) index toward higher values, and indeed, the very important value of (K-L) = 3.22 fully confirms this interpretation, a dust temperature of 600K being derived if K and L fluxes are assumed to be entirely due to dust emission.

The source C which is fainter, but still prohominent at 10 μm, presents color indices (see Fig. 2) which are rather close to those of source B, and especially a strong (K-L) value indicating here also a very hot dust component with similar temperature as for B. This rules out that C can be a standard star forming region. Due to the strong common behaviour of B and C we shall follow the proposal of Combes et al. (private communication), based on CO measurements, that C is in fact the nucleus of a third galaxy involved in the interaction, and not a "classical" star forming region.

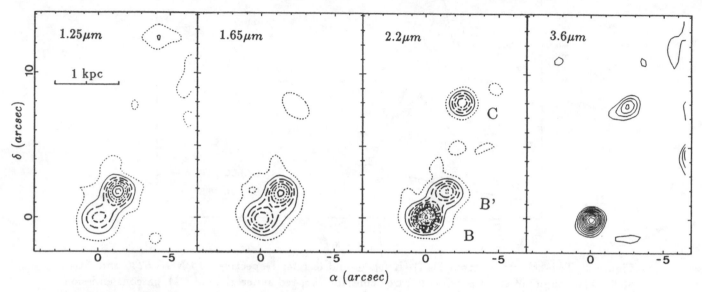

Figure 3. Isophotes maps of NGC 3690 at J, H, K and L. B is the nucleus of NGC 3690, B' corresponds to a star forming region, and C, the nucleus of a third interacting galaxy. In J, H and K maps, contours are separated by 0.32 $mJy/arcsec^2$, lowest contours are 0.32 $mJy/arcsec^2$. In L map, the separation is 3.2 $mJy/arcsec^2$ and lowest contour is 8 $mJy/arcsec^2$.

III. OTHER RESULTS

3.1 PAH in the Edge-on Galaxy NGC 891

It has been recently proposed that a new component of the interstellar medium, large aromatic molecules (PAHs), are responsible for the group of bands observed in the IR at 3.3, 6.2, 7.7 8.6 and 11.3 μm in regions rich in UV radiation. The hypothesis that the excess of the diffuse IRAS 12 μm in the galactic plane was also due to this component, through its 11.3 μm contribution, has led to the search and the discovery by the balloon-borne experiment AROME of such an extended emission in the 3.3 μm band in most of the Milky Way[17].

From this result, it was logic to conclude that such a diffuse emission must also exist in external normal spiral galaxies, and we have started a program to try to detect it in edge-on galaxies through IR spectro-imaging. We report the discovery of such an emission from the only object of the program we had the time to observe during a recent run at CFHT.

NGC 891 is an almost perfectly edge-on galaxy, at a distance of 10 Mpc, and is thought to be very similar to our own galaxy. Our observations at J, 3.185 and 3.285 μm have been made on a region centered on the dust obscuration, at the limit of the external radius of the bulge.

The results are the following:

i) The stellar disk population is well identified on the J image as an elongated ridge. Closely following the same contours, the 3.3 μm emission is also clearly detected. This disk structure, and the scale of the line emitting region, larger than 350 pc, points clearly to an extended diffuse component rather than a bright isolated source.

ii) We have selected the region of maximum brightness (typically 50 $arcsec^2$) to evaluate the average line contrast $F(3.28)/F(3.185)$. This ratio is 1.6, with a low uncertainty thanks to the large number of involved pixels. The figure 4 shows the two measured spectral points superimposed on the spectrum of a typical galactic PAH emitting region, together with the points measured by the AROME experiment for the Milky way. Taking into account the differences in spectral resolution, the agreement on the line contrast appears to be excellent. Note that such a high ratio can have no other explanation but an emission line, since the slope of the continuum would be to steep, and in any case of opposite sign because stellar radiation still dominates in this wavelength range.

iii) The $F(3.3)/F(J)$ ratio in NGC 891 is very close to the one measured for the Milky Way; together with the good correspondance between the 3.3 μm and the J image, this result reinforces the basic hypothesis that PAHs are transiently heated by the stellar photons in very analog conditions in both galaxies.

This very first result tends thus to prove that PAHs are, as predicted, an important component of the diffuse interstellar medium in spiral galaxies. This program will be continued.

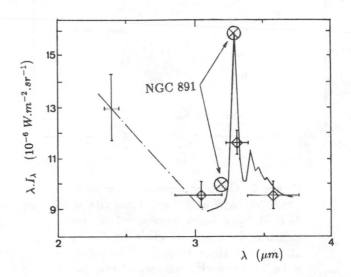

Figure 4. PAH $3.3\mu m$ emission line, as detected by Arome in the Milky Way ($\diamond$) and CIRCUS in NGC 891 ($\otimes$). The values for NGC 891 are divided by 8. Solid line deals with a typical galactic PAH emission from IRAS 21282+5050.

3.2 The Gravitational Mirage Q0957+561

The double quasar Q0957+561 was discovered at optical wavelengths by Walsh et al.[17] in 1979, and is the first observed gravitational mirage. It consists in two images of a same object and was identified by optical spectroscopy. Optical images obtained by Stockton[18] show a faint extent to the component B, corresponding to the image of the lens galaxy. Infrared multi-apertures studies[19,20] showed that the component B is three times brighter than component A, because the lens galaxy dominates at infrared wavelengths.

The image presented in figure 5 results in co-addition of 30 sec integration time elementary exposure and corresponds to a total integration time of 28 min on the source, after deglitching and elementary images selection. It shows clearly two sources which are the infrared counterparts of the A and B components. The angular separation between the centers of gravity of these two sources is 5.7" ± 0.4".

Component A is not resolved while component B is obviously extended and represents as far as we know the first direct image of this object at infrared wavelengths. However, this component is not resolved in two objects because of the small distance between the quasar and the galaxy, but is coherent with a superposition of a point-like source with an extended object.

Despite the moderate value of the signal to noise ratio and the faint magnitude of the object ($m_K = 15.4$), the surface photometry of the galaxy can be done by averaging pixel fluxes on circular rings centered on the best estimate of the galaxy center. To avoid flux contamination by the southern quasar image (assuming a flux ratio between the two quasar images of 0.76 [21]), we have considered only the rings with diameter larger than 3 *arcsec*. The result of this evaluation is shown on figure 6 as the total flux $F(r)$ in diaphragm of diameter r, for both components A and galaxy. One can check that component A is unresolved and that the galaxy is clearly extended over a 6 arc-sec diameter, with a behaviour of the brightness $F(r) \propto r^{0.76 \pm 0.15}$, in good agreement with a de Vaucouleurs's law transposed in integrated fluxes.

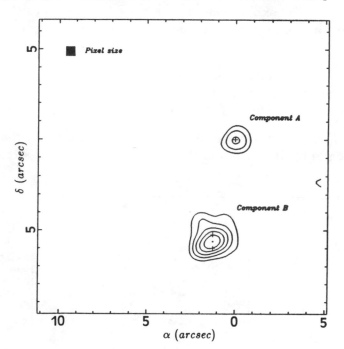

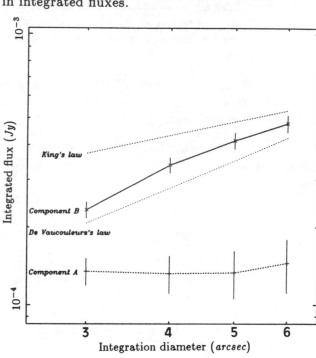

Figure 5. Contour representation of QSO 0957+561 A,B at 2.2μm; Pixel size is indicated by a black square. The crosses indicate the positions given by Young et al. for the three sources. The levels, in $mJy/(arc-sec)^2$, are respectively 0.032, 0.047, 0.063, 0.078, 0.093, 0.109.

Figure 6. Flux density integrated in disks of increasing diameter, for component A and galaxy. The de Vaucouleurs's and King's law are plotted at arbitrary positions (for slope comparison). Error bars are $\pm 1\sigma$.

In conclusion, these short examples give a good idea of the kind of studies in the extragalactic field now possible with the infrared cameras on large telescopes.

References:

1. Tiphène, D., Rouan, D. and Lacombe, F., 1987, *Infrared Astronomy with Arrays* , Eds C.G. Wynn-Williams and E.E. Becklin, Hilo, Hawaii, march 24-26 1987.
2. Lacombe, F., Tiphène, D., Rouan, D., Léna, P. and Combes, M., 1989, *Astron. Astrophys.*, in press.
3. Trinchieri, G., Fabbiano, G. and Palumbo, G.G.C., 1985, *Astrophys. J.*, **290**, 96.
4. Bohlin, R.C., Cornett, R.H., Hill, J.K., Smith, A.M. and Stecher, T.P., 1983, *Astrophys. J. (Letters)*, **274**, L53.
5. Pastoriza, M.G., 1975, *Astrophys. Spa. Sci.*, **33**, 173.

6. Turner, J.L., Ho, T.P. and Beck, S.C., 1987, *Astrophys. J.*, **313**, 644.
7. Telsco, C.M., Decher, R. and Ramsey, D., 1986, in *Star Formation in Galaxies*, C.J. Lonsdale Persson (Editor), NASA Conference Publication 2466, p.497.
8. Telesco, C.M., 1988, *Ann. Rev. Astr. Ap.*, **26**, 343.
9. Campbell, A.W. and Terlevich, R., 1984, *Mont. Not. R. Astron. Soc.*, **211**, 15.
10. Wood, and Andrews,, 1974, *Mon. Not. R. Astron. Soc.*, **167**, 13.
11. Handa, T., Nakai, N., Sofue, Y., Hayashi, M. and Fujimoto, M., 1988, *Publ. Astron. Soc. Japan*, submitted.
12. Condon, J.J., Condon, M.A., Gisler, G. and Puschell, J.J., 1982, *Astrophys. J.*, **252**, 102.
13. Keel, C.W., 1987, in *Observationnal Evidence of Activity in Galaxies*, IAU Symposium n°121, Kachikian et al. (eds), p.255.
14. Shlosman, I.,Frank, J. and Begelman, M., 1989, *Nature*, **338**, 45.
15. Fowler, A.M., Gillett, F.C., Gregory, B., Joyce, R.R., Probst, R.G. and Smith, R., 1987, *Infrared Astronomy with Arrays* , Eds C.G. Wynn-Williams and E.E. Becklin, Hilo, Hawaii, march 24-26 1987.
16. Giard, M., Pajot, F., Lamarre J.M., Serra, G., Caux, E., Gispert, R., Leger, A. and Rouan, D., 1988, *Aston. Astrophys.*, **201**, L1.
17. Walsh,D., Carswell, R.F. and Weymann, R.J., 1979, *Nature*, **279**, 381.
18. Stockton, A., 1980, *Astrophys. J. (Letters)*, **242**, L141.
19. Soifer, B.T., Neugebauer, G., Matthews, K., Becklin, E.E., Wynn-Williams, C.G. and Capps, R., 1980, *Nature*, **285**, 91.
20. Lebofsky, M.J., Rieke, G.H., Walsh, D. and Weymann, R.J., 1980, *Nature*, **285**, 385.
21. Young, P., Gunn, J.E., Kristian, J., Oke, J.B. and Westphal, J.A., 1981, *Astrophys. J.*, **244**, 736.

SESSION 5

The Infrared Space Observatory

Chair
Jean-Pierre Swings
Institut d'Astrophysique/Université de Liège (Belgium)

The Infrared Space Observatory (ISO) and its Instruments

M.F. Kessler

Astrophysics Division, Space Science Department of ESA,
ESTEC, Postbus 299, 2200AG Noordwijk, The Netherlands.

ABSTRACT

The Infrared Space Observatory (ISO), a fully approved and funded project of the European Space Agency (ESA), is an astronomical satellite, which will operate at wavelengths from 3–200μm. ISO will provide astronomers with a unique facility of unprecedented sensitivity for a detailed exploration of the universe ranging from objects in the solar system right out to the most distant extragalactic sources. The satellite essentially consists of a large cryostat containing superfluid helium to maintain the telescope and its scientific instruments at temperatures around 2–3 K. The telescope has a 60-cm diameter primary mirror and is diffraction-limited at a wavelength of 5μm. A pointing accuracy of a few arc seconds is provided by a three-axis stabilisation system. ISO carries four instruments, namely: an imaging photo-polarimeter (3–200μm), a camera (3–17μm), a short wavelength spectrometer (3–45μm) and a long wavelength spectrometer (45–180μm). ISO will be launched in early 1993 by an Ariane 4 rocket into an elliptical orbit (apogee 70000 km and perigee 1000 km) and will be operational for at least 18 months. In keeping with ISO's role as an observatory, two-thirds of its observing time will be made available to the general astronomical community.

1. INTRODUCTION

The Infrared Astronomical Satellite (IRAS) used a cryogenically-cooled telescope high above the disturbing effects of the Earth's atmosphere to give astronomers their first clear look at the infrared universe. In a mission lasting a bare 10 months, IRAS sent back so much high-quality data that, 6 years later, they are still being analysed and yielding fresh science. The IRAS catalogues, maps and spectra, containing more than 250,000 individual sources, have already become an indispensible tool for astronomical research. However, with the end of the IRAS mission due to depletion of its liquid-helium coolant, instruments with sufficient sensitivity to observe many of these sources are no longer available. The Infrared Space Observatory (ISO), an observatory rather than a survey mission, will make high-sensitivity and versatile observing facilities routinely available to astronomers for detailed observations of individual sources.

ISO resulted from a proposal submitted to ESA in 1979 in response to a call to the scientific community for ideas for new missions. Following various scientific and technical studies and assessments, including a phase-A (feasibility) study in 1981-2, ISO was chosen in March 1983 to be the next new start in the ESA Scientific Programme. This selection carried with it approval of the necessary ESA funds for the entire mission. After a 'Call for Experiment and Mission Scientist Proposals' to the European and U.S. astronomical communities, four focal-plane instruments and five Mission Scientists were selected in mid-1985. The industrial system design (phase B) study started in December 1986 and was successfully completed in March 1988. Currently the spacecraft is in its main development phase (C/D).

The design and status of ISO and its instruments were detailed in a previous SPIE volume[1-5]. Since then, the entire project has advanced from the conceptual design phase to integration and testing of hardware. Major changes have been: the replacement of the dual cryogen (hydrogen/helium) system by one using superfluid helium only; and the adoption of an orbit with a 24-hour, rather than a 12-hour, period.

Figure 1: Computer Graphic Schematic of the ISO Satellite.

The ISO satellite (depicted in figure 1) includes many areas where new technologies are being applied to astronomy. For the spacecraft, the entire cryogenic system is a first for Europe and demonstrates the growing maturity of this technology. The need to test large optical systems at liquid-helium temperatures has presented fresh challenges. The scientific instruments all contain state-of-the-art infrared detectors—single elements and arrays—with their associated read-out electronics, all operating at a few degrees Kelvin. Many special mechanisms, with very low power dissipations and lifetimes up to 2 years, have been developed for the instruments for use in space under cryo-vacuum conditions.

2. SCIENTIFIC RATIONALE

In the years since observational astronomy finally escaped from confinement to the narrow visible region of the electromagnetic spectrum, it has become clear that a full understanding of the properties and physics of astronomical sources can only be obtained by studying them across the widest possible frquency range. The region of the spectrum covered by ISO is of great scientific interest, not only because it is here that cool objects (15–300K) radiate the bulk of their energy, but also because of its rich variety of atomic, ionic, molecular and solid-state spectral features. Measurements at these wavelengths permit determination of many physical parameters, for example energy balance, temperatures, abundances, densities and velocities. Owing to the much reduced extinction, infrared observations are particularly well-suited to probing the properties of objects obscured at visible wavelengths.

Observations in the infrared from ground-based telescopes are limited to a small range of wavelengths –the so-called "atmospheric windows"– at which the Earth's atmosphere is transparent. The available wavelength coverage can be extended by placing telescopes on-board high-flying aircraft and balloons, but the total amount of observing time remains relatively limited. A second problem is that thermal emission from the atmosphere and telescope optics provides an undesired background against which much weaker astronomical signals have to be distinguished; the photon shot noise due to this background can be the dominant noise source in the measurement. These restrictions are avoided by operating a cryogenically-cooled telescope in space. ISO will be offering high sensitivity and sophisticated observing facilities for this difficult spectral region, and it is expected that its scientific programme will touch upon virtually every field of astronomy, ranging from solar system studies to cosmology.

3. SPACECRAFT AND MISSION DESIGN

The complete satellite will be 5.3 m high, 2.3 m wide and will weigh around 2400 kg at launch. It is divided into a payload module (the upper cylindrical part of figure 1) and a service module. These modules are built up of sub-systems, which are described in the next two sections.

3.1 Payload Module

The payload module is essentially a large cryostat containing the telescope and the scientific instruments. A cutaway schematic is shown in figure 2.

- **Helium Sub-system:** This sub-system provides the cooling power to maintain inter alia the scientific instruments and telescope at temperatures between 1.8 and 4 K for an operational lifetime in-orbit of at least 18 months. The main toroidal HeII tank, equipped with a porous-plug phase separator, contains 2250 litres of superfluid helium at a temperature of 1.8 K. Some of the infrared detectors are directly coupled to this helium tank; all other units are cooled using the cold boil-off gas from the liquid helium. This gas is first routed through the optical support structure to cool the telescope and the scientific instruments. It is then passed along the optical baffles and radiation shields before being vented to space. A small auxiliary tank, containing about 60 litres of normal liquid helium, fulfils all of ISO's cooling needs for the last 72 hours before launch.
- **Optical Sub-system:** The main components of this sub-system are the telescope, the set of baffles and the sunshade. Suspended in the middle of the main helium tank is the telescope, which has an aplanatic Ritchey-Chrétien configuration with an effective aperture of 600 mm and an overall f/ratio of 15. A four-sided pyramid mirror distributes the 20' total unvignetted field of view of the telescope among the four instruments, which are mounted on the side of the optical support structure opposite to the primary mirror. Each instrument simultaneously receives a 3' unvignetted field centred on an axis at an angle of 8.5' to the telescope optical axis. A weight-relieved fused-silica (Herasil I) primary mirror and a solid fused-silica secondary mirror have been selected as the telescope optics. The optical quality of these mirrors is adequate for diffraction-limited performance at a wavelength of 5 μm.

Stringent control of stray light, particularly from bright infrared sources outside the telescope's field of view, is necessary in order to ensure that the system sensitivity is not degraded. This control is accomplished by (i) imposition of viewing constraints (ii) by equipping the mirrors with baffles (iii) by the main optical baffle, which protects from off-axis straylight and thermal self-emission from the sunshade and (iv) the sunshade, which prevents earth and sun radiation from entering the telescope.

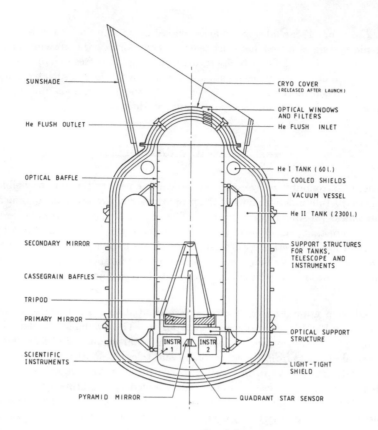

Figure 2: Schematic of the Payload Module.

- **Structure and Insulation Sub-system:** The largest component is the vacuum vessel, which is composed of three forged and machined parts, rigidly flanged to each other. Multi-layer insulation (MLI) is used on the outside of the vacuum vessel. All internal units are suspended from the vacuum vessel via glass-fibre and carbon-fibre straps and spatial frameworks. The three gas-cooled radiation shields are each covered with MLI and there is an additional shield to provide a light-tight enclosure for the instruments. Mounted on the outside of the vacuum vessel is a sunshield, which prevents the sun from shining directly on the cryostat.
- **Cryostat Cover Sub-system:** This cover provides many facilities beyond its basic purpose of closing the cryostat on the ground. It contains two windows which transmit visible radiation, thereby permitting the optical alignment of the telescope and the instruments to be monitored even when they are at cryogenic temperatures. To aid instrument testing, the cover carries 2 infrared sources which can "illuminate" the instruments and, additionally, the cover's innermost radiation shield can be cooled to below 5 K with a liquid-helium flush so as to provide a low thermal radiation background. The cover is secured by a clampband and it will be ejected about 14 days after launch after the spacecraft has outgassed sufficiently.
- **Electrical Sub-system:** This supplies the power, cabling, instrumentation and commanding facilities needed for the module.

3.2 Service Module

As its name indicates, the service module provides the "classical" support services to the entire satellite. These include:
- the structure and the load path to the launcher,
- the solar array mounted on the sunshield, delivering 580 W at the end of the mission,
- sub-systems for thermal control, data handling, power conditioning, telemetry (nominal rate 32768 bps of which about 24 kbps are available for the scientific instruments) and telecommand (2000 bps),
- the "attitude and orbit control" subsystem. This provides the three-axis stabilisation and the raster pointing facilities needed for the mission. The requirement on relative pointing error (equivalent to jitter) is 2.7" ($2\,\sigma$, half cone, over a period of 30secs and that on the absolute pointing error (the angular separation between the commanded direction and the instantaneous actual direction) 11.7" ($2\,\sigma$, half cone). Sensors used are: sun acquisition sensors to provide coarse information on the position of the sun; fine sun sensors for accurate sun position information; earth limb sensors, covering both "forbidden" and "warning" zones for the spacecraft attitude with respect to the Earth; star trackers as the prime pointing sensors; a quadrant star sensor on the optical axis of the telescope to calibrate the mis-alignment between the star trackers and the telescope axis; and four rate-integrating gyros in an all-skewed configuration. The main actuators are four

reaction wheels, also in an all-skewed configuration. These wheels can be unloaded by use of the hydrazine reaction control subsystem, which is also used for orbit acquisition and maintenance.

An Ariane-4 vehicle will launch ISO into a transfer orbit with a perigee height of around 200 km and an apogee height of around 70000 km. ISO's hydrazine reaction control system will then be used to raise the perigee to attain the operational orbit (24-hour period, perigee 1000 km and apogee 70000 km). The inclination to the equator will be between 5° and 20° (to be finalised later). ESA plans to supply only one ground station, enabling ISO to make astronomical observations during the best 14 hours of each orbit. The mission's scientific return, however, could be greatly increased by the addition of a second ground station, which would permit ISO to be operated for the entire time that it spends outside the main part of the Earth's radiation belts. An international collaboration is being sought by ESA to provide this second ground station.

4. SCIENTIFIC INSTRUMENTS

The ISO scientific payload consists of four instruments which, although being developed separately, have been designed as a package to offer complementary facilities to the observers. Each instrument is being built by a consortium of scientific institutes using national non-ESA funding and will be delivered to ESA for in-orbit operation. Details of the individual instruments are given in table 1. The scientific capabilities of the total payload for spectroscopy, photometry, polarimetry and imaging are shown in figure 3. The four instruments view different adjacent patches of the sky, but, in principle, only one will be operational at a time. However, when the camera is not the prime instrument, it can be operated in a so-called parallel mode, either to gather additional astronomical data or to assist another instrument in acquiring and tracking its target. In order to maximise the scientific return of the mission, the ISOPHOT instrument will be operated during as many satellite slews as possible so as to make a partial sky survey at a wavelength of 200 μm, a region not explored by IRAS.

Instrument and Principal Investigator	Main Function	Wavelength (Microns)	Spectral Resolution	Spatial Resolution	Outline Description
ISOCAM (C. Cesarsky, CEN-Saclay, F)	Camera and Polarimetry	2.5 - 17	Broad-band, Narrow-band, and Circular Variable Filters	Pixel f.o.v.'s of 1.5, 3, 6 and 12 arc seconds	Two channels each with a 32x32 element detector array
ISOPHOT (D. Lemke, MPI für Astronomie, Heidelberg, D)	Imaging Photo-polarimeter	2.5 - 200	Broad-band and Narrow-band Filters. Near IR Grating Spectrometer with R = 90	Variable from diffraction - limited to wide beam	Four sub-systems: i) Multi-band, Multi-aperture photo-polarimeter (3-110 μm) ii) Far-Infrared Camera (30-200 μm) iii) Spectrophotometer (2.5-12 μm) iv) Mapping Array (18-28 μm)
SWS (Th. de Graauw, Lab. for Space Research, Groningen, NL)	Short-wavelength Spectrometer	2.5 - 45	1000 across wavelength range and 2×10^4 from 15 - 30 μm	10×20 and 20×30 arc seconds	Two gratings and two Fabry-Pérot Interferometers
LWS (P. Clegg, Queen Mary College, London, GB)	Long-wavelength Spectrometer	45-180	200 and 10^4 across wave-length range	1.65 arc minutes	Grating and two Fabry-Pérot Interferometers

Table 1: Characteristics of the ISO Instruments.

The ISOCAM (figure 4) instrument[6,7] consists of two optical channels, each with a 32 x 32 element detector array, operating in the wavelength ranges 2.5–5μm and 5–17μm. The short wavelength array uses an InSb detector with a CID readout and the long wavelength detector is made of Si:Ga with a direct read out (DRO). Each channel contains a wheel for selecting various filters (including circular variable filters, CVF) and a second wheel for choosing a pixel field of view of 1.5, 3, 6, or 12 arc secs. Polarisers are mounted on an entrance wheel common to both channels. A sixth wheel carries mirrors for selecting between the channels, of which only one is operational at a time.

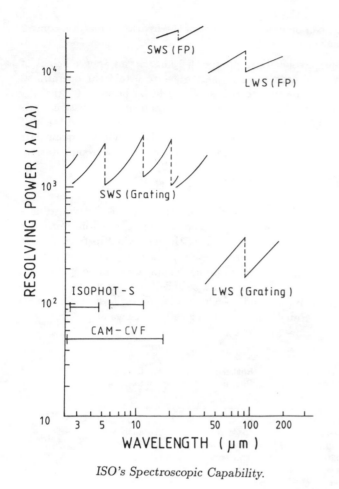

ISO's Spectroscopic Capability.

Wavelength Range (µm)	No. of Pixels	Pixel f.o.v. (arc secs)
2.5–5	32x32	1.5, 3, 6, 12
5–17	32x32	1.5, 3, 6, 12
18–28	8x8	19
30–60	3x5	31
60–120	3x3	44
120–200	2x2	90

ISO's Imaging Capability.

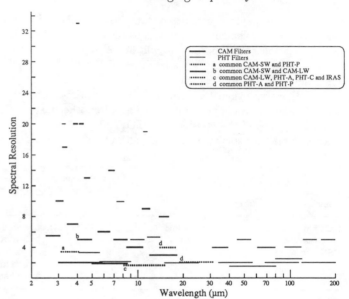

ISO's Photometric and Polarimetric Capability.

Figure 3: Scientific Capabilities of the ISO Payload.

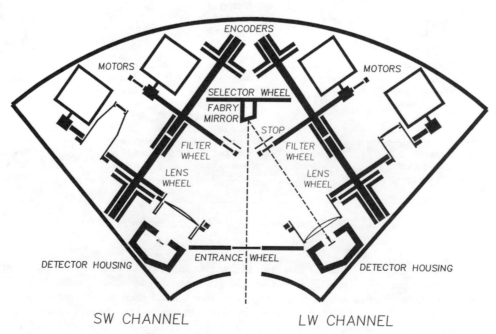

Figure 4: Schematic of the ISOCAM.

The LWS (figure 5) instrument consists of a reflection diffraction grating used in 1st and 2nd order with an array of 10 discrete detectors to provide a spectral resolving power of ~200 over the wavelength range from 45μm to 180μm. The detectors are made of Ge:Be (to be confirmed) and Ge:Ga (stressed and unstressed) material. Two Fabry-Pérot interferometers are mounted in a wheel and either can be rotated into the beam to increase the resolving power to ~10^4 across the entire wavelength range.

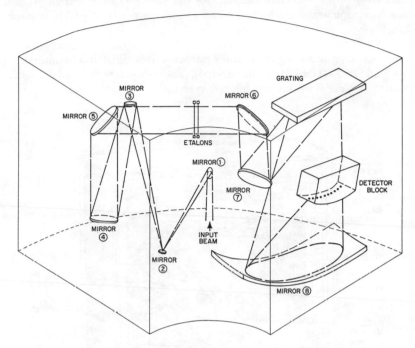

Figure 5: Schematic of the Long Wavelength Spectrometer (LWS).

The SWS (figure 6) instrument provides a resolving power of between 1000 and 2000 across the wavelength range from 2.4μm to 45μm by means of two reflection diffraction gratings used in 1st, 2nd and 3rd orders. Filters for order-sorting are placed at the instrument's various entrance apertures. Detectors made from InSb, Si:Ga, Si:P and Ge:Ga material are used. Over a part (14–30μm) of the SWS's operating range, the resolution can be increased to ~2 x 10^4 by directing the incident radiation through either of two Fabry-Pérot interferometers.

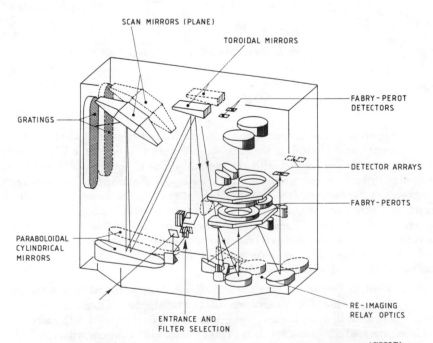

Figure 6: Schematic of the Short Wavelength Spectrometer (SWS).

The ISOPHOT (figure 7) instrument[8] consists of four sub-systems:
- ISOPHOT-C: a photopolarimeter which also provides imaging capability at close to the diffraction limit in the wavelength range from $30\mu m$ to $200\mu m$,
- ISOPHOT-P: a multi-band, multi-aperture photopolarimeter for the wavelength range from $30\mu m$ to $110\mu m$,
- ISOPHOT-A: an multi-band array of 8 x 8 discrete elements for the wavelength range from $\sim12\mu m$ to $28\mu m$,
- ISOPHOT-S: a dual grating spectrophotometer which provides a resolving power of ~90 in two wavelength bands simultaneously (2.5–5μm and 6–12μm).

A focal plane chopper with a beam throw of up to 3′ is also included in ISOPHOT. Selection between the different modes of the various sub-systems is achieved with appropriate setting of three ratchet wheels. ISOPHOT contains a total of 223 infrared detectors made of Si:Ga, Si:P, Ge:Be and Ge:Ga (stressed and unstressed). These detectors are read out by specially designed cryogenic electronics, which exists in both multiplexed and 'un-multiplexed' versions.

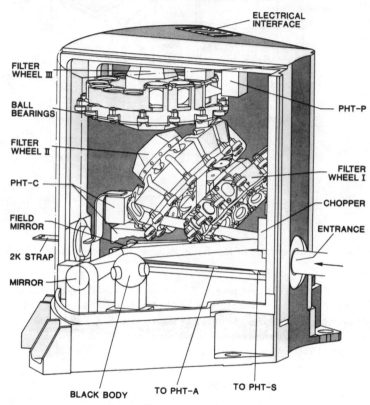

Figure 7: Schematic of the ISOPHOT.

5. OPERATIONS

The in-orbit operations of the spacecraft and instruments will be carried out by a team of scientists and engineers located at the ISO Control Centre in Villafranca near Madrid, Spain. This site is currently used by the IUE Observatory. During scientific use, the satellite will always be in real-time contact with the ground segment; however, ISO will be operated according to a detailed, pre-planned schedule in order to maximise the overall efficiency of the mission. The required astronomical flexibility will be provided by the concepts of "branched" and "linked" observations. In the former, a default and one (possibly more) optional sets of operations will be defined and prepared in advance of the observation. Then, based on an immediate examination of the incoming data, a decision can be made, in real-time, to branch from one option to another. For safety reasons, there will be restrictions on the range of choices available in a branch. For linked observations, a "test" exposure will be made on an orbit; the results examined over the course of a day or so; and a decision made, off-line, as to the final parameters to be used for the "main" observation to be scheduled several orbits later.

Examination of the scientific data will be carried out both on- and off-line. In close to real-time, a "quick-look" output, adequate for an initial estimate of the success or failure of an observation will be available to the Resident Astronomer and Guest Observer (if present). This assessment will be used to make the branching decisions. A final product with more detailed data reduction and calibration will be supplied later; the goal is within a few days. This product will be the one with which observers make their astronomical analyses.

6. OBSERVING TIME

The majority of ISO's observing time will be available to the scientific community via the submission and selection (by peer review) of proposals. In addition to this *Open Time*, there will also be *Guaranteed Time* for the groups who provide the instruments, for the Mission Scientists and for the Observatory Team, who will be responsible for all scientific operations. The division of time between these two categories will vary as the mission progresses. After launch, it is anticipated that there will be a period of up to 8 weeks during which the operational orbit will be attained, the spacecraft sub-systems switched on and checked out and the scientific performance of the instruments established. Following this, there will be a 1-month period, consisting of 50% *open time* and 50% *guaranteed time*, during which astronomical observations, designated by the *Observing Time Allocation Committee* as being of the highest priority, will be carried out. For the rest of the mission (at least 15 months), 65% of the time will be *open time*.

The first *Call for Observing Proposals* will be issued 18 months before launch. It will contain details of expected instrument performances and will solicit proposals for observations to be carried out in the period from 3 to 10 months after launch. Due to the large number of observations expected to be proposed for ISO, the proposal-handling system will be automated as much as is feasible. Thus, proposals must be submitted electronically. Observing time on ISO will be allocated on a "per object" basis, as was the case for EXOSAT, rather than on a "per shift" basis as is done with IUE. In order that the best use can be made of ISO's limited lifetime, there will be a review of the implementation of the observing programme about 5 months after launch; if actual instrument performances differ from those predicted, the *Observing Time Allocation Committee* will recommend suitable adjustments to the programme.

7. STATUS AND SCHEDULE

The spacecraft entered its detailed design, development, integration and test phase (the so-called phase C/D) in March 1988. The industrial team is led by Aerospatiale, Cannes, France and contains about 35 sub-contractors. Following reviews of all sub-systems, the *System Design Review* is currently under way with the aim of assessing the satellite design in order to (i) release the 'Structural and Thermal Model' of the payload module for integration and (ii) release the 'Qualification Models' of the electrical system units for manufacture. Assuming a successful outcome, testing of the structural and thermal model of the payload module will start in early 1990. The foreseen launch date is May 1993.

Four models are expected to be delivered to ESA for each of the scientific instruments. These are (i) the alignment, mass and thermal model (AMTM) (ii) the engineering qualification model (EQM) (iii) the flight model and (iv) the flight spare model. The AMTM's have either been or are being delivered to ESA. Activities are well advanced on the EQM's, due for delivery in Spring 1990.

8. CONCLUSION

ISO is a fully-approved and funded mission, which will offer astronomers unique and unprecendented observing opportunities in the infrared spectral region for a period of at least 18 months. Both the spacecraft and its selected complement of instruments are in their main development phase and the scheduled launch date is May 1993.

9. REFERENCES

1. M.F.Kessler,"The Infrared Space Observatory (ISO)",, Proc. SPIE 589, 201–207 (1985).
2. F. Sibille **et al**, "ISOCAM: an infrared camera for ISO" Proc. SPIE 589, 170–173 (1985).
3. Th. de Graauw **et al**, "The Short Wavelength Spectrometer for ISO", Proc. SPIE 589, 174–180 (1985).
4. D. Lemke, "ISOPHOT – Photometer for the Infrared Space Observatory", Proc. SPIE 589, 181–186 (1985).
5. R.J. Emery **et al**, "The Long Wavelength Spectrometer (LWS) for ISO", Proc. SPIE 589, 194–200 (1985).
6. C. Cesarsky, F. Sibille and L. Vigroux, "ISOCAM, a Camera for the Infrared Space Observatory", this volume.
7. E. Atad-Ettedgui, "Optical Design of ISOCAM", this volume.
8. D. Lemke, M. Burgdorf, Ch. Hajduk and J. Wolf, "Detectors and Arrays of ISO's Photopolarimeter", this volume.

ISOCAM, a camera for the Infrared Space Observatory

C. Cesarsky[1], F. Sibille[2], L. Vigroux[1]

1) Service d'Astrophysique, DPhG, CEN Saclay, F91191 Gif sur Yvette cedex
2) Observatoire de Lyon, F69230, Saint Genis Laval

Abstract

The ISO camera (ISOCAM) is an instrument designed to map selected areas of the sky in the spectral region from 2.5 to 17 μm at various spatial and spectral resolutions, polarization mapping will also be possible. At 10 μm the sensivity limitation (1mJy in 10 min) will be mainly that imposed by the astronomical background. Spatial resolution will be limited to a few arcseconds by diffraction in the telescope and by the satellite pointing. A very wide range of astrophysical problems can be tackled with ISOCAM. Examples of current interest include : a systematic search for and survey of circumstellar disks or proto-planetary clouds, a probe for dark matter in the form of low mass stars, the nature and distribution of the emitters of the 'unidentified' (PAH?) infrared features, the low mass end of the initial mass function in star-forming regions ; mapping nearby galaxies.

ISOCAM will provide imaging capability across a 3 arc min field of view with two arrays of 32x32 infrared detectors. Each array is mounted in one optical channel : the short wavelength channel operates in the 2.5 to 5.5 μm wavelength range with an InSb CID array, made by la Société Anonyme des Télécommunications ; the long wavelength channel operates from 4 to 17 μm, with a Si:Ga direct read out array (DRO) made by LETI-LIR. Different magnification factors for matching the fixed pixel size to the desired pixel field of view on the sky are provided by four different lenses, which are mounted on a wheel. Choice of 1.5, 3, 6 or 12 arcsec. are possible, thereby determining the spatial resolution of the camera. The spectral range of the observations can be selected in each channel by a set of about 10 fixed band-pass filters and Continous Variable Filters (CVF), all mounted on a wheel. The spectral resolution is about 50 for the CVF and ranges from 2 to 100 for the filters.

ISOCAM is being developed by an european consortium of laboratories led by the Service d'Astrophysique of CEN Saclay.

I) INTRODUCTION

In the european astronomical community excitment about the first results from the IRAS satellite was turning high when the European Space Agency selected the Infrared Space Observatory ISO as its next mission. IRAS had demonstrated the great advantage of space cryogenics missions for infrared astronomy : getting rid of the damaging effects of the earth atmosphere, its absorption and also its emission; limiting the emission from the telescope and the instruments by cooling them down to superfluid helium temperatures, it becomes possible to explore the infrared universe in unprecedented ways. Thanks to IRAS, our views on comets, on grains in the interstellar medium, on the main energy sources in galaxies and on the origin of quasars are radically changed. In 1983, IRAS has mapped the whole sky in four wide bands around 12, 25, 60 and 100 microns; it remains to ISO, to be launched in 1993, with enhanced sensitivities, better angular resolution and a wide range of spectroscopic and polarimetric capabilities, to scrutinize chosen regions of the sky and establish a solid basis for the understanding of the physics of the infrared sky.

This paper is devoted to a description of one of the four focal plane instruments to be flown in the ISO mission : the camera, aiming to image the sky at various spatial resolutions in the range 2.5 to 17 microns. A general outline of the ISO satellite and of the three other instruments can be found in this volume in the paper given by M. Kessler.

II) ISOCAM OPERATIONAL FRAMEWORK

Operating from space, ISOCAM is not limited to the atmospheric windows, which in its bandpass are : the L window, around 3.6 μm, the M window, around 5 μm and the N band around 10 μm, but can observe throughout the region of the spectrum for which its detectors are sensitive. Rid of the emissivity of the atmosphere and of the instruments, which have such overwhelming effects on the capabilities of ground based instruments and telescopes (see Appendix), ISO will still have to contend with a non negligible bother: the zodiacal background. Fig. 1 shows the background expected at the north galactic pole. This background is of course much lower than the atmospheric background, but it is worthwhile to notice that, at a wavelength of 10 μm the zodiacal background for ISOCAM (using the 6 arcsec pixel field of view) is only lower by a factor less than 10 than the atmospheric background around 1.5 μm for UKIRT (with an 0.5 arcsec pixel field of view) . Thus the experience which is being presently gathered by observers using infrared arrays in the near infrared will prove to be useful for optimizing ISOCAM operations at 10 μm.

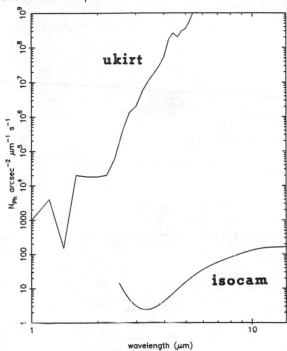

figure 1: comparison between the background flux at instrument level for a focal plane instrument in the cool 60 cm IR telescope in ISO and the ground based UKIRT telescope on top of Mauna Kea in Hawaii. The backgrounds are expressed in photon arcsec^{-2} μm^{-1}s^{-1}.

The spatial resolution of the 60 cm ISO telescope will be at the diffraction limit for wavelengths greater than 5 μm ; the diameter of the Airy circle is 4 arcsec at 5 μm and 14 arcsec at 17 μm. The random pointing error of the satellite will be 2.7 arcsec/30 seconds. Thus the space resolution achievable with ISOCAM will be about 10 times better than that of IRAS. Given that ISOCAM's gain in sensitivity with respect to IRAS is by a factor of 10^3, source confusion could have become an important concern. In fact, at high galactic latitudes, A. Franceschini et al. (personal communication) find that at b > 20° and for a pixel field of view of 6 arcsec the confusion limit is only reached at 10 μJy for the IRAS 12 μm band (8 μm to 15 μm). For a wide band around 3.5 μm, it is reached at 30 μJy, and can marginally be a problem. On the galactic plane, ISOCAM sensitivity will indeed be limited by confusion to the 0.1-1 mJy range.

III) ISOCAM CONCEPT

ISOCAM is an infrared camera whose main characteristics were defined in the model payload description of ISO : wavelength coverage from 2.5 to 17 μm with pixel field of view (PFOV) adapted to the resolution of the telescope and with a set of broadband and narrowband filters and low resolution Circular Variable Filters (CVF). These scientific specifications led to a 2 channel instrument: a short wavelength channel for the range 2.5 -5.5 μm, and a long wavelength one for 5 to 17 μm. Each channel has a filter wheel containing individual filters and CVFs, and a lens wheel supporting 4 lenses giving PFOV of 1.5, 3, 6 and 12 arcsec. A selection wheel allows to direct the sky light through one or the other channel, or to illuminate the detectors with an internal calibration source. Polarimetry capabilities have been added by placing three polarizers on an entrance wheel, see figure 2. The optical design of the camera is described in detail elsewhere in this conference (Atad-Ettedgui,1989), and the list of filters is given in figures 3a and 3b.

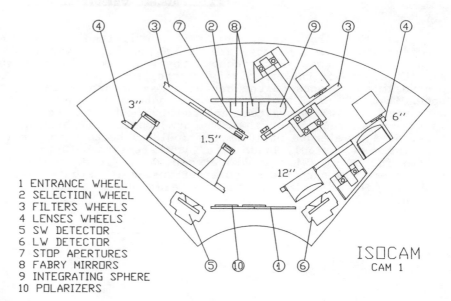

figure 2: Shematic lay-out of the IR camera, ISOCAM. The optical beam enters in the camera through the entrance wheel and can be directed to a short or a long wavelength channel by field mirrors fixed on the selection wheel. Each channel includes a filter wheel and a lens wheel.

1 ENTRANCE WHEEL
2 SELECTION WHEEL
3 FILTERS WHEELS
4 LENSES WHEELS
5 SW DETECTOR
6 LW DETECTOR
7 STOP APERTURES
8 FABRY MIRRORS
9 INTEGRATING SPHERE
10 POLARIZERS

TABLE I : ISOCAM is built by a consortium of laboratories. We give here the list of coinvestigators and the distribution of hardware tasks among the laboratories.

ISOCAM
Scientific Consortium.

Principal investigator:
C.CESARSKY (SAP, Saclay).

S.CAZES	I.A.S. Orsay
D.CESARSKY	I.A.P. Paris
A.CHEDIN	L.M.D. Palaiseau
M.COMBES	Meudon Observatory
M.GORISSE	S.A.P. Saclay
T.HAWARDEN	R.O.E. Edinburgh
P.LENA	Meudon Observatory
M.S.LONGAIR	R.O.E. Edinburgh
R.MANDOLESI	T.E.S.R.E. Bologna
L.NORDH	Stockholm Observatory
P.PERSI	I.A.S. Frascati
D.ROUAN	Meudon Observatory
A.SARGENT	Caltech, U.S.A
F.SIBILLE (project scientist)	Lyon Observatory
L.VIGROUX	S.A.P. Saclay
R.WADE	R.O.E. Edinburgh

ISOCAM
HARDWARE RESPONSIBILITIES

SAp - Saclay	Management. Long wavelenght detector. Read out electronics. Instrument command electronics
Meudon Observatory	Short wavelength detector. Read out electronics On board calibration source.
IAS (Orsay)	Integration and calibration facility.
ROE (Edinburgh)	Optical concept. Optical components.
Stockholm Observatory	Filters
Italian laboratories	Ground Support equipement Observatory Ground Sements

The optical bench is subcontracted to AEROSPATIALE

Project Manager: D. Imbault (SAp Saclay)

The ISO mission has several particularities. The elongated 24 hrs orbit selected offers the possibility of long exposures on a single astronomical target. The drawback is that the satellite has to cross the proton and electron belts to reach the low altitude perigee and is subjected to a high radiation dose. The thermal requirments also are very stringent. All the focal plane components must be operated at a temperature as low as 2.4 K and with low thermal dissipation. The allocation for each experiment is 10 mW as a mean value with peak dissipation less than 50 mW. To satisfy all these constraints, several new technological developments have been undertaken which represent significant improvements on the existing space or ground based infrared cameras. We now describe the most prominent developments.

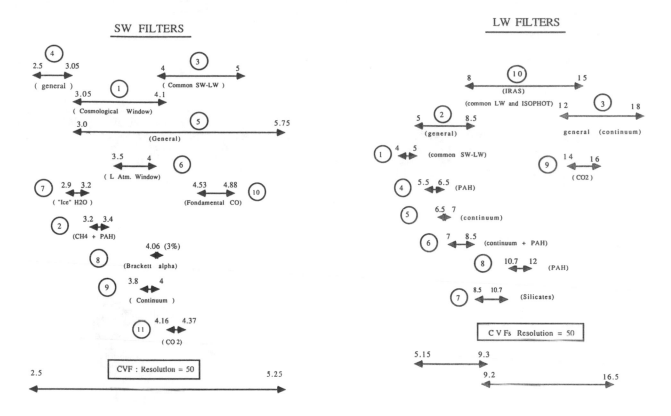

figure 3: list of filters and Circular Variable Filters of ISOCAM

a) Cryomechanisms

In addition to the normal space condition: vacuum during all the mission and high vibration levels during the launch, the mechanisms in ISOCAM must whithstand cryogenic temperatures and heavy duty cycles. These mechanisms must fulfill five major constraints: i) be able to operate at room temperatures , ii) operate at helium temperatures satisfying the ISO thermal requirements, iii) withstand the vibrations during the launch, iv) have a long life time, and v) posess an encoding system on each wheel .

For availability reasons, a superconductor stepper motor from SAGEM was selected. This motor had already been space qualified and had the advantage of a small thermal dissipation. Due to its superconducting wires, it has only self losses and no Joule losses. Drawbacks are a higher current as compared with a motor using regular wires, and a small number of steps per turn, 24. A demultiplication gear train is required between the wheel and the motor since some optical components,e.g. the CVFs, requires angular motion smaller than 15 degree.

Positional encoding can be obtained by counting the number of motor steps; for reliability reasons, it was decided to add an external absolute encoding system. Capacitive encoders were considered but finally an encoding system based on magnetoresistors was designed. The resistance of a magnetoresistor changes with the magnetic field. The magnetoresistor (5mm X 5mm) is glued on a small magnet and tied to a fixed part in front of the edge of the wheel. The successive passages of the teeth of the gear modulate the magnetic field which can be monitored by measuring the resistance of the magnetoresistors. The encoding system has two magnetoresistors phased at 90 degree on the motor pinion, which are used to control the number of steps executed by the motor, and one on the wheel which provides an absolute reference (figure 4). In addition to their encoding utility, the magnets give a resistive torque that ensures a highly reproducible and stable position of the wheel. The center of the optical components must be aligned with the teeth. Magnetoresistors must therefore be carefully positioned: their distance to the wheel must fulfill the magnetic field requirements and their angular location must ensure the correct positioning of the optical components along the optical path. The only difficulty in the use of magnetoresistors is the strong variation of the resistance with the temperature. Since this variation is device dependent, magnetoresistors must be selected from their characteristics at 4 K.

The design of the gear has to satisfy opposing constraints: large play to survive vibrations during the launch, smooth rotation to have a long lifetime, and operations at low frequency to minimize the thermal dissipation. The magnetic resistive torque at each tooth position complicates the situation. A low frequency combined with this torque and the backlash of the gear leads to shocks on the tooth's edges at each step causing a rapid wear of the mechanisms. Now, estimates of ISOCAM utilization suggest some 100,000 motions of the selection wheel and of the filter wheels; the mechanisms must withstand them. After several trials, the solution adopted is: allow a large backlash in the gear, 0.1mm radial and 0.15mm transverse, operate the motor in the frequency range 150 to 200 Hz , use a motor pinion in VESPEL, a composite material made of polyimides and MoS_2. This material has several advantages: i) a good mechanical behavior at low temperature with a large enough elasticity to withstand the vibrations, ii) no danger of adherence with the titanium of the wheel in the vacuum, and iii) a low friction coefficient that does not require a deposit of solid lubrifiant on the wheel gear. With this design, the mechanism has survived without noticeable degradations more than 200,000 cycles at 4 K during the lifetime test performed at Aerospatiale.

figure: 4

principle of cryomechanism. Each wheel has a dedicated motor situated on the wheel edge. The motor rotation is transmitted trough a gear at one end of the motor axle, and a gear on the edge of the wheel. Motor steps can be counted by sensing 2 magnetoresistors situated in front of a pinion at the other side of the motor axle (C1 and C2). A third magnetoresistor provides an absolute zero reference, C3.

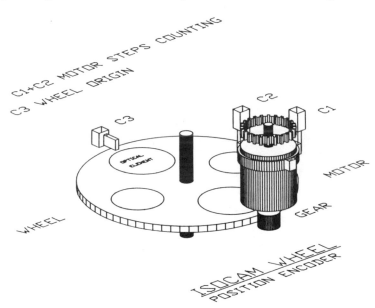

b) Detectors

The constraints on the detectors are: an operating temperature as low as 3 K, a total heat dissipation less than 10 mW and a total radiation dose above 5 krad. The operating temperature prohibits using any kind of hybrid CCD readout which would freeze below 20 K. The low dissipation leads to the use of cold multiplexing to reduce the number of wires and of low preamplification.

For the short wavelength channel, the basic device is a 32 x 32 pixel CID InSb array manufactured by Société Anonyme de Télécommunications (SAT) (Figure 5a). The detection is performed in metal insulator semiconductor (MIS) capacitors used in inverted mode; a pixel is divided in 2 capacitors, one connected to the row, the other to the column lines. Measurements of the charge can be done by sensing the row line voltage and sequentially injecting the charges in the substrate through column voltage clocking. These devices were already qualified with military acceptance tests and presented the advantages of a low operating temperature and a large radiation tolerance compatible with the ISO mission. Upgrade of the existing devices has been done along several tracks: increment of the pixel pitch to 100 μm, increment of the filling factor to 89%, and new design of the ceramic support to decouple the row and column addressing lines to reduce the electric crosstalk. A prototype detector has been extensively tested in a ground based astronomical camera, CIRCUS (Tiphène et al, 1989). The dark current arises from a tunnel effect; it is low and increases as the logarithm of the integration time. The readout noise is 1000 e/px; however, the performance of the detector is adequate for ISOCAM purposes because the device allows very long integration times - of up to several minutes, and the signal-to-noise ratio is proportional to the square root of a single integration time, T_i (see Appendix).

Three hybrid circuits, in the close vicinity of the CID chip, and wire bound to it, perform the signal processing, drive the CID clocks and multiplex the outputs. All the cold electronics and part of the detector are surrounded by a cover which is insulated from the mechanical ground. This cover also provides a radiation shield to decrease the total dose to 1.5 krads. Since the detector performances are almost independent of the temperature in the

ISOCAM expected range, no thermal regulation is necessary; thermal straps are applied between the dissipative components and the ISO Optical Support Structure (OSS) to keep the array close to the OSS temperature.

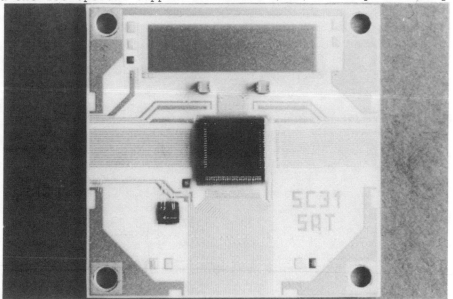

figure 5a: the 32 **X** 32 InSb CID array used as the short wavelength detector of ISOCAM. The CID is glued on a ceramic baseplate with printed row and column adressing lines. The column lines are separated in odd and even frames, on each edges of the detector. Column and row lines are separated to minimize the cross-talk.

At the time of the ESA Call for Proposals, there was no detector available in Europe for the long wavelength channel. A specific development was undertaken at the Laboratoire d'Infrarouge du CEA-LETI Grenoble (LIR) to build a 32x32 array. The design is a hybrid circuit with a 32x32 photoconductive Si:Ga array connected by indium bumps to direct voltage readout circuits (DVR) (figure 5b). The Si:Ga photoconductor was selected for its long wavelength cut off (> 17 μm). The dopant concentration of 10^{16} cm^3 gives a resistivity of 10^{12} Ω cm^{-2} and a quantum efficiency of 0.25. The electrical field line geometry is given by an equipotential conductive surface on the front surface, and a metallic reflector surface on the back surface between the bumps. The surface filling factor is 100%. There is a small sensitivity variation inside a pixel due to the different optical index of the ohmic connector zone above the indium bump. An external guard, 3 pixel wide, has been added around the 32x32 array to prevent field line distorsions at the edges of the pixels on the periphery of the array. The DVR circuit is made of silicon MOS. The integration capacitance is low (0.1 pF), optimizing the device for low flux applications. The integration capacitance gives an output signal in the 1 mV range, even for low charge levels, and therefore no additional cold electronics is required (Agnese et al, 1989). A readout noise of 300 e/px has already been achieved in qualification model devices at 4 K. The performance depends on the temperature and we have designed a thermal regulation system which can keep the detector between 3 and 10 K with an accuracy of 0.05 K. The detector housing includes a radiation shield, a copper base plate which holds both the detector and a hybrid circuit

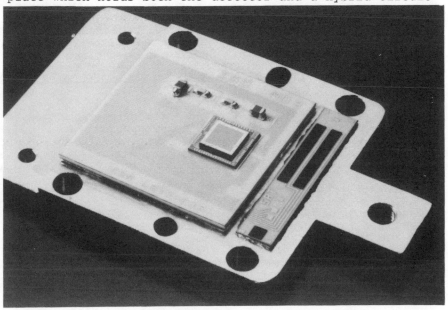

figure 5b: the 32 X 32 Si:Ga detector used in the long wavelength channel. The photo-conductor is hybridized by indium bumps to the Direct Voltage Readout circuits. The detector is glued on a ceramic which is soldered on a copper baseplate. Also soldered on this baseplate, is a hybrid circuit with heating resistors and diode temperature probes which is used for the thermal regulation of the detector.

with heating resistors and temperature probes. This housing is connected to a titanium bracket with sandwiches of kapton and small disks made of a composite of carbon-carbon. The kapton provides the electrical insulation while the carbon-carbon composite thermally insulates the copper plate from the OSS and allows its thermal regulation (Blondel et al, 1988).

The external signal processing chain includes a preamplification unit, 32 channels for each array, located just outside the ISO helium tank and a warm unit with amplifiers and sample and hold circuits, again 32 for each detector. Each channel is multiplexed and feeds a 12-bit analog-to-digital converter. In order to both properly sample the noise and keep the full dynamic range of the array, the signal must be coded over at least 14 bits. However, no high reliability rad-tolerant A/D converter is available off the shelf. It would have been very cumbersome to qualify a hybrid 14 bit converter and ESA strongly advised against its use. Instead, we added an additional amplifier with switchable gain, front-ending the 12-bit A/D converter to reach the accuracy required for very low intensity measurements.

c) The internal calibration system

An internal calibration system was designed to provide a rough absolute calibration flux and to give an accurate flat field source. This system is based on integrating spheres located on the selection wheel, which can be made to intersect the optical path. The sphere is fed by a infrared emitter providing a variable flux. There are two major difficulties in this system, an optical one, which is to fill the beam etendue in all the camera configuration, and a thermal one, which is to achieve a black body with the very low fluxes needed for the LW channel. On the one hand, to cover the 3 arcmin. field of view, the sphere must have an output porthole diameter larger than 8.5 µm. On the other hand, the lack of room in the selection wheel environment restricts the diameter of the sphere. Therefore there may be as few as one or two reflections in some directions and a good emittance uniformity can be obtained only with high scattering coefficient surface. This is achieved by machining the sphere in a single block and by an electrochemical erosion of the internal surface. Two spheres are included in the system, one for each channel, with entrance holes adapted to the flux level required for each detector.

The infrared emitter is a small resistor (0.8 mmx0.9 mmx0.15 mm) mounted on a 50 µm thick kapton film. A mechanical support has been designed to avoid the displacement of the emitter by compensating the thermal dilatation when the emitter is heated or cooled. The temperature of the emitter can vary in the range 150 to 350 K and is controlled by a 12 bit programmable DC current generator. This system is now qualified, and its output uniformity is better than 1% at pixel scale over the whole 3 arcmin field.

d) Electrical design

The electrical architecture is standard for a space experiment. It is organized around a 16 bit 80C86 microprocessor, powered by hybrid DC/DC converters using the satellite 28 volt power line. Redundancy is obtained by mounting two independent microprocessor units and DC/DC units which can be selected by external switches. The major difficulty lies in the high radiation level all along the mission. Heavy shielding, >7 mm of equivalent aluminum, has to surround the detector and the sensitive parts of the electronics. Also, rad-hard components must be used, which are not so readily available, expensive, and power-hungry. No rad hard version of the 80C86 micro-processor is available. A rad tolerant microprocessor will be used and the electrical power will be switched off while the satellite goes through the radiation belts, since this device and its peripherals can stand a dose of more than 100 krad when turned off, but only 30 krad in operation.

IV) ISOCAM PERFORMANCES AND MAIN LIMITING PARAMETERS

The expected performances of the camera are displayed in fig. 6. For the computation, the optical parameters for the telescope have been taken from ISO documents, and the reflectivity of the mirrors is assumed to be 95%. Measured transmissions have been used for the filters; for the CVFs, which are not yet available, we assumed a transmission of 0.80%. For the detectors, we have used the noise measured on the qualification models.

The effects of other characteristics of the observation chain have been estimated. Flat field corrections turn out to be the main concern. A faint source has to be measured against a large background. Residuals in the flat field correction leave a fixed pattern noise which prevents a good background substraction and decreases the sensitivity. This effect increases with the background, and is of course most important for our wide IRAS like filter. For a 6 arcsec pixel field of view, a change from 0.01 to 0.001 in the flat fielding accuracy decreases the sensitivity limit by a factor of order 10. Thus much care will have to be taken with flat fields : by having an homogeneous and stable calibration source, by taking into account the known non-linearities of the LW detectors when doing the flat fielding corrections, and by using raster pointing techniques to microscan over the source.

As seen above, the detectors will be submitted to radiation impacts : cosmic ray protons over the whole orbit, and trapped electrons when traversing the electron Van Allen belt. The SW detector is very insensitive to radiation, and can operate adequately in the electron belts. For the LW detector, which is much thicker (400 μm), charged particles or bremstrahlung photons induced by trapped electrons are an important source of glitches. In addition, due to the geometry of the pixels, 100 μm wide and 400 μm deep, the charged particles cross several pixels, ~8.5 for protons and ~2.5 for electrons. Deglitching algorithms can be used but good restitution of the signal-to-noise ratio is obtained only if less than 8% of pixels are glitched in a single frame. The overall effect is to limit the individual exposure time T_i. Outside the electron belts, the integration time will be limited for the LW to a few tens seconds, while it will be only a few seconds in the electron belts. Since in a readout noise limited observations, as ISOCAM will be in most cases, the sensitivity increases as the square root of the integration time, cosmic ray glitches limit the ISOCAM sensitivity, even in the good part of the orbit.

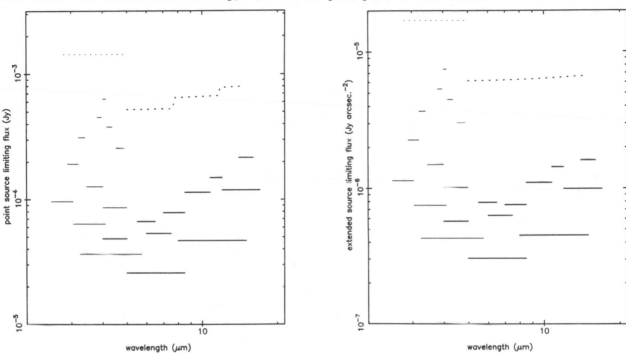

figure 6: expected performances of ISOCAM. These have been computed using the measured characteristics of qualification models of the optical elements and of the detectors. The sensitivity has been calculated for each filter and for the CVFs. It is represented by a line, thin for the SW channel and thick for the LW, with length corresponding to the FWHM of the filter (see fig. 3). The CVFs are represented by dotted lines. The sensitivity has been computed for point sources and for extended sources for a detection limit at 3 σ in 1 h exposure. The individual integration time, T_i is 10 s for the LW detector and 60 s for the SW

V) OBSERVING WITH ISOCAM

A very wide range of astrohysical problems can be tackled with ISOCAM. We just give two examples here, to illustrate the use of the camera:

a) Deep survey of an area of the sky.

The aim of this programme is to explore a field of (3x3) arcmin^2 at high galactic latitude, with a detection limit in the range 40-100 mJy, comfortably above the confusion limit. Typically, in such a survey, we expect to detect ~40 normal galaxies (spirals, ellipticals, irregulars or S0) and ~3 to 4 normal stars at a wavelenght of 3.6 μm, and ~2 normal galaxies and one normal star at 12 μm (Franceschini, private communication). The intention is of course to discover more interesting objects, e.g. bright infrared galaxies of the type of Arp 220 at cosmological distances, or nearby brown dwarfs. Using data available at present, A.Franceschini estimates that ~3.5 such active star forming galaxies should be seen in each frame at 3.6 μm, and only ~0.1 at 12μm. As for brown dwarfs: Bahcall (1984) argues that 0.09M_O/pc^3 are "missing" in the solar neighbourhood (but see Bienaymé et al., 1986). If this mass were hidden in brown dwarfs of mass 0.05M_O, luminosity 5.10^{-5} M_O

and temperature 1200°K, such as the companion of GICLAS 29-38 (Zuckerman and Becklin, 1987), we would expect to detect about one such object per deep survey frame.

To have some information on the spectrum of the objects detected, and in particular to recognize low mass stars and normal galaxies, it is essential to use at least three filters suitably chosen over the ISOCAM wavelength range; these can be wide band filters to enhance the sensitivity (e.g. filters, SW 5 and LW 2 and 10). Most sources detected will be very distant galaxies, of apparent diameter 5 arcsec. When combined with the diffraction due to the telescope and with the random pointing error of the satellite, the images of these galaxies will be spread over 10 arcsec at 3 μm and 17 arcsec at 12 μm; thus a reasonable sampling of these objects will be obtained using the 6 arcsec pixel field of view.

To have accurate flat fielding, it is best to raster scan : using a 6 arcsec pixel field of view and raster scanning with steps of 12 arcsec, over both directions, so that in the end a matrix of 3x3 pointings is obtained. Taking into account all overheads, wheel motions, dark fields, flat fields and raster scans, such a programme takes ~4 hours.

b) Photometry of sources in a molecular cloud, e.g.S 140.

The region Sharpless 140 is a typical example of a dense molecular cloud associated to a very luminous infrared source. Far infrared measurements of this source indicate that the dust temperature is 30 to 40 K. The infrared source is a star or a stellar cluster of high luminosity, recently formed; but it does not provide enough flux to keep the cloud at such a temperature. It may be that the extra energy source is a cluster of dimmer stars, much less luminous than the known infrared sources, embedded totally or partially in the cloud, whose opacity is high ($A_V > 20$ magnitudes).

The aim of this programme is to search for such stars in the infrared where the dust absorption is weak ($< 0.02\ A_V$), and to attempt to determine their luminosity function. The intention is to detect all stars more massive than 0.4 M_O at two wavelengths, ~3 and ~6 μm, and also to obtain photometric data at ~12 μm for stars more massive than 1 M_O. At the distance of S140, 1Kpc, this corresponds to $m_L = m_B = 14,5$ and $m_N = 13.4$, not including the absorption in the cloud. The size of the field to be surveyed is 9 arcminx9 arcmin. In such a field, ~10 field stars should be detected; any excess can be attributed to a stellar population related to the cloud.

This programme is best achieved with a series of raster scans with steps of12 arcsec, over nine 3 arcminx3 arcmin fields. Including all overheads, the duration is ~5 hours for a survey with three filters.

VI) CONCLUSION

We have presented a brief overview of the concept of ISOCAM and of its expected performances at the current stage of development. At present, all subsystems of ISOCAM have undergone succesfully qualification tests, and the manufacturing of the first complete model (Engineering Qualification Model) is well underway (figure 7). The ISOCAM team is looking forward to the manufacture of the flight model and , after nearly ten years of conception, building and testing of the instrument, to the operational phase, hoping that all promises will be fulfilled.

figure 7: the present state of the optical bench for the engineering qualification model. On each side, the filter wheel and the lens wheel, in front, seen from the back, the selection wheel and entrance wheel in the foreground. Above the wheels, one can see the flexible printed board circuits and the connectors for the 2 detectors.

REFERENCES

Agnese,P., Lucas, C.,Maillart, P., Mottier, P., Lepennec Y., Masse,P., SPIE/SPSE Symposium on Electronic Imaging: Advanced Devices and Systems, Los Angeles, 15-20 January 1989, in press
Atad-Ettedgui, E. This conference (1989)
Bahcall,J.N., Astrophys. J., **287**, 926 (1984)
Bienaymé,O., Robin,A.C., Crézé,M., Astron. & Astrophys., **180**, 94 (1987)
Blondel,C., Roquessalane,R., Testard,O.A., Latimier,F., and Viratelle, D., Cryogenics,**29**, 569 (1989)
Kessler,M. This conference, (1989)
Tiphene,D., Rouan,D., Lacombe,F., Combes,M., in Infrared Astronomy with Arrays, University of Hawaii at Hilo, G. Wynn-Williams and E.E. Becklin edts.1989
Zuckerman, B. and Becklin, E.E., Nature, **330**, 138 (1987)

APPENDIX:

comparaison between sensitivity of ground based and space telescopes

In this section, we compare the limiting sensitivity of astronomical observations : i) with a large ground based telescope (diameter $\approx$ 8 meters, like ESO's VLT or Keck Telescope), and ii) with a small cryo-cooled space telescope (diameter $\approx$ .6 meter for ISO or .9 meter for SIRTF).

The formula giving the Signal to Noise ratio S/N exhibits the complexity of this comparison :

$$S/N = \frac{G\ QE\ Fs\ n\ Ti}{[(e\ G\ QE\ Fb\ n\ Ti)^2 + 2\ G^2\ QE\ Fb\ n\ Ti + n\ Nr^2]^{1/2}}$$

In this formula : G.QE is the photoconductive gain times the quantum efficiency product of the detector. n is the number of coadded frames, Ti is the integration time for one frame, or between two read outs of the array, so that nTi is the total observation time. The read out process introduces an amount of noise charges Nr, which we assumed to be fixed. Fs and Fb are respectively the Signal and the Background flux on a pixel, in photon per second. e is the flat fielding error : if K is the transfer coefficient for any given pixel, or the output signal (in Volt) per input detected photon, e = dK/K, where dK is the uncertainty in our knowledge of K.

Depending upon which of the three terms of the noise predominates the denominator, the S/N may evolve in three different regimes :

1 - Read noise limted (RNL) : n Nr^2 predominates. Then S/N $\approx$ Ti $n^{1/2}$ $\approx$ $(T\ Ti)^{1/2}$. This may be the case in space near 3 µm, or from the ground at shorter wavelengths, and generally every times the beam étendue and the spectral band pass are reduced to a very small value.

2 - Background photon noise limited (BLIP) : 2 G^2 QE Fb n Ti predominates. Then S/N $\approx$ $(Ti\ n)^{1/2}$ $\approx$ $(T)^{1/2}$. This may be the situation in space at and above 5 µm, and generally on the ground with wide band pass or large beam étendue.

3 - Flat field noise limited (FFL) : (e G QE Fb n Ti)^2 predominates. Then S/N = Fs/(eFb) is a constant. If e is not zero, when n increases, both regimes 1 and 2 ultimately run into regime 3 and S/N asymptotically tends towards this limit. Once in regime 3, there is no gain in spending more time on an observation, except if this additional measurement time allows to improve the value of e.
Writing Nc = G QE Fb Ti :

$$\frac{S/N}{(S/N)lim} = [1 + \frac{1}{n\ Nc\ e^2}(2G + \frac{Nr^2}{Nc})]^{-1/2}$$

Given the importance of this transition from two regimes where S/N increases with time to a regime where S/N saturates, we first estimate the time Tlim needed to reach this transition, which we characterize by S/N = 0.7 (S/N)lim. This gives Tlim = 2 /(e^2 QE Fb), assuming that Nr^2 << 2 G Nc. We calculate :

Fb = 2.5 10^{-11}A (PFOV)^2 (filter bandpass) Ib

where A is the area of the pupil of the telescope in cm^2, PFOV stands for the Pixel Field of View in arc second and Ib is the backgound intensity. In space Ib is mainly due to emission and scattering by dust grains in the solar system and in the plane of the galaxy, while on the ground, Ib' is the emission of the optics of the telescope, assimilated to a blackbody at 280 K of emissivity 0.07. It's interesting to note that Ib'/Ib is almost constant of the order of 10^6. We assume that in one can achieve e = 10^{-3} while on the ground, with more sophisticated chopping techniques, one can reach e' = $5\ 10^{-5}$. We take PFOV = 6 arc sec , PFOV' = 0.3 arc sec , and QE = .25 .

wavelength (μm)	10	5	3	
Ib (space)	$3\,10^9$	$3\,10^8$	$4\,10^7$	
Ib'(ground)	$2.4\,10^{15}$	$2.4\,10^{14}$	$2.4\,10^{12}$	
band pass (μm)	5	1	1	(atmospheric windows)
Tlim (space)	3 min	2,5 hr	270 hr	
Tlim'(ground)	0.3 sec	15 sec	1600 sec	
band pass (μm)	.1	.05	.03	(R = 100)
Tlim (space)	2.5 hr	2 days	1 year	
Tlim' (ground)	15 sec	5 min	15 hr	

$$\text{Tlim}/\text{Tlim'} = \left[\frac{e'\ D'\ PFOV'}{e\ D\ PFOV}\right]^2 \frac{Ib'}{Ib} \approx 600 \qquad \text{from 3 to 17 μm}$$

Even in space, the flat field limited condition is reached at 10 μm in quite a short time. But at shorter wavelength, since Fb decreases very rapidly, unrealistic observing time are needed, which means that one stays in regime 1 or 2, and in particular with spectroscopic modes even of quite moderate resolution.

In regime 3, we can define a factor of merit M between the observations from the space and from the ground :

$$M = \frac{(S/N)\text{lim, space}}{(S/N)\text{lim, ground}} = \frac{Fs\ e'\ Fb'}{Fs\ e\ Fb}$$

For a point source, assuming that the PFOV are larger than the size of the PSF of the instrument :

$$M = \frac{e'\ Ib'\ (PFOV')^2}{e\ Ib\ (PFOV)^2}$$

and for an extended source :

$$M = \frac{e'\ Ib'}{e\ Ib}$$

M = 100   for a point source,
M = $4\ 10^4$ for an extended object (or PFOV = PFOV').

This result shows the dramatic advantage of observations in the space over observations from the ground, in particular when dealing with extended objects. But one should remember that this factor of merit compares results which are not obtained in the same amount of observation time. The following table gives, in μ Jy, the limiting flux which can be measured with S/N ≥ 3 in 1 hour on a point source, and the prevailing limiting condition.

wavelength (μm)	10	5	3	
band pass (μm)	5	1	1	(atmospheric windows)
Space	55 FFL	75 RNL	45 RNL	
Ground	5400 FFL	270 FFL	1,6 FFL	

The above comparison is valid for point sources for which we admit that the PSF of the instrument covers just one pixel. For the ground based 8 meter telescope, this require a very good seeing and even using adaptive optics techniques which concentrate the image spread by the atmospheric turbulence.

A similar comparison, adressing the case of extended objects observations will give a result even more in the advantage of the space when one increases PFOV'. But in any case, a large telescope is not well suited for this kind of work since a large PFOV implies a large beam étendue, that is a very fast optics and/or a large pixel size, which are both difficult to achieve.

Optical Design of ISOCAM

E Atad-Ettedgui

Applied Physics Group, Royal Observatory, Edinburgh, EH9 3HJ Scotland

ABSTRACT

The Infrared Space Observatory Camera (ISOCAM) is one of four instruments attached to the ISO satellite due to be launched by an Ariane 4 rocket in 1993. The camera is designed to operate at 4K and uses two channels to cover the spectral range from 2.5 to 17 μm. Geometrical aberrations and diffraction were studied by a complete ray–tracing of the system including the f/15 Ritchey–Chretien telescope. Curvatures, aspheric coefficients and positions of the various optical components are optimised to reduce spherical as well as off–axis aberrations (coma and astigmatism). Chromatic aberrations are reduced by a suitable choice of infrared materials: Germanium for the 5 to 17 μm range and silicon for the 2.5 to 5 μm. A Monte–Carlo statistical approach was used to evaluate the effect of manufacturing and assembly errors on the 90% encircled energy diameter of the Point Spread Function. Special effects as deformation and possible existence of ghost images in the system are presented. A test facility including a f/15 simulator and a cryogenically cooled camera simulator has been developed in ROE to test the optics at 4K by measuring its PSF. Recent measurements show a good agreement with the computed PSF.

1. INTRODUCTION

The detection of infrared radiation emanating from astronomical objects is limited by the atmospheric absorption, the thermal background of the optical instrument used for observation and the detector noise [1,2]. ISO and its four instruments (infrared camera, photopolarimeter and short– and long–wavelength spectrometers) will orbit the earth at a perigee of 1000km and an apogee of 70000km. The entire telescope and its instruments will operate at 4K and use highly sensitive two–dimensional detectors arrays. The telescope which feeds all four instruments via a fixed pyramid is a f/15 Ritchey–Chretien with a 600mm aperture and an unvignetted field of view of 3 arcmin. The camera required has to be designed with a minimum number of optical components. Two channels are needed: a short–wavelength (SW) channel from 2 to 5 μm using a InSb detector with 32 x 32 arrays (100 μm size), and a long–wavelength (LW) channel from 5 to 17 μm using a SiGa detector with 32 x 32 arrays (100 μm size). Each channel is required to work at four magnifications giving pixel fields of view of 12, 6, 3 and 1.5 arcsec for a 100 μm pixel. Polarisers, interference filters and circular variable filters will also be needed in the system.

2. OPTICAL DESCRIPTION

The object is focused onto an off–axis movable mirror M which separates the two channels from 2.5 to 5 and from 5 to 17 μm. The radius of this mirror (R=55.5mm) is chosen to give a small image (D=2mm) of the telescope secondary mirror (D=90mm) at a distance of 26mm from M. At this position of the pupil the CVF is inserted as well as the filters. A relay lens is then used to reimage the object onto the detector. A schematic drawing of the camera is shown in Figure 1. A ray–tracing of the chief and margin rays for three different objects–on–axis, +1.5 arcmin and −1.5 arcmin is represented in Figure 2 for the 12 arcsec lens and in Figure 3 for the 1.5 arcsec lens.

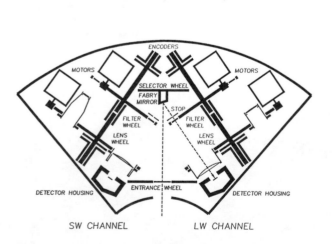

Figure 1. *Infrared Space Observatory Camera (ISOCAM).*

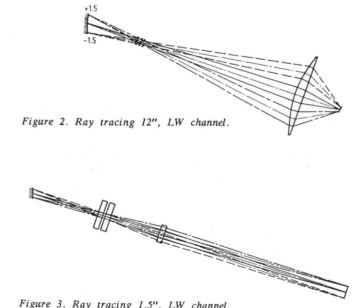

Figure 2. *Ray tracing 12", LW channel.*

Figure 3. *Ray tracing 1.5", LW channel.*

3. LENS MATERIAL

The first task was to choose a suitable material for the imaging lenses. ZnSe was the first choice due to its relatively high transmission in the visible spectrum and useful for the alignment. Its high dispersion from 5 to 17 μm introduces an unacceptable level of chromatic aberration. Instead n-type optical grade monocrystalline germanium and silicon were chosen.

Germanium has low dispersion, excellent homogeneity ($\Delta n = 2 \times 10^{-4}$) and is diamond turned making easier the manufacture of the aspheric surface in the lens. Its absorption above 15 μm becomes almost negligible when it is cooled to 4K [3]. The refractive index at low temperature (77K) has been measured by Wolfe et al [4] and extrapolated to 4K. The following values have been chosen:

Wavelength (μm)	5	6	12	18
Refractive index	3.937	3.9305	3.925	3.925

Antireflection (AR) coatings have been designed and deposited on Ge by OCLI. The transmission of a 3mm thick Ge sample with both sides Ar-coated at 77K is greater than 93% from 5 to 15 μm, between 80% and 90% from 15 to 16.5 μm and around 60% for 17 μm.

Silicon has low dispersion between 3 and 5 μm and is diamond turned. Its refractive index has also been measured at 77K [4] and extrapolated to 4K. The following values have been chosen:

Wavelength (μm)	3	4	5
Refractive index	3.397	3.392	3.387

The measured transmission for a 1mm thick silicon sample with both sides Ar-coated is greater than 90% from 2 to 5 μm.

Thermal expansion data for Ge and Si are given in reference 5.

4. OPTIMISATION: CHOICE OF VARIABLES AND MERIT FUNCTION

The lens was optimised by minimising in a least-square sense an error function comprised of ray aberrations for 24 rays in the pupil traced for zero field, +1.5 arcmin and −1.5 arcmin and for $\lambda=4$ μm for the SW channel and for $\lambda=12$ μm for the LW channel. We used CODEV software, choosing as variables the curvature and the aspheric coefficient of the convex part of the lens. The distances between the mirror M and lens and between the lens and detector were varied while the distance between the mirror M and detector was held fixed at 125.3mm in order to get the required magnification.

5. CHROMATIC ABERRATION

The remaining chromatic aberrations for the LW and SW lenses are shown in Figures 4 and 5. It is expressed as a change in focus for the spectral band 5 to 17 μm and 2 to 5 μm respectively. Its effect on geometrical aberrations is shown for the most sensitive lens LGe12 in Figure 6.

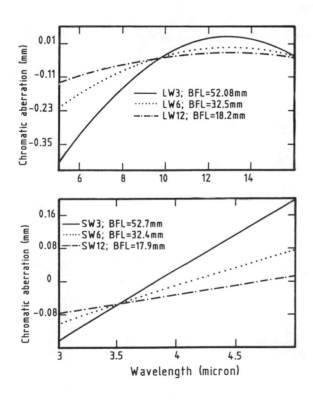

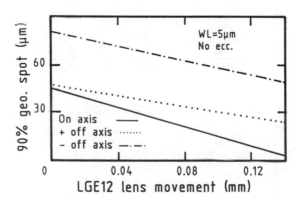

Figure 4. Chromatic aberration for LW lens.

Figure 6. Effect of defocus on geometrical spot.

Figure 5. Chromatic aberration for SW lens.

6. EFFECT OF AXIAL DISPLACEMENT, LATERAL DISPLACEMENT and TILT OF THE LENS ON THE IMAGE QUALITY AND IMAGE SHIFT

6.1. Axial displacement of the lens

The focus is adjusted in the test facility by moving the lens along the optical axis. The corresponding focal shifts (mm) are given in Table 1. This adjustment is necessary to compensate for tolerances on radius of curvature, separations, thermal contraction and changes in refractive index. No significant effect on image quality is noticed.

6.1.1. Lateral displacement of the lens. The lens and its mount are inserted in a wheel. The accumulated tolerance could reach 0.3mm of eccentricity relative to the optical axis. The corresponding lateral displacement of the image are also given in Table 1. There is no effect on image quality for the 1.5, 3 and 6 arcsec lenses, although there is an effect for the 12 arcsec lens on the diffraction intensity profile LSF for off-axis objects as shown in Figure 7 to 9.

6.1.2. Lens tilt. No effect on image quality has been noticed for a tilt of ±1 mrad.

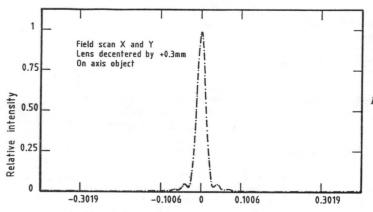

Figure 7. *Effect of decenter on on-axis object.*

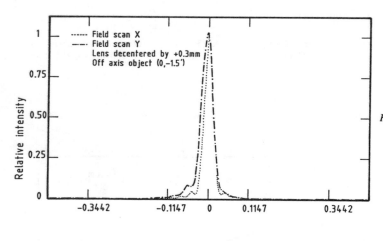

Figure 8. *Effect of decenter on −1.5 arcmin off-axis object.*

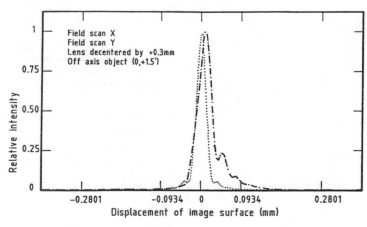

Figure 9. *Effect of decenter on +1.5 arcmin off-axis object.*

Table 1. *Effect of axial and lateral displacement of the lens*

Lens (Arcsec)	Focal length (mm)	Conjugate distance from the lens (mm)		Image Displacement (mm)	
		Object(s)[c]	Image(s')[d]	Axial[a]	Lateral[b]
12	16.28	102.40	19.36	+0.096	0.36
6	24.35	88.90	33.54	+0.085	0.42
3	30.28	70.60	53.02	+0.042	0.54
1.5	29.63	49.60	73.59	-0.10	0.75

a. The lens is moved +0.1mm along the optical axis towards the detector plane.
b. The lens is moved 0.3mm perpendicular to the optical axis.
c. s is the distance between the object at the moving mirror and the lens.
d. s' is the distance between the lens and the image at the detector plane.

7. EFFECT OF THE LENS DEFORMATION OF IMAGE QUALITY

An error in manufacturing such as the irregularity of the surfaces introduces a wavefront error and an increase in the spot size. This error and a deformation of the lens after mounting it in its barrel are simulated by changing the sag equation of the aspheric and of the plano surfaces by a term in Ay^4. There is a compensation effect if the two faces of the lens are deformed by the same number of fringes (visible interferometry). The wavefront error introduced by the aspheric face is compensated by the wavefront error introduced by the plano surface of the lens. Evaluation of the effect of irregularity of filters, mirror M and the lens on aberrations has been carried out and is shown in Figure 10. The data used for this evaluation are: 1 fringe for each face of the filters (3 filters: 2 in Ge, 1 in CaF2) on a 3mm aperture, ½ fringe for the mirror M on a 9mm aperture, and the difference between the number of fringes for the 2 lens surfaces on a 32mm aperture.

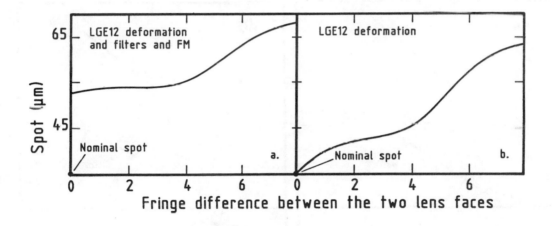

Figure 10.   a) Effect of optical deformation on spot size.
              b) Effect of lens deformation on geometrical spot.

8. POINT SPREAD FUNCTION: PSF

The PSF of the optical system was calculated using the CODEV software package. The diffraction integral giving the complex amplitude of the wavefront at a point (x, y) in the image plane A(x,y) is computed by evaluating the integral:

$$\iint B(u,v)\exp(-i\Phi(u,v))\exp(i2\pi/\lambda R\ (ux+vy))du\ dv$$
exit pupil area

where $\Phi(u,v)=(2\pi/\lambda)OPD$ is the wave-aberration phase function difference of the ray through point (u,v) in the exit pupil (resulting from an optical path difference equal to OPD). The evaluation is performed by CODEV using a FFT algorithm. The intensity P(x,y) is then calculated by calculating $|A(x,y)|^2$.

An example of a 3-D PSF for on and off axis objects is given in Figures 11 and 12.

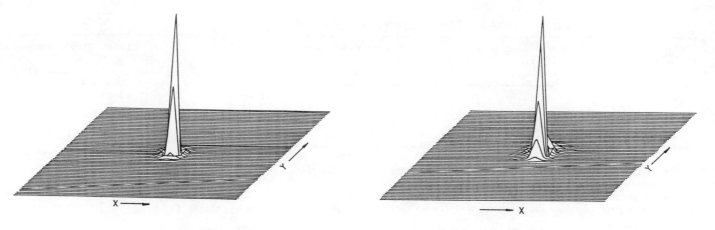

Figure 11. 3-D PSF for on-axis object.

Figure 12. 3-D PSF for +1.5' off axis object.

Results for the 90% encircled energy diameter of the PSF are given in Figures 13 and 14. This includes as well a Monte-Carlo statistical run of the manufacturing errors such as radius of curvature, separations and assembly errors such as tilt, decentration and deformation.

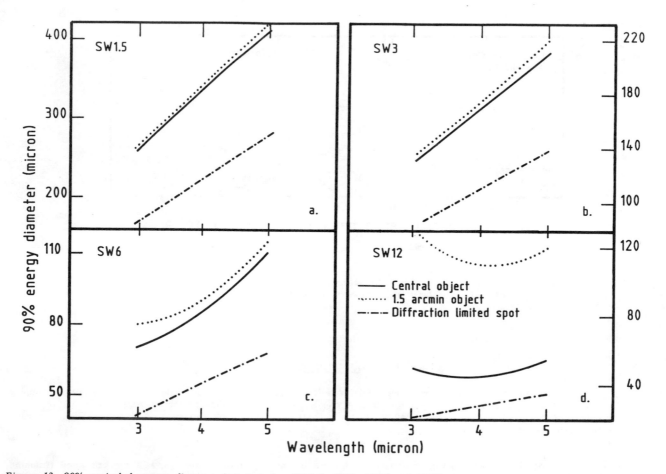

Figure 13. 90% encircled energy diameter (micron) for SW1.5, SW3, SW6 and SW12.

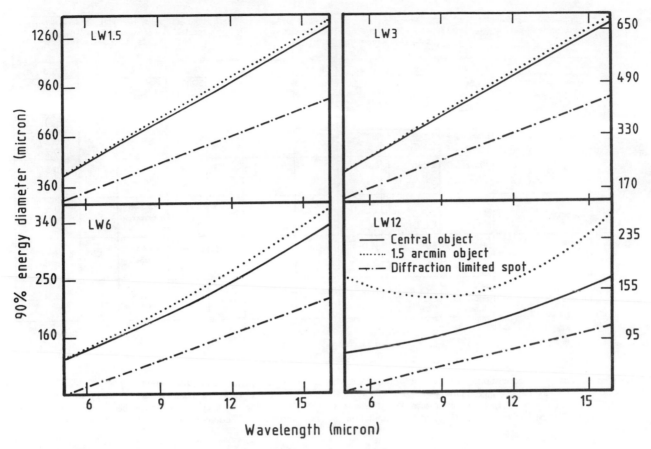

Figure 14. 90% encircled energy diameter (micron) for LW1.5, LW3, LW6 and LW12.

9. OPTICAL DESIGN DATA FOR LW and SW band

A summary of all the data obtained after optimizing and tolerancing the system is given in Tables 2 and 3. We also added the polariser specification which could be inserted in the entrance wheel.

Table 2

Component identification	Surface number	Radius (mm) tol (+ −)	Thickness or separation (mm)		Clear aperture diameter (mm)	Physical diameter (mm)	Irregularity (fringes)	Wedges (TIR) (mm)	Optical material	Aspheric coefficient ($-e^2$)	Tilt (mrad) (+ −)	Decentration (mm) (+ −)
Polarizer	0	plano 2fr	1209	1	21.5	25	1	0.01	KRS5		1	0.3
Mirror	1	55.50 0.2	105		$8.7^{+0.1}_{-0}$		1/2		6080 Alumin alloy	−		
Stop	2	plano	22.0	0.1			−	−			3	0.2
CVF	3	plano 2fr	4.0	0.1	$4.6^{+0.1}_{-0}$	$7.5^{+0}_{-0.1}$	1	0.01	Germanium	−	3	0.2
	4	plano 2fr		0.1				0.01		−	3	0.2
Blocker	5	plano 2fr	1	0.1	$4.6^{+0.1}_{-0}$	$7.5^{+0}_{-0.1}$	1	0.01	CAF2			
	6	plano 2fr	2.03	0.1								
LGe1.5ISO Image 1.5"	7	85.44 0.08	19.3	0.1	$6.5^{+0.5}_{-0}$	$10^{+0}_{-10.1}$	1/2	0.003	Germanium	0 sphere	1	0.3
	8	plano 2fr	2.0	0.1			1/2				1	
	9	plano −	72.9	0.1			−					
LGe3ISO Image 3"	7	87.37 0.09	40.165	0.1	$14.5^{+0.5}_{-0}$·	$18.5^{+0}_{-0.1}$	1/2	0.003	Germanium	−4.55 hyperboloid	1	0.3
	8	plano 2fr	2.0	0.1			1/2					
	9	plano −	52.08	0.1			−					
LGe6ISO Image 6"	7	70.53 0.07	58.735	0.1	$31.0^{+0.5}_{-0}$	$35.0^{+0}_{-0.1}$	1/2	0.003	Germanium	−3.71 hyperboloid	1	0.3
	8	plano 2fr	3.0	0.1			1/2					
	9	plano −	32.5	0.1			−					
LGe12ISO Image 12"	7	47.20 0.05	72.04	0.1	$32.0^{+0.5}_{-0}$	$36.0^{+0}_{-0.1}$	1/2	0.003	Germanium	−4.57 hyperboloid	1	0.3
	8	plano 2fr	4.0	0.1			1/2					
	9	plano −	18.2	0.1			−					

Table 3

Component identification	Surface number	Radius (mm) tol (+−)	Thickness or separation (mm)	Clear aperture diameter (mm)	Physical diameter (mm)	Irregularity (fringes)	Wedges (TIR) (mm)	Optical material	Aspheric coefficient ($-e^2$)	Tilt (mrad) (+ −)	Decentration (mm) (+ −)
Polarizer	0	plano 2fr	1209 1	21.5	29	1	0.01	KRS5		1	0.3
Mirror	1	55.50 0.2	105	$8.7^{+0.1}_{-0}$		1		6080 Alumin alloy	—		
Stop	2	plano	22.0 0.1	$4^{+0.1}_{-0}$						3	0.2
CVF	3	plano 2fr	4.0 0.1	$4.6^{+0.1}_{-0}$	$7.5^{+0.1}_{-0}$	1	0.01	Silicon	—	3	0.2
	4	plano 2fr	2.175 0.1				0.01		—	3	0.2
LSI1.5ISO Image 1"	5	70.82 0.07	21.45 0.1	$6.0^{+0.5}_{-0}$	$10^{+0}_{-10.1}$	1	0.003	Silicon	0 sphere	1	0.3
	6	plano 2fr	2.0 0.1								
	7	plano —	73.675 0.1								
LSI3ISO Image 3"	5	72.38 0.07	42.4 0.1	$14.5^{+0.5}_{-0}$	$18.5^{+0}_{-0.1}$	1	0.003	Silicon	−3.558 hyperboloid	1	0.3
	6	plano 2fr	2.0 0.1								
	7	plano —	52.7 0.1								
LSI6ISO Image 6"	5	58.20 0.06	60.7 0.1	$31.0^{+0.5}_{-0}$	$34.0^{+0}_{-0.1}$	1	0.003	Silicon	−2.645 hyperboloid	1	0.3
	6	plano 2fr	4.0 0.1								
	7	plano —	32.4 0.1								
LSI12ISO Image 12"	5	38.9 0.07	74.2 0.1	32.0	34.0	1	0.003	Silicon	−3.178 hyperboloid	1	0.3
	6	plano 2fr	5.0 0.1								
	7	plano —	17.9 0.1								

10. GHOST IMAGES

A ghost analysis has been done taking into account reflections on the surfaces of the CVF and filters. The distance between the reflected image and the primary image plane (D1), the geometrical diameter of the reflected beam at the primary image plane (D2) and the magnification m(ratio of the size of the reflected image to the size of the primary image) have been calculated. Table 4 gives the results of a first order ray-tracing of a combination of two surfaces reflections. This analysis shows the presence of multiple ghosts.

To evaluate the effect of the ghosts we need to know the reflectivity of each surface and compare the total amount of light transmitted by the CVF and filters with the light reflected by 2 surfaces. From the data given by filter manufacturer we expect the ghost intensity to be less than 1% than the real image intensity. Therefore we do not expect the ghosts to affect the image quality of the camera.

Table 4
Ghost analysis

Lens (arcsec)	Refl 1	Refl 2	D1	D2	m
12	2	1	− 0.06	0.02	0.99
	3	1	− 0.12	0.04	0.97
	4	1	− 0.22	0.08	0.93
	3	2	− 0.09	0.03	0.98
	4	2	− 0.19	0.07	0.95
	4	3	− 0.12	0.04	0.97
6	2	1	− 0.17	0.03	0.98
	3	1	− 0.44	0.08	0.95
	4	1	− 0.80	0.15	0.91
	3	2	− 0.30	0.05	0.97
	4	2	− 0.68	0.13	0.93
	4	3	− 0.42	0.08	0.96
3	2	1	− 0.65	0.06	0.97
	3	1	− 1.69	0.16	0.93
	4	1	− 3.04	0.30	0.87
	3	2	− 1.16	0.10	0.95
	4	2	− 2.57	0.26	0.89
	4	3	− 1.62	0.16	0.93
1.5	2	1	− 2.07	0.10	0.95
	3	1	− 5.86	0.30	0.86
	4	1	−10.3	0.60	0.76
	3	2	− 4.0	0.2	0.91
	4	2	− 8.8	0.5	0.80
	4	3	− 5.6	0.3	0.87

11. COMPARISON WITH EXPERIMENT

A test facility including a f/15 telescope simulator and a cryogenically cooled camera simulator has been built in ROE to carry out optical tests on the mirror M, lenses, filters and CVF elements. BFL, Magnification, and PSF will be determined. A schematic layout is shown in Figure 15. The results of these tests will be compared to the values expected from the theoretical optical design. Recent measurements are shown in Table 5.

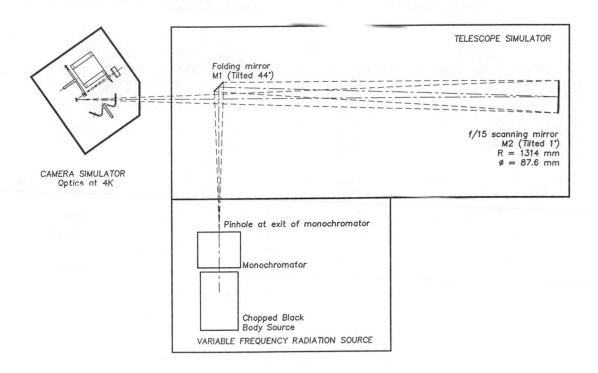

Figure 15. ISOCAM Test Facility

Table 5. 80% encircled energy diameters (microns) Comparison between theory and Experiment

Theory	Experiment	Wavelength (μm)	Lens (arcsec)
180	206	5	LGe1.5
245	295	9	LGe1.5
374	360	15	LGe1.5
100	104	3.5	LSi3
110	104	4.5	LSi3
110	123	5	LGe3
124	157	9	LGe3
195	213	15	LGe3
160	181	3.5	LSi1.5
167	181	4.5	LSi1.5

12. CONCLUSION

The purpose of this study was to describe the optical design of ISOCAM and assess its performance in terms of PSF and encircled energy diameters. Aspheric surfaces for the lenses were used to improve the image quality of the camera.

13. REFERENCES

1. "Infrared Space Observatory ESA, Report on the phase A Study", SCI(82) 6, November (1982).
2. Proposal to ESA: ISOCAM, January (1985).
3. Collins, R.J. and Fan, H.Y., Phys. Rev. 93 674 (1954).
4. Wolfe, W.L., De Bell, A.G. and Palmer, J.M., Proc. SPIE 245, 164 (1980).
5. Browden, J.S. and Ballard, S.S., Appl. Opt. 16, 3214 (1977).

Detectors and arrays of ISO's photopolarimeter

D. Lemke, M. Burgdorf, Ch. Hajduk, J. Wolf

Max-Planck-Institut für Astronomie
D-6900 Heidelberg-Königstuhl, Germany

1. DESIGN GOALS

The Infrared Space Observatory's (ISO) photometer experiment ISOPHOT provides 4 sub-systems, as described in LEMKE 1985, which optimizes the different ways of photometric measurements. They allow multiband - multiaperture photopolarimetry, multicolor - polarimetric imaging and spectrophotometry. In order to cover the wide wavelength range $2.5...240 \mu$m five different detector materials have to be used. They are arranged according to their application as 2D-arrays, linear arrays and single detectors, a total of 223 detectors are present, see tab. 1.

Table 1. The 4 experiment subsystems use different detector arrangements with different materials to cover certain wavelength ranges [μm].

PHT-S	2 linear arrays		
	64 pixel row	Si:Ga	2.5...5.0
	64 pixel row	Si:Ga	6.0..12.0
PHT-A	2D-array		
	8x8 pixels	Si:P	8...30
PHT-C	2D-arrays		
	C50 3x5 pixels	Ge:Be	30...55
	C100 3x3 pixels	Ge:Ga	60..120
	C200 2x2 pixels	Ge:Ga	120..240
		stressed	
PHT-P	3 single detectors		
		Si:Ga	3...17
		Si:P	15...28
		Ge:Ga	40...110

A design goal of ISOPHOT was to meet all natural and physical limits imposed on the experiment by the sky-background and the satellite. For instance, the detection sensitivities should be limited only by the photon noise of the thermal radiation of interplanetary and interstellar dust at faint sky regions. Spatial resolution should approach the diffraction limit of the 60 cm telescope at all wavelengths, with a provision to perform "super-resolution" on bright sources. On the other hand, scientifically important observations of faint extended sources should be possible in the widest beams, only limited by vignetting.

2. NOISE SOURCES IN DETECTOR ASSEMBLIES

Several noise sources contribute to the total noise of a detector assembly, as indicated in fig. 1. The instrumental noise should be minimized in order to be limited only by the thermal background noise of the sky. With the integrating preamplifier circuit used, only its read noise and the detector's dark current noise are important. With a sensitive area of 1x1 mm^2 typical of all detectors, and a background of $Q_B = 10^8$ photons cm^{-2} s^{-1}, the third term of the equation in fig. 1 representing the photon shot noise dominates if the read noise is smaller than a few hundred electrons/s and the dark current through a detector is $I_d < 10^5$ e/s. While all other noise sources can be neglected under the operational conditions of the cold telescope, the spike noise caused by ionizing radiation penetrating the detectors can at times be large and will be considered in section 5.

3. INTEGRATING PREAMPLIFIER

The basic design of a cold read-out circuit (CRE) is shown in fig. 1. Several chips have been developed to fit the needs of the different detector array geometries. All CRE's for arrays (CRE66, 66-2D, 17, 11, 6) include a cold multiplexer, which is missing on PHT-P's CRE1. Tests of the second generation of these newly developed circuits exhibit a read noise of < 400e at 4 K, according to manufacturers' tests (IMEC, Leuven). Dynamic range, offsets, stability and crosstalk are satisfactory and are intended to be further improved in another redesign. Some more details of the CRE's are given by WOLF et al. 1989.

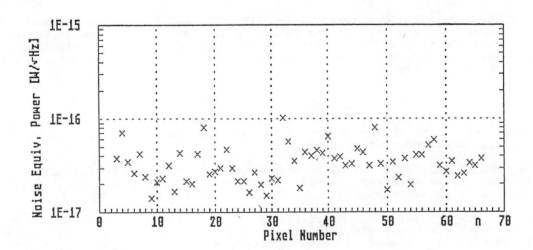

ISOPHOT - Detector Assemblies (Si:X, Ga:X + CRE)

NEP and Total Noise

$$NEP = \frac{e}{R} \; N_{tot} \; \left[\frac{2}{t_{int}} \right]^{1/2}$$

responsivity   integration time

$$N_{tot}^2 = N_R^2 \, (t_{int}) + 2 \, \frac{I_D}{e} \, t_{int} + 2 \, \eta G^2 Q_B \, t_{int} \left[1 + \frac{1}{e^{hc/\lambda kT_{B-1}}} \right]$$

readout noise   dark current   photon noise

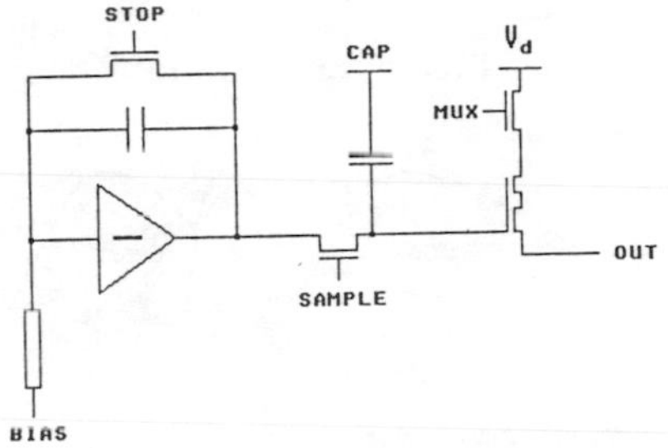

Figure 1. Noise-Equivalent-Power (NEP) and major contributions to the total noise number N of noise electrons in ISOPHOT's detector assemblies including integrating pre-amplifier (t_{int}=integration time, G=photoconductive gain, Q_B background flux).

4. DETECTOR ASSEMBLIES

4.1 The 64 pixel linear Si:Ga arrays

Two of these devices coupled to CRE66 sample the two low resolution spectra of PHT-S (see tab. 1). The Qualification Models of these assemblies are almost completed, test results are shown in fig. 2.

Figure 2. NEP[$WHz^{-\frac{1}{2}}$] measurements of the 64 pixel Si:Ga array PHT-S2 read-out by a CRE66. Background flux 10^8 photons $cm^{-2}s^{-1}$, difference signal 1.4 10^{-14}W, chopper frequency 0.68 Hz, integration time 0.48s (Battelle Test).

4.2 The two-dimensional 8x8 pixel Si:P camera

The detector chip consists of a $8\times8\times1$ mm^3 wafer almost saw cut on its back side by 950 μm deep grooves. Pixel separation on the flat front side is by a 120 μm wide metallic grid. Connection to the CRE66-2D is via gold balls plus silver filled epoxy, a variation of the more elaborate indium bump technology. An engineering model of this assembly connected to a CRE17 exhibited reasonable behaviour, except for the crosstalk, which was in the order of a few percent. At present an improved qualification model with an average goal NEP$\sim$3 10^{-17} WHz$^{-\frac{1}{2}}$ is being manufactured.

4.3 The two-dimensional Ge:X cameras

These three cameras own common design principles. Individually made detector crystals are arranged in a 2D-block to form the arrays described in table 1 and figure 3. Each detector is housed in a separate cavity with an entrance field lens made of germanium (C200, C100) or silicon (C50).

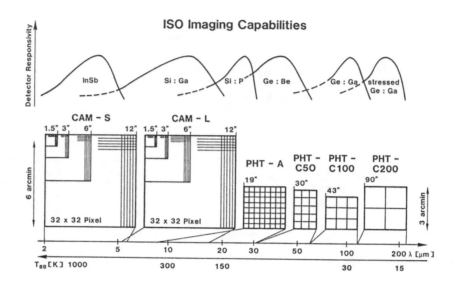

Figure 3. The far-infrared cameras of ISO are contained in the ISOPHOT-experiment (PHT-A, PHT-C...). The size of the camera is limited by the 3 arcmin unvignetted field of view and the pixels are sized to the diffraction image at the longest wavelength. The near-infrared cameras contained in the ISOCAM-experiment are also presented at this conference.

The engineering model of the 3x3 pixel Ge:Ga-camera exhibited good performance (NEP$\sim$5 10^{-17} WHz$^{-\frac{1}{2}}$) when read out by transimpedance amplifiers. At present, the qualification model is assembled to the CRE11.

The production of the 3x5 pixel Ge:Be-camera is somewhat behind schedule because of imperfections of the detector material: too high dark current and too large scatter of individual pixel parameters.

The 2x2 pixel camera made of stressed Ge:Ga is one of the most important devices on-board. It covers the unexplored 110...240 μm range during regular pointed observations and it will additionally be used to serendipitously survey the sky at 200 μm during satellite slews. The engineering prototype showed good performance (NEP$\sim$3 10^{-17} WHz$^{-\frac{1}{2}}$, responsivity $\sim$7 AW^{-1}). Since these detectors exhibit the largest dark current, careful measurements were made at different temperatures. As shown in fig. 4, an operational temperature of T$\sim$1.8 K available on ISO has to be chosen in order to suppress an otherwise dominating dark current noise. Individual bias lines supply the four detectors in order to match the low bias of these detectors ($\sim$30 mV) to CRE's with an input offset scatter in the mV-range.

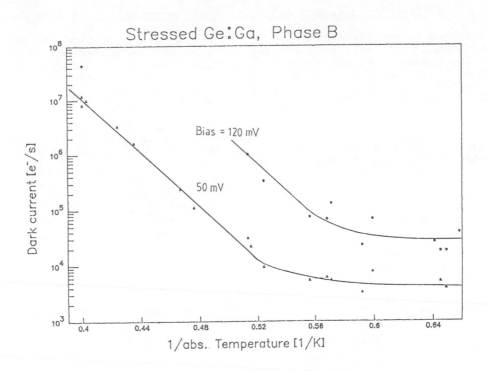

Stressed Ge:Ga, Phase B

Figure 4. Dark current of the stressed Ge:Ga detector ($\lambda < 240\,\mu$m) versus the inverse operational temperature for two different biases.
The required detector temperature of ~1.8 K ($I_D < 10^5 e^- s^{-1}$) will be achieved by a
copper cooling strap between sensor and ISO's helium tank (< 1.8 K).

4.4 The single detectors

These three sensors are selected for highest performance in the single beam photopolarimeter. Their common design principle is (i) cavity housing, (ii) read-out by CRE's
and (iii) individual field mirrors or lenses. The completed qualification model of the P3-
assembly is shown in fig. 5.

Figure 5. PHT-P3-Ge:Ga detector assembly. On the left the detector/preamp housing and its
entrance aperture are visible. It is connected by a cold harness to the stress-
relief device of the plug internal to the focal plane unit.

5. HIGH ENERGY RADIATION EFFECTS ON DETECTORS

ISO passes once a day the earth's radiation belts. The detectors respond by increased spike noise and drifts of their current responsivity. The latter effect was investigated by simulating the passage through the electron belt (dose rate 80 mrad/h) by a radioactive source (^{60}Co) emitting gamma radiation (1.1 MeV). While all Si:X detectors suffered from responsivity shifts of a few percent, the effect was most dramatic in the stressed Ge:Ga. As shown in fig. 6 the calibration factor is changed by an order of magnitude, details of these investigations are reported by BLUM et al. 1989. After passage of the radiation belts the sensors will be cured by either bias boosts or a short time temperature increase. While bias boosting can only safely be applied to sensors with rather low bias voltages (Ge:X), the Si:X-detectors will be heated up to < 15 K. Including all drift and stabilization times the whole process might require several minutes.

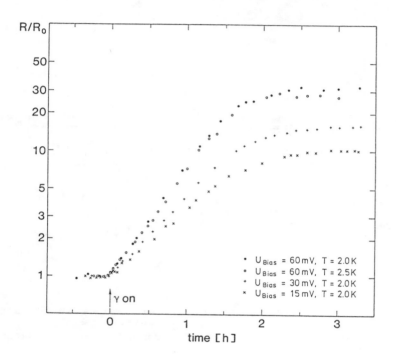

Figure 6. Responsivity drifts of a stressed Ge:Ga-detector after irradiation by a gamma source simulating the ionizing dose of ISO's passage through the (outer) electron belts.

6. ACKNOWLEDGEMENT

The ISOPHOT project is funded by the Bundesministerium für Forschung und Technologie (BMFT), Bonn. The industrial contracts are managed by DLR, Porz. Battelle Europa, Frankfurt/M, manufactures the detector assemblies; IMEC, Leuven, develops the CRE-circuits; Dornier, Friedrichshafen builds the warm electronics. We appreciate many interesting technical discussions with all companies. A. Salama, now with ESA, Noordwijk, contributed to the high energy radiation measurements when still in Heidelberg.

7. REFERENCES

1. Blum, J., Hajduk, Ch., Lemke, D., Salama, A., Wolf, J., accepted for Infrared Physics, 1989.
2. Wolf, J., Lemke, D., Burgdorf, M., Grözinger, U., Hajduk, Ch., Proceedings of the 3rd Infrared Detector Technology Workshop, ed. C.R. Mc Creight, NASA AMES Research Center, 1989.
3. Lemke, D., SPIE-Proceedings 589, 181, 1985.

AUTHOR INDEX